Math 8

A Reference Guide

Book Staff and Contributors
Lisa White *Content Specialist*
Ellen Loeb *Text Editor*
Suzanne Montazer *Creative Director, Print and ePublishing*
Stephanie Shaw Williams *Senior Print Visual Designer, Cover Designer*
Carol Leigh, Jacquie Rosenborough *Visual Designers*
Meredith Condit, Charlotte Fullerton *Media Editors*
Susan Raley *Senior Manager, Writers and Editors*
Alison Gold *Project Manager*
Abhilasha Parakh *Senior Project Manager*

Paul Thomas *Senior Director, Content and Assessment*
Kelly Engel *Director, Mathematics Content Specialists*
Michelle Kitt *Director, Instructional Design*
Jason Golomb *Senior Director, Program Management Product Development*
Christopher Frescholtz *Senior Director, Program Management*

Lisa Dimaio Iekel *Director, Print Production and Manufacturing*

About K12 Inc.
K12 Inc., a technology-based education company, is the nation's leading provider of proprietary curriculum and online education programs to students in grades K–12. K[12] provides its curriculum and academic services to online schools, traditional classrooms, blended school programs, and directly to families. K12 Inc. also operates the K[12] International Academy, an accredited, diploma-granting online private school serving students worldwide. K[12]'s mission is to provide any child the curriculum and tools to maximize success in life, regardless of geographic, financial, or demographic circumstances. K12 Inc. is accredited by CITA. More information can be found at www.K12.com.

ISBN: 978-1-60153-508-5 (online book)
ISBN: 978-1-60153-501-6 (printed book)

Printed by Quad Graphics, Versailles, KY, USA, May 2016

Contents

Lines

Systems of Equations

Function Basics

Linear Data Models

Basic Geometric Shapes

Volume

Transformation, Congruence, and Similarity

Real Numbers

The Pythagorean Theorem

Appendices

K12 Summit Curriculum

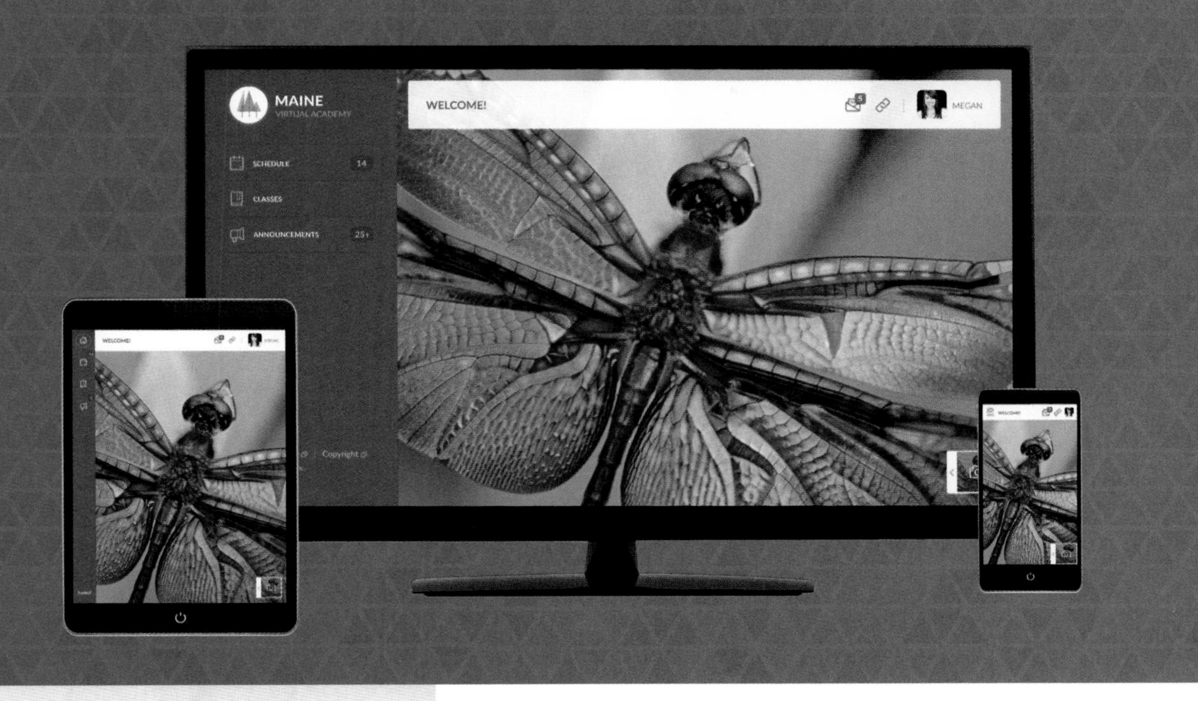

And remember: The pages in your book are also online!

Go to the online course to look for these digital resources in your lessons:

Videos will introduce you to each topic.

math CAST

Visual learning with animations and interaction will help you master key skills.

Solve problems with the help of stepped examples.

Use real-world examples to practice what you've learned.

Number Properties

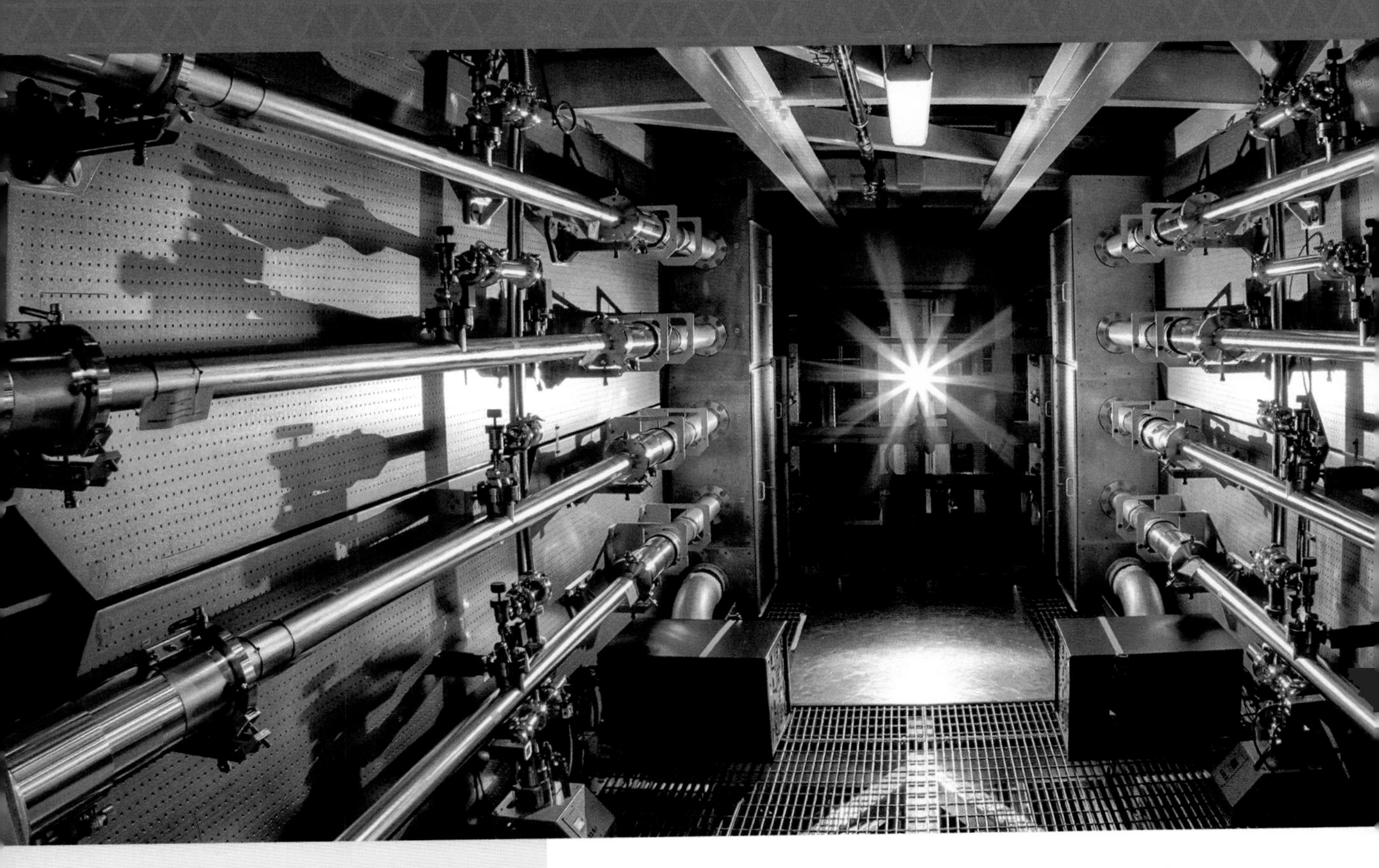

Topic List

- Expressions
- The Distributive Property
- Positive Exponents
- Negative Exponents
- Working with Exponents
- Scientific Notation
- Orders of Magnitude
- Working with Scientific Notation

Lawrence Livermore National Laboratory's National Ignition Facility uses lasers to create fusion reactions. In one experiment, the facility produced 5 quadrillion neutrons. That's a 5 with 15 zeros after it. Scientific notation can help you work with and make sense of huge numbers like this.

Expressions

A **numerical expression** consists of numbers and one or more operations.

Here are some examples of numerical expressions:

$18 - 2$ $\quad$ $7 + 2 \bullet 3$ $\quad$ $4 + 2[3 - 4 \div (12 - 8)]$ $\quad$ $\dfrac{(5+3)^2}{10 - 3(4 - 2)}$

Think About It

NOTATION 8^2 An exponent indicates repeated multiplication, so $8^2 = 8 \bullet 8$.

To find the value of a numerical expression, you need to simplify the expression or evaluate the expression. To simplify a numerical expression, perform the indicated operation(s).

Consider the expression $7 + 2 \bullet 3$. If you add and then multiply, you get the value 27. But if you multiply and then add, you get the value 13. Because an expression can have only one value, mathematicians have agreed on a process to follow so that everyone simplifies expressions the same way. This process is the **order of operations**.

Order of Operations

Step 1 Perform operations within grouping symbols. For nested grouping symbols, simplify in the innermost group first.

Step 2 Evaluate powers (as indicated by exponents).

Step 3 Multiply and divide from left to right.

Step 4 Add and subtract from left to right.

> **Think About It** You can use "**P**lease **E**xcuse **M**y **D**ear **A**unt **S**ally" to remember the order of operations.
>
> P: Parentheses
> E: Exponents
> M/D: Multiply and Divide
> A/S: Add and Subtract

The correct way to simplify $7 + 2 \cdot 3$ is to multiply and then add.

$$7 + 2 \cdot 3 = 7 + 6 = 13$$

The most common grouping symbols are parentheses ( ). Grouping symbols can affect the value of an expression. Nested grouping symbols (grouping symbols within grouping symbols) sometimes contain brackets [ ] and sometimes contain braces { }.

Simplifying Expressions With and Without Grouping Symbols

EXAMPLE 1

Simplify.

A $5 \cdot 2 + 7$

SOLUTION

$5 \cdot 2 + 7 = \mathbf{10} + 7$	Multiply.
$= 17$	Add.

B $5 \cdot (2 + 7)$

SOLUTION

$5 \cdot (2 + 7) = 5 \cdot (\mathbf{9})$	Add first because addition appears inside parentheses.
$= 45$	Multiply.

▶ **Think About It** The expression $5 \bullet (2+7)$ is also written as $5(2+7)$.

Simplifying Expressions with Several Operations

EXAMPLE 2

Simplify.

A $3 \bullet 7 - 10 \div 2 \bullet 3$

SOLUTION

$3 \bullet 7 - 10 \div 2 \bullet 3 = \mathbf{21} - 10 \div 2 \bullet 3$	Multiply and divide in order from left to right.
$= 21 - \mathbf{5} \bullet 3$	
$= 21 - \mathbf{15}$	
$= 6$	Subtract.

B $4 + 2[3 - 4 \div (12 - 8)]$

SOLUTION

$4 + 2[3 - 4 \div (12 - 8)] = 4 + 2[3 - 4 \div \mathbf{4}]$	Parentheses are nested within brackets. Subtract.
$= 4 + 2[3 - \mathbf{1}]$	Divide inside the brackets.
$= 4 + 2[\mathbf{2}]$	Subtract inside the brackets.
$= 4 + \mathbf{4}$	Multiply.
$= 8$	Add.

C $\frac{2}{3} + \frac{1}{3} \cdot 27 \div 3 - 2$

SOLUTION

$\frac{2}{3} + \frac{1}{3} \cdot 27 \div 3 - 2 = \frac{2}{3} + \mathbf{9} \div 3 - 2$ Multiply and divide in order from left to right.

$= \frac{2}{3} + \mathbf{3} - 2$

$= \mathbf{3\frac{2}{3}} - 2$ Add and subtract in order from left to right.

$= 1\frac{2}{3}$

D $68.3 - 5[4.2 + 3.6(4 - 1.5)]$

SOLUTION

$68.3 - 5[4.2 + 3.6(4 - 1.5)] = 68.3 - 5[4.2 + 3.6(\mathbf{2.5})]$ Subtract inside the parentheses, which are nested inside the brackets.

$= 68.3 - 5[4.2 + \mathbf{9}]$ Multiply inside the brackets.

$= 68.3 - 5[\mathbf{13.2}]$ Add inside the brackets.

$= 68.3 - \mathbf{66}$ Multiply.

$= 2.3$ Subtract. ■

Simplifying an Expression with a Fraction Bar

A fraction bar indicates division. It is also a grouping symbol, separating the numerator from the denominator.

EXAMPLE 3

Simplify.

$$\frac{(5 + 3)^2}{1 + 2^5 - 23}$$

SOLUTION

Treat the fraction bar as a grouping symbol. Simplify the numerator and denominator, and then divide.

$$\frac{(5+3)^2}{1+2^5-23} = \frac{(8)^2}{1+2^5-23}$$ Perform the operation inside the parentheses.

$$= \frac{\mathbf{64}}{1+\mathbf{32}-23}$$ Evaluate the powers: $8^2 = 8 \bullet 8 = 64$ and $2^5 = 2 \bullet 2 \bullet 2 \bullet 2 \bullet 2 = 32$.

$$= \frac{64}{\mathbf{10}}$$ Add and subtract from left to right to simplify the denominator.

$$= \frac{32}{5} = 6.4$$ Reduce the fraction or divide to simplify.

▶ **Think About It** In Example 3, the expression can be written as $(5+3)^2 \div (1+2^5-23)$.

Placing Grouping Symbols to Get a Specified Value

You can get different values for an expression by changing the placement of grouping symbols.

EXAMPLE 4

Place grouping symbols in the expression $2 \bullet 8 + 2^3 \bullet 10$ to get expressions that have these values: 20,000 and 80,000.

SOLUTION

The method is trial and error. Some possible placements of grouping symbols are $2 \bullet (8+2)^3 \bullet 10$, $[2 \bullet (8+2)]^3 \bullet 10$, and $(2 \bullet 8 + 2)^3 \bullet 10$. Evaluate these expressions, and try other placements if necessary. The two correct expressions are shown.

First Expression

$2 \cdot (8+2)^3 \cdot 10 = 2 \cdot (\mathbf{10})^3 \cdot 10$	Perform the operation inside the parentheses.
$= 2 \cdot \mathbf{1000} \cdot 10$	Evaluate the power: $10^3 = 10 \cdot 10 \cdot 10 = 1000$.
$= \mathbf{2000} \cdot 10$	Multiply from left to right.
$= 20{,}000$	Multiply.

Second Expression

$[2 \cdot (8+2)]^3 \cdot 10 = [2 \cdot (\mathbf{10})]^3 \cdot 10$	Perform the operation inside the parentheses.
$= [\mathbf{20}]^3 \cdot 10$	Perform the operation inside the brackets.
$= \mathbf{8000} \cdot 10$	Evaluate the power: $20^3 = 20 \cdot 20 \cdot 20 = 8000$.
$= 80{,}000$	Multiply. ■

The Distributive Property

You can use the distributive property to find the product of a number and a sum or the product of a number and a difference.

Distributive Property

Let a, b, and c be real numbers.

$$a(b+c) = a \cdot b + a \cdot c \text{ and } a(b-c) = a \cdot b - a \cdot c$$

Using the Distributive Property to Evaluate Expressions

Sometimes expressions are easier to evaluate when you apply the distributive property. The distributive property can also help you evaluate expressions using mental math.

EXAMPLE 1

Use the distributive property to evaluate the expression.

A $11 \cdot 62$

SOLUTION

$11 \cdot 62 = (10+1) \cdot 62$	Write 11 as the sum of 10 and 1.
$= 10 \cdot 62 + 1 \cdot 62$	Distributive Property
$= 620 + 62$	Multiply.
$= 682$	Add.

B $8 \cdot 14 + 8 \cdot 6$

SOLUTION

$8 \cdot 14 + 8 \cdot 6 = 8(14 + 6)$	Distributive Property
$= 8 \cdot 20$	Add.
$= 160$	Multiply. ■

Like Terms

The distributive property is also the property that allows you to combine like terms. Terms that contain the same variables raised to the same powers are **like terms**. In other words, like terms have identical variable parts.

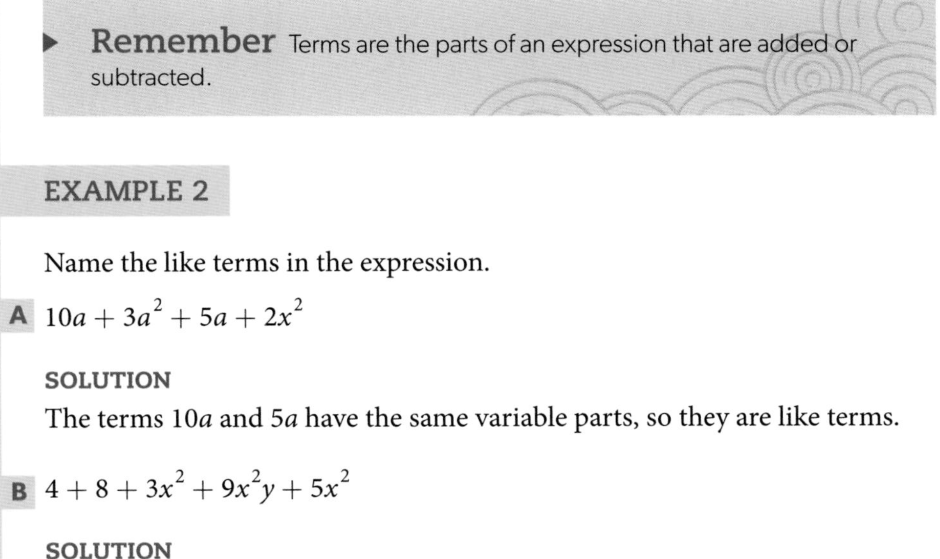

▶ **Remember** Terms are the parts of an expression that are added or subtracted.

EXAMPLE 2

Name the like terms in the expression.

A $10a + 3a^2 + 5a + 2x^2$

SOLUTION

The terms $10a$ and $5a$ have the same variable parts, so they are like terms.

B $4 + 8 + 3x^2 + 9x^2y + 5x^2$

SOLUTION

The terms $3x^2$ and $5x^2$ have the same variable parts, so they are like terms. The constant terms 4 and 8 are also like terms. ■

EXAMPLE 3

Combine the like terms in the expression.

A $10a + 3a^2 + 5a + 2x^2$

SOLUTION

From Example 2, you know the terms $10a$ and $5a$ are like terms. Simplify the expression.

$$\begin{aligned} 10a + 3a^2 + 5a + 2x^2 &= 10a + 5a + 3a^2 + 2x^2 \\ &= 15a + 3a^2 + 2x^2 \end{aligned}$$

B $4 + 8 + 3x^2 + 9x^2y + 5x^2$

SOLUTION

From Example 2, you know $3x^2$ and $5x^2$ are like terms, as are 4 and 8. Simplify the expression.

$$\begin{aligned} 4 + 8 + 3x^2 + 9x^2y + 5x^2 &= 4 + 8 + 3x^2 + 5x^2 + 9x^2y \\ &= 12 + 8x^2 + 9x^2y \end{aligned}$$

Terms may also have common factors. A **common factor** occurs when terms have at least one identical factor.

▶ **Think About It** Like terms always have a common factor.

EXAMPLE 4

Name the common factors of the terms $9x^3$, $3x^2$, and $6x$.

SOLUTION

Write the factors of each term.

$$9x^3 = \mathbf{3} \cdot 3 \cdot \boldsymbol{x} \cdot x \cdot x$$

$$3x^2 = \mathbf{3} \cdot \boldsymbol{x} \cdot x$$

$$6x = 2 \cdot \mathbf{3} \cdot \boldsymbol{x}$$

Each term has one 3 and one x. So the common factors are 1, 3, x, and $3x$.

Using the Distributive Property to Simplify Expressions

You can also use the distributive property to remove parentheses when simplifying expressions. To completely simplify an expression, remove any grouping symbols and combine all like terms.

EXAMPLE 5

Simplify.

A $3(y + 4) + 2y$

SOLUTION

$3(y + 4) + 2y = 3 \cdot y + 3 \cdot 4 + 2y$	Distributive Property
$= 3y + 12 + 2y$	Multiply.
$= 3y + 2y + 12$	Commutative Property of Addition
$= 5y + 12$	Combine like terms.

B $-8 + 2(x - 15) - x$

SOLUTION

$-8 + 2(x - 15) - x = -8 + 2 \cdot x - 2 \cdot 15 - x$	Distributive Property
$= -8 + 2x - 30 - x$	Multiply.
$= -8 - 30 + 2x - x$	Commutative Property of Addition
$= -38 + x$	Combine like terms.
$= x - 38$	Commutative Property of Addition ■

Application: Cost

EXAMPLE 6

A plumber charges $75 for the first hour of service and $60 per hour for each additional hour. Write an equation to find the total cost, C, in terms of time in hours, h.

SOLUTION

Step 1 Write a verbal model. Then write an equation.

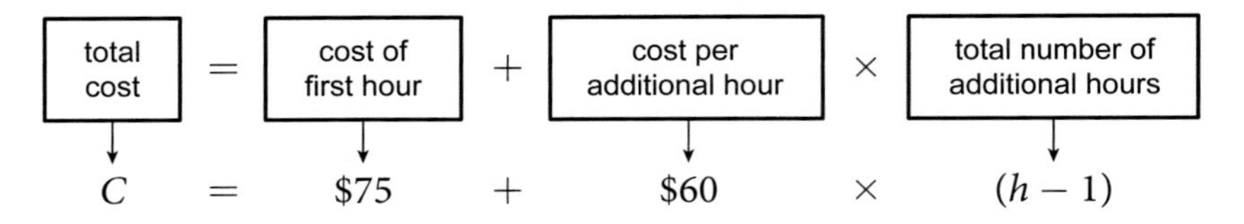

Step 2 Simplify the expression on the right side of the equation.

$$\begin{aligned} C &= 75 + 60(h - 1) \\ &= 75 + 60h - 60 \\ &= 15 + 60h \\ &= 60h + 15 \end{aligned}$$

The equation $C = 60h + 15$ can be used to find the total cost of the plumber's service. ■

Positive Exponents

A **power** is a special kind of product.

A power has a **base** and an **exponent**. In the power a^n, a is the base and n is the exponent. Read a^n as "a to the nth power." You can read a^2 as "a squared" and a^3 as "a cubed."

▶ **Think About It** Exponents are normally written above and to the right of the base.

Simplify a power by multiplying. The exponent tells how many times to use the base as a factor.

Positive Exponents

For any real number a and natural number n,

$$a^n = \underbrace{a \cdot a \cdot a \cdot a \cdot \ldots \cdot a}_{n \text{ factors}}$$

Simplifying Powers

EXAMPLE 1

Simplify.

A 2^4

SOLUTION

$2^4 = 2 \cdot 2 \cdot 2 \cdot 2$ Use 2 as a factor 4 times.

$= 16$ Multiply.

B $(-4)^2$

SOLUTION

$(-4)^2 = (-4) \cdot (-4)$ Use -4 as a factor 2 times.

$= 16$ Multiply the factors.

▶ **Think About It** Writing a power as a product first will help you avoid mistakes. In Example 1B, write $(-4) \cdot (-4)$, and then multiply.

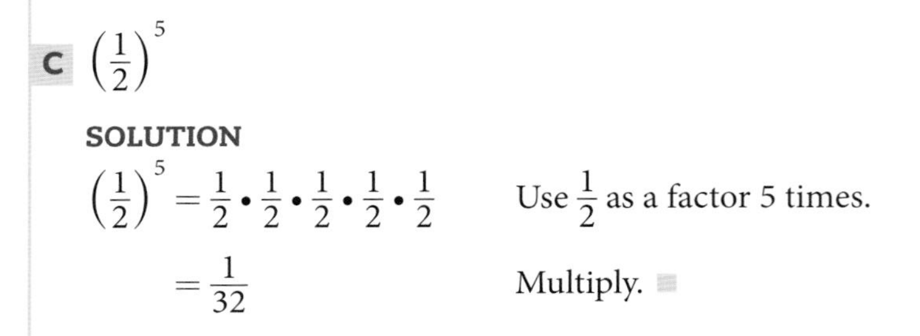

C $\left(\frac{1}{2}\right)^5$

SOLUTION

$\left(\frac{1}{2}\right)^5 = \frac{1}{2} \cdot \frac{1}{2} \cdot \frac{1}{2} \cdot \frac{1}{2} \cdot \frac{1}{2}$ Use $\frac{1}{2}$ as a factor 5 times.

$= \frac{1}{32}$ Multiply. ■

Exponents 0 and 1

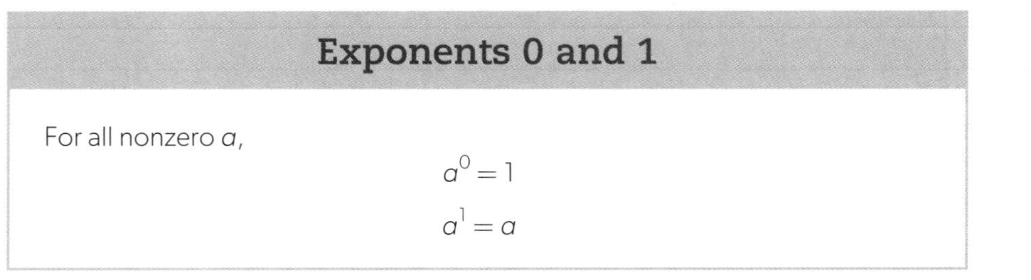

Exponents 0 and 1

For all nonzero a,

$$a^0 = 1$$

$$a^1 = a$$

EXAMPLE 2

Simplify.

A $4^0 \bullet 3^3$

SOLUTION

$4^0 \bullet 3^3 = \mathbf{1} \bullet 3^3$	Use $a^0 = 1$ to simplify 4^0.
$= 1 \bullet \mathbf{3} \bullet \mathbf{3} \bullet \mathbf{3}$	Use 3 as a factor 3 times.
$= 27$	Multiply.

B $(9 - 6)^2 + 2^1$

SOLUTION

$(9 - 6)^2 + 2^1 = 3^2 + 2^1$	Subtract inside the parentheses.
$= \mathbf{9} + 2^1$	Simplify 3^2.
$= 9 + \mathbf{2}$	Simplify 2^1.
$= 11$	Add.

C -4^2

SOLUTION

$-4^2 = -(4 \bullet 4)$	Use 4 as a factor 2 times.
$= -(16)$	Multiply the factors.
$= -16$	Simplify. ■

▶ **Think About It** Notice that, unlike in Example 1B, the negative is not inside the parentheses, so the answer remains negative.

Writing a Number as a Power

When a number can be written in the form a^n (where n is an integer), the number is a **power** of a.

EXAMPLE 3

A Write 16 as a power of 2.

SOLUTION

$16 = 2 \cdot 2 \cdot 2 \cdot 2$ Use 2 as a factor 4 times.

$= 2^4$ Write using an exponent.

▶ **Think About It** Divide the final product, 16, by the base, 2, and then divide the quotient by 2 again. Repeat until the final quotient is 1. The number of times the division is carried out is the exponent. This process is called repeated division.

B Write 125 as a power of 5.

SOLUTION

$125 = 5 \cdot 5 \cdot 5$ Use 5 as a factor 3 times.

$= 5^3$ Write using an exponent. ■

Evaluating Expressions with Variables and Exponents

To evaluate an expression with variables, first substitute the given values. Then simplify using the order of operations.

▶ **Think About It** Unless it appears after parentheses, an exponent applies only to a single number or variable.

$$-6b^3 = -6 \cdot b \cdot b \cdot b$$

On the other hand,

$$(-6b)^3 = (-6b) \cdot (-6b) \cdot (-6b).$$

EXAMPLE 4

Evaluate.

A $-6b^3$ when $b = 4$

SOLUTION

$-6b^3 = -6 \cdot 4^3$	Substitute 4 for b.
$= -6 \cdot 64$	Evaluate 4^3.
$= -384$	Multiply.

B $4m^3n^2$ when $m = -2$ and $n = 5$

SOLUTION

$4m^3n^2 = 4 \cdot (-2)^3 \cdot 5^2$	Substitute -2 for m and 5 for n.
$= 4 \cdot (-8) \cdot 25$	Evaluate $(-2)^3$ and 5^2.
$= -800$	Multiply.

▶ **Think About It** A negative number raised to an even power is positive. A negative number raised to an odd power is negative.

C $2x^3y^2$ when $x = 3$ and $y = -4$

SOLUTION

$2x^3y^2 = 2 \cdot 3^3 \cdot (-4)^2$	Substitute 3 for x and -4 for y.
$= 2 \cdot 27 \cdot 16$	Evaluate 3^3 and $(-4)^2$
$= 864$	Multiply. ■

Application: Genealogy

EXAMPLE 5

You can use exponents to model the number of ancestors in each generation of a person's family tree.

In this family tree, M stands for "Mother" and F stands for "Father."

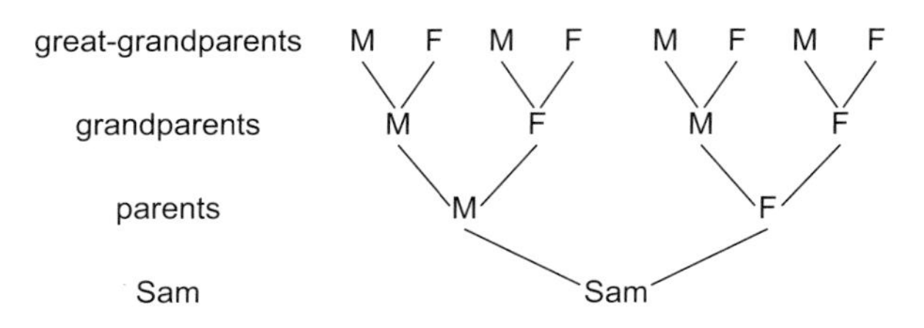

A How many people are 1 generation above Sam in the family tree? Write the number as a power of 2.

SOLUTION

There are 2 people. Sam's **2** parents are **1** generation above Sam.

$$2 = 2^1$$

B How many people are 2 generations above Sam in the family tree? Write the number as a power of 2.

SOLUTION

There are 4 people. Sam's **4** grandparents are **2** generations above Sam.

$$4 = 2^2$$

C Use the pattern to predict. How many people were in the sixth generation above Sam?

SOLUTION

There are 2^n people in the generation that is n generations above Sam. So there were 2^6, or 64, people in that generation. Sam has 64 great-great-great-great-grandparents. ■

Negative Exponents

A positive exponent means repeated multiplication.
A negative exponent means repeated division.

A power in which the exponent is a negative number can be simplified using the properties of negative exponents.

Properties of Negative Exponents

For all nonzero a and integer n,

$$a^{-1} = \frac{1}{a} \qquad a^{-n} = \frac{1}{a^n} \qquad \frac{1}{a^{-n}} = a^n$$

Simplifying Negative Exponents

EXAMPLE 1

Simplify.

A 10^{-1}

SOLUTION

$10^{-1} = \frac{1}{10^1}$ Write the expression using a positive exponent.

$= \frac{1}{10}$ Simplify.

▶ **Think About It** When you simplify a power that has a negative exponent, the result can be a positive number.

B 4^{-2}

SOLUTION

$4^{-2} = \frac{1}{4^2}$ Write the expression using a positive exponent.

$= \frac{1}{16}$ Simplify.

C $\frac{1}{2^{-3}}$

SOLUTION

$\frac{1}{2^{-3}} = 2^3$ Write the expression using a positive exponent.

$= 8$ Simplify. ■

Simplifying Expressions with Negative Exponents

To simplify expressions with negative exponents, follow the order of operations.

EXAMPLE 2

Simplify.

A $\frac{4}{3^{-2}}$

SOLUTION

$\frac{4}{3^{-2}} = 4 \bullet \frac{1}{3^{-2}}$ Write the fraction as a product.

$= 4 \bullet 3^2$ Write the expression using a positive exponent.

$= 4 \bullet 9$ Evaluate the power.

$= 36$ Multiply.

▶ **Think About It** Think of a negative exponent as a command telling you to move the power to the other level of the fraction. Once the command has been carried out, drop the negative sign.

B $\frac{4^{-3}}{8^{-2}}$

SOLUTION

$\frac{4^{-3}}{8^{-2}} = 4^{-3} \bullet \frac{1}{8^{-2}}$ Write the fraction as a product.

$= \frac{1}{4^3} \bullet 8^2$ Write the expression using positive exponents.

$= \frac{1}{64} \bullet 64$ Evaluate each power.

$= 1$ Multiply.

C $\frac{(3-5)^{-2}}{3 \bullet 5^{-3}}$

SOLUTION

$\frac{(3-5)^{-2}}{3 \bullet 5^{-3}} = \frac{(-2)^{-2}}{3 \bullet 5^{-3}}$ Subtract inside the parentheses.

$= \frac{5^3}{3(-2)^2}$ Write the expression using positive exponents.

$= \frac{125}{3 \bullet 4}$ Evaluate each power.

$= \frac{125}{12}$ Multiply. ■

Solving Equations with Negative Exponents

You can use exponential properties to solve equations.

EXAMPLE 3

Solve.

A $6^n = \frac{1}{36}$

SOLUTION

$$
\begin{aligned}
6^n &= \frac{1}{36} \\
&= \frac{1}{6^2} && \text{Write 36 as } 6^2. \\
&= 6^{-2} && \text{Write the positive exponent as a negative exponent.}
\end{aligned}
$$

Since $6^n = 6^{-2}$, $n = -2$.

▶ **Remember** Solutions to an equation are those values for variables that make the equation true.

B $x^{-3} = \frac{1}{27}$

SOLUTION

$$
\begin{aligned}
x^{-3} &= \frac{1}{27} \\
&= \frac{1}{3^3} && \text{Write 27 as } 3^3. \\
&= 3^{-3} && \text{Write the positive exponent as a negative exponent.}
\end{aligned}
$$

Since $x^{-3} = 3^{-3}$, $x = 3$. ■

Working with Exponents

To simplify or evaluate expressions with powers, apply the properties of exponents.

Multiplying Powers

Product of Powers Property

For all real numbers a, m, and n,

$$a^m \cdot a^n = a^{m+n}.$$

To multiply powers with equal bases, add the exponents. Then simplify the resulting expression.

EXAMPLE 1

Simplify.

$$2^3 \cdot 2^2$$

SOLUTION

Both powers have a base of 2. Let the base remain as 2 and add the exponents.

$$2^3 \cdot 2^2 = 2^{3+2} = 2^5 = 32$$ ■

▶ Think About It

$$2^3 = 2 \cdot 2 \cdot 2 \text{ and } 2^2 = 2 \cdot 2$$

$$\text{So } 2^3 \cdot 2^2 = (2 \cdot 2 \cdot 2) \cdot (2 \cdot 2)$$
$$= 2^5$$
$$= 32$$

Dividing Exponents

Quotient of Powers Property

For all real numbers a, m, and n, and $a \neq 0$,

$$\frac{a^m}{a^n} = a^{m-n}.$$

When you divide powers with equal bases, subtract the exponents. Then simplify the resulting expression.

EXAMPLE 2

Simplify.

A $\frac{4^4}{4^6}$

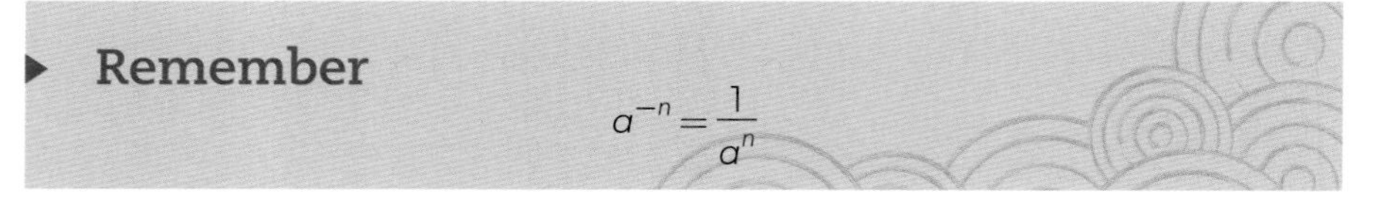

SOLUTION

Both powers have a base of 4. Let the base remain as 4 and subtract the exponents.

$$\frac{4^4}{4^6} = 4^{4-6} = 4^{-2} = \frac{1}{4^2} = \frac{1}{16}$$

Think About It

$$\begin{aligned} \frac{4^4}{4^6} &= \frac{\cancel{4} \cdot \cancel{4} \cdot \cancel{4} \cdot \cancel{4}}{\cancel{4} \cdot \cancel{4} \cdot \cancel{4} \cdot \cancel{4} \cdot 4 \cdot 4} \\ &= \frac{1}{4 \cdot 4} \\ &= \frac{1}{4^2} \\ &= \frac{1}{16} \end{aligned}$$

B $\frac{2^3 \cdot 2^5}{2^4}$

SOLUTION

Apply the product of powers property to simplify the numerator, and then apply the quotient of powers property.

▶ **Think About It** When you divide powers with equal bases, always subtract the exponent in the denominator from the exponent in the numerator.

$$\frac{2^3 \cdot 2^5}{2^4} = \frac{2^{3+5}}{2^4} \quad \text{Product of Powers Property}$$

$$= \frac{2^8}{2^4} \quad \text{Simplify.}$$

$$= 2^{8-4} \quad \text{Quotient of Powers Property}$$

$$= 2^4 \quad \text{Simplify.}$$

$$= 16$$

Raising a Power to a Power

Power of a Power Property

For all real numbers a, m, and n,

$$(a^m)^n = a^{mn}.$$

To raise a power to another power, multiply the exponents. Then simplify the resulting expression.

EXAMPLE 3

Simplify.

A $\left(2^3\right)^2$

SOLUTION

$$\begin{aligned}\left(2^3\right)^2 &= 2^{3 \cdot 2}\\ &= 2^6\\ &= 64\end{aligned}$$

▶ **Think About It**

$$\begin{aligned}\left(2^3\right)^2 &= 2^3 \cdot 2^3\\ &= (2 \cdot 2 \cdot 2) \cdot (2 \cdot 2 \cdot 2)\end{aligned}$$

B $\dfrac{\left(4^2\right)^3}{4^7}$

SOLUTION

Apply the power of a power property to simplify the numerator. Then apply the quotient of powers property.

$$\begin{aligned}\frac{\left(4^2\right)^3}{4^7} &= \frac{4^{2 \cdot 3}}{4^7} && \text{Power of a Power Property}\\ &= \frac{4^6}{4^7} && \text{Simplify.}\\ &= 4^{6-7} && \text{Quotient of Powers Property}\\ &= \frac{1}{4} \;\blacksquare\end{aligned}$$

Scientific Notation

When a number has lots of zeros, you can use scientific notation to represent very great or very small values.

A number is written in **scientific notation** when it is written as the product of a number that is greater than or equal to 1 but less than 10 multiplied by an integer power of 10.

Scientific notation is especially useful for writing very large or very small numbers that may have many zeros.

Scientific Notation and Standard Form

Converting from Scientific Notation to Standard Form

To convert a number that is in the form $a \times 10^n$ from scientific notation to standard form,

$n > 0$ Move the decimal n places to the right.

$n < 0$ Move the decimal n places to the left.

EXAMPLE 1

Write the number in standard form.

A 7.5×10^9

SOLUTION

$7.5 \times 10^9 = 7.500000000$ Move the decimal point 9 places to the right and add zeros as needed.

$= 7{,}500{,}000{,}000$

B 3.95×10^{-6}

SOLUTION

$3.95 \times 10^{-6} = 000003.95$ Move the decimal point 6 places to the left and add zeros as needed.

$= 0.00000395$

Converting from Standard Form to Scientific Notation

To convert a number from standard form to scientific notation,

number > 10 Move the decimal to the left until the number is between 1 and 10. Add "$\times 10^n$," where n is the number of places you moved the decimal.

number < 1 Move the decimal to the right until the number is between 1 and 10. Add "$\times 10^{-n}$," where n is the number of places you moved the decimal.

EXAMPLE 2

Write the number in scientific notation.

A 35,000,000

SOLUTION

$35{,}000{,}000 = 35{,}000{,}000.$ Move the decimal point 7 places to the left.

$= 3.5 \times 10^7$

▶ **Think About It** To remember whether to use a positive or negative power of 10, ask yourself if you want to make the first factor greater or lesser. To make it greater, use a positive exponent. To make it lesser, use a negative exponent.

B 0.0000024

SOLUTION

$0.0000024 = .0000024$ Move the decimal point 6 places to the right.

$= 2.4 \times 10^{-6}$ ■

Using Scientific Notation to Add and Subtract Numbers

Adding Numbers with Scientific Notation

To add numbers that are written in scientific notation, rewrite the addends in scientific notation with the same power of 10. Use the distributive property to regroup the numbers and the power of 10. Then add the numbers, keeping the power of 10 the same.

EXAMPLE 3

Add. Write the sum in scientific notation.

A $\left(7.36 \times 10^3\right) + \left(4.9 \times 10^5\right)$

▶ **Think About It** Although you can rewrite the numbers using either power of 10, it will be easier to rewrite these numbers using the power with the least exponent, 10^3.

SOLUTION

$$\begin{aligned}(7.36 \times 10^3) + (4.9 \times 10^5) &= (7.36 \times 10^3) + (490 \times 10^3) && \text{Rewrite the numbers with the same power of 10.}\\ &= (7.36 + 490) \times 10^3 && \text{Distributive Property}\\ &= 497.36 \times 10^3 && \text{Add.}\\ &= 4.9736 \times 10^5 && \text{Write in scientific notation.}\end{aligned}$$

B $0.0000277 + (8.6 \times 10^{-6})$

▶ **Think About It** When one of the numbers is written in standard form, you will need to write the number in scientific notation first before solving the problem.

SOLUTION

$$\begin{aligned}0.0000277 + (8.6 \times 10^{-6}) &= (2.77 \times 10^{-5}) + (8.6 \times 10^{-6}) && \text{Write the decimal number in scientific notation.}\\ &= (27.7 \times 10^{-6}) + (8.6 \times 10^{-6}) && \text{Rewrite the numbers with the same power of 10.}\\ &= (27.7 + 8.6) \times 10^{-6} && \text{Distributive Property}\\ &= 36.3 \times 10^{-6} && \text{Add.}\\ &= 3.63 \times 10^{-5} && \text{Write in scientific notation.}\end{aligned}$$

Subtracting Numbers with Scientific Notation

To subtract numbers that are written in scientific notation, rewrite the numbers in scientific notation with the same power of 10. Use the distributive property to regroup the numbers and the power of 10. Then subtract the numbers, keeping the power of 10 the same.

EXAMPLE 4

Subtract. Write the difference in scientific notation.

A $(9.3 \times 10^8) - (2.1 \times 10^7)$

SOLUTION

$(9.3 \times 10^8) - (2.1 \times 10^7) = (93 \times 10^7) - (2.1 \times 10^7)$ Rewrite the numbers with the same power of 10.

$= (93 - 2.1) \times 10^7$ Distributive Property

$= 90.9 \times 10^7$ Subtract.

$= 9.09 \times 10^8$ Write in scientific notation.

B $(6.67 \times 10^{-4}) - (0.0000525)$

SOLUTION

$(6.67 \times 10^{-4}) - (0.0000525) = (6.67 \times 10^{-4}) - (5.25 \times 10^{-5})$ Write the decimal number in scientific notation.

$= (66.7 \times 10^{-5}) - (5.25 \times 10^{-5})$ Rewrite the numbers with the same power of 10.

$= (66.7 - 5.25) \times 10^{-5}$ Distributive Property

$= 61.45 \times 10^{-5}$ Subtract.

$= 6.145 \times 10^{-4}$ Write in scientific notation.

Using Scientific Notation to Multiply and Divide Numbers

Multiplying Numbers with Scientific Notation

To multiply numbers that are written in scientific notation, first use the commutative and associative properties to regroup the numbers and the powers of 10. Then multiply the numbers.

EXAMPLE 5

Multiply.

A $(3.2 \times 10^2) \bullet (1.05 \times 10^3)$

SOLUTION

$(3.2 \times 10^2) \bullet (1.05 \times 10^3) = 3.2 \bullet 1.05 \bullet 10^2 \bullet 10^3$	Commutative and Associative Properties of Multiplication
$= 3.36 \bullet 10^2 \bullet 10^3$	Multiply.
$= 3.36 \bullet 10^{(2+3)}$	Product of Powers Property
$= 3.36 \times 10^5$	Write in scientific notation.

B $(1.6 \times 10^2) \bullet (4.5 \times 10^{-3})$

SOLUTION

$(1.6 \times 10^2) \bullet (4.5 \times 10^{-3}) = 1.6 \bullet 4.5 \bullet 10^2 \bullet 10^{-3}$	Commutative and Associative Properties of Multiplication
$= 7.2 \bullet 10^2 \bullet \frac{1}{10^3}$	Simplify exponents. Multiply.
$= 7.2 \bullet \frac{10^2}{10^3}$	Multiply.
$= 7.2 \bullet \frac{1}{10}$	Quotient of Powers Property
$= 7.2 \times 10^{-1}$	Write in scientific notation.

Dividing Numbers with Scientific Notation

To divide numbers that are written in scientific notation, first use the commutative and associative properties to regroup the numbers and the powers of 10. Then divide the numbers.

EXAMPLE 6

Divide. Write the quotient in scientific notation.

A $\left(8.4 \times 10^5\right) \div \left(1.5 \times 10^3\right)$

SOLUTION

$$\left(8.4 \times 10^5\right) \div \left(1.5 \times 10^3\right) = (8.4 \div 1.5) \times \left(10^5 \div 10^3\right)$$ Commutative and Associative Properties of Multiplication

$$= 5.6 \times \left(10^5 \div 10^3\right)$$ Divide.

$$= 5.6 \times 10^{(5-3)}$$ Quotient of Powers Property

$$= 5.6 \times 10^2$$ Write in scientific notation.

B $\left(4.914 \times 10^2\right) \div \left(6.3 \times 10^{-4}\right)$

SOLUTION

$$\left(4.914 \times 10^2\right) \div \left(6.3 \times 10^{-4}\right) = (4.914 \div 6.3) \times \left(10^2 \div 10^{-4}\right)$$ Commutative and Associative Properties of Multiplication

$$= 0.78 \times \left(10^2 \div \frac{1}{10^4}\right)$$ Divide.

$$= 0.78 \times \left(10^2 \times 10^4\right)$$ Multiply by the reciprocal.

$$= 0.78 \times 10^6$$ Product of Powers Property

$$= 7.8 \times 10^5$$ Write in scientific notation. ■

Application: Astronomy

EXAMPLE 7

The speed of light is about 299,800 km/s.

How many kilometers can light travel in 1 day? Write the answer in scientific notation.

SOLUTION

$299{,}800 \times 60 = 17{,}988{,}000$	Find the number of kilometers light travels in 1 min.
$17{,}988{,}000 \times 60 = 1{,}079{,}280{,}000$	Find the number of kilometers light travels in 1 h.
$1{,}079{,}280{,}000 \times 24 = 25{,}902{,}720{,}000$	Find the number of kilometers light travels in 1 day.
$25{,}902{,}720{,}000 = 2.59 \times 10^{10}$	Write in scientific notation.

Light travels about 2.59×10^{10} km in 1 day. ■

Orders of Magnitude

Orders of magnitude help you make rough estimates of large or small numbers.

Estimating Very Large or Small Numbers

One way to estimate a very large or very small number is to express the number as a product of a single digit and a power of 10. First write the number in scientific notation. Then round the decimal factor to the nearest whole number.

EXAMPLE 1

Solve.

A China's population in 2013 was 1,347,350,000. Estimate China's population. Express your estimate as the product of a single digit and a power of 10.

SOLUTION

Step 1 Write China's population in scientific notation.

$$1{,}347{,}350{,}000 = 1.34735 \times 10^9$$

Step 2 Round 1.34735 to the nearest whole number.

$$1.34735 \times 10^9 \approx 1 \times 10^9$$

China's population was about 1×10^9.

▶ **Think About It** In 2013, China was the most populous country in the world. Its residents made up about 19% of the world's population.

B The diameter of a water molecule is 0.00000000027 m. Estimate the diameter. Express your estimate as the product of a single digit and a power of 10.

SOLUTION

Step 1 Write the diameter of a water molecule in scientific notation.

$$0.000000000275 = 2.75 \times 10^{-10}$$

Step 2 Round 2.75 to the nearest whole number.

$$2.75 \times 10^{-10} \approx 3 \times 10^{-10}$$

A water molecule's diameter is about 3×10^{-10} m. ■

Making Comparisons

To compare two numbers that are expressed as the product of a single digit and a power of 10, simply compare the powers of 10. The number with the greater exponent is greater. If the exponents are equal, compare the single digit factors.

EXAMPLE 2

Compare. Use $>$, $<$, or $=$.

A $2 \times 10^{6} \blacksquare 1 \times 10^{7}$

SOLUTION

The exponent 6 is less than the exponent 7. Therefore, $2 \times 10^{6} < 1 \times 10^{7}$.

B $3 \times 10^{-5} \blacksquare 5 \times 10^{-8}$

SOLUTION

The exponent -5 is greater than the exponent -8. Therefore, $3 \times 10^{-5} > 5 \times 10^{-8}$.

C $4 \times 10^{-3} \blacksquare 6 \times 10^{-3}$

SOLUTION

In both numbers, the power of 10 has an exponent of -3, so compare the single digit factors. Since 4 is less than 6, $4 \times 10^{-3} < 6 \times 10^{-3}$. ■

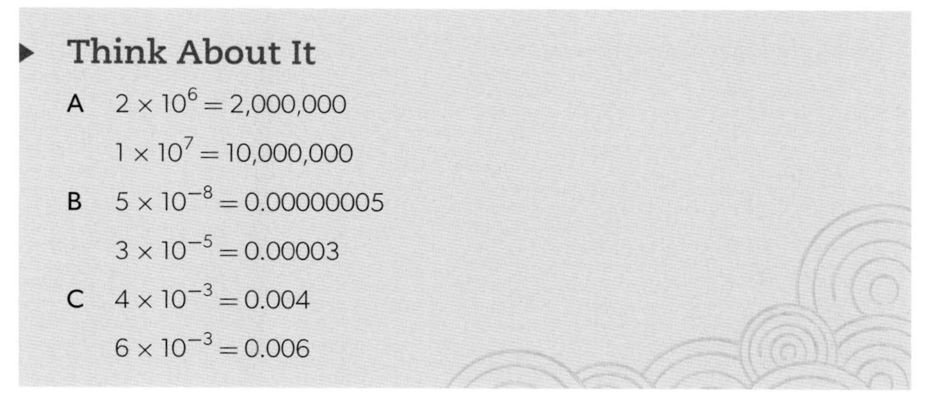

Think About It

A $2 \times 10^6 = 2{,}000{,}000$

$1 \times 10^7 = 10{,}000{,}000$

B $5 \times 10^{-8} = 0.00000005$

$3 \times 10^{-5} = 0.00003$

C $4 \times 10^{-3} = 0.004$

$6 \times 10^{-3} = 0.006$

You can compare two numbers in scientific notation by using division. By dividing the numbers, you will find how many times greater one value is than the other.

EXAMPLE 3

Determine how many times greater the first number is than the second number.

A 9×10^6 and 3×10^2

SOLUTION

Divide 9×10^6 by 3×10^2.

Remember For all real numbers a, m, and n, if $a \neq 0$,

$$\frac{a^m}{a^n} = a^{m-n}.$$

$$\begin{aligned}\frac{9 \times 10^6}{3 \times 10^2} &= \frac{9}{3} \times \frac{10^6}{10^2} \\ &= 3 \times 10^4 \\ &= 30{,}000\end{aligned}$$

So 9×10^6 is 30,000 times greater than 3×10^2.

B 4×10^{-3} and 8×10^{-5}

SOLUTION

Divide 4×10^{-3} by 8×10^{-5}.

$$\frac{4 \times 10^{-3}}{8 \times 10^{-5}} = \frac{4}{8} \times \frac{10^{-3}}{10^{-5}}$$
$$= 0.5 \times 10^{2}$$
$$= 50$$

So 4×10^{-3} is 50 times greater than 8×10^{-5}. ■

EXAMPLE 4

Use estimation and scientific notation to determine about how many times greater one value is than the other.

A Jupiter is the largest planet in our solar system, with a diameter of 1.42984×10^{8} m. Mercury is the smallest planet in our solar system, with a diameter of 4.879×10^{6} m. About how much greater is Jupiter's diameter than Mercury's diameter?

SOLUTION

Estimate each diameter. Then divide the estimates.

Jupiter: $1.42984 \times 10^{8} \approx 1 \times 10^{8}$

Mercury: $4.879 \times 10^{6} \approx 5 \times 10^{6}$

$$\frac{1 \times 10^{8}}{5 \times 10^{6}} = \frac{1}{5} \times \frac{10^{8}}{10^{6}}$$
$$= 0.2 \times 10^{2}$$
$$= 20$$

Jupiter's diameter is approximately 20 times greater than Mercury's diameter.

B The mass of one atom of platinum is approximately 3.2394×10^{-22} g, and the mass of one atom of carbon is 1.9927×10^{-23} g. How much heavier is one atom of platinum than one atom of carbon?

SOLUTION

Estimate each mass. Then divide the estimates.

platinum: $3.2394 \times 10^{-22} \approx 3 \times 10^{-22}$

carbon: $1.9927 \times 10^{-23} \approx 2 \times 10^{-23}$

$$\begin{aligned} \frac{3 \times 10^{-22}}{2 \times 10^{-23}} &= \frac{3}{2} \times \frac{10^{-22}}{10^{-23}} \\ &= 1.5 \times 10^{1} \\ &= 15 \end{aligned}$$

The mass of one atom of platinum is approximately 15 times greater than the mass of one atom of carbon.

Estimating Numbers to Nearest Order of Magnitude

In some instances, you may only need a rough estimate of a number. In those situations, estimate the number to its nearest order of magnitude.

Definition

An **order-of-magnitude estimate** is an estimate expressed as a power of 10.

To find the best order-of-magnitude estimate of a number, determine the power of 10 to which the number is nearest in value.

EXAMPLE 5

The average height of a female giraffe is 15 ft. What is the best order-of-magnitude estimate of the giraffe's height in feet?

SOLUTION

Fifteen lies between 10 and 100, so $10^1 < 15 < 10^2$. The number 15 is closer in value to 10^1 than 10^2. Therefore, the best order-of-magnitude estimate for the height of the giraffe is 10^1, or 10 ft. ■

> ▶ **Think About It** The best order-of-magnitude estimate for a person who is 6 ft tall is 10^1 ft because 6 is closer $10^1 = 10$ than $10^0 = 1$.

EXAMPLE 6

A red blood cell has a diameter of about 0.000008 m. What is the best order-of-magnitude estimate for the diameter of a red blood cell in meters?

SOLUTION

The decimal 0.000008 is between 0.000001 and 0.00001, so $10^{-6} < 0.000008 < 10^{-5}$. The decimal 0.000008 is closer in value to 0.00001 than 0.000001. Therefore, the best order-of-magnitude estimate for the diameter of a red blood cell is 10^{-5} m. ■

> ▶ **Think About It** The difference between 0.00001 and 0.000008 is less than the difference between 0.000008 and 0.000001.
>
> $$0.00001 - 0.000008 = 0.000002$$
>
> $$0.000008 - 0.000001 = 0.000007$$
>
> $$0.000002 < 0.000007$$
>
> Therefore, 0.000008 is closer to 0.00001, or 10^{-5} in value.

EXAMPLE 7

According to one study, the median number of texts a teen sends in a day is 60. What is the best order-of-magnitude estimate for the number of texts a teen sends in a year?

SOLUTION

There are 365 days in a year, so multiply 60 by 365.

$$60 \times 365 = 21{,}900$$

The number 21,900 is between 10,000 and 100,000, but it is closer to 10,000. Therefore, the best order-of-magnitude estimate for the number of texts a teen sends in a year is 10^4, or 10,000 texts.

Working with Scientific Notation

You can use scientific notation to solve problems involving very large or very small numbers.

Converting Units Expressed in Scientific Notation

To convert units, use a process called dimensional analysis. Multiply the given quantity by appropriate unit rates so that unwanted units divide out and the desired units remain.

EXAMPLE 1

Convert 50 m/s to kilometers per hour.

SOLUTION

Approach this problem in two steps. First convert kilometers to meters. Then convert seconds to hours.

Step 1 Multiply the rate by $\frac{1 \text{ km}}{1000 \text{ m}}$ to get kilometers per second.

$$\frac{50 \text{ m}}{1 \text{ s}} \bullet \frac{1 \text{ km}}{1000 \text{ m}} = \frac{\overset{1}{\cancel{50}} \cancel{\text{m}}}{1 \text{ s}} \bullet \frac{1 \text{ km}}{\underset{20}{\cancel{1000}} \cancel{\text{m}}}$$ Divide common factors and units.

$$= \frac{1 \text{ km}}{20 \text{ s}}$$ Multiply,

$$= \frac{1}{20} \text{ km/s}$$ Simplify.

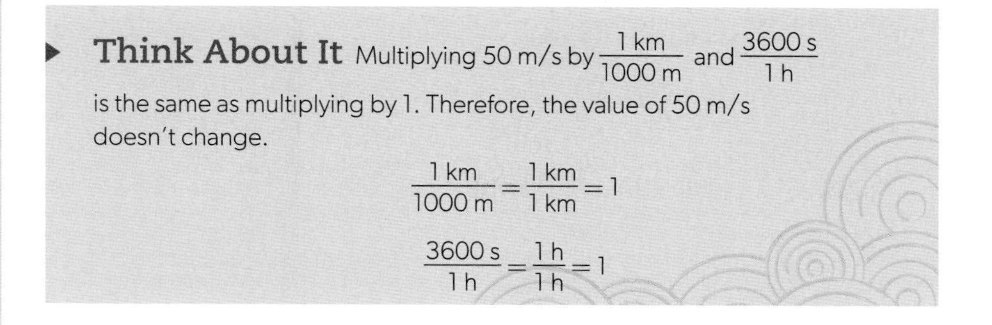

Think About It Multiplying 50 m/s by $\frac{1\text{ km}}{1000\text{ m}}$ and $\frac{3600\text{ s}}{1\text{ h}}$ is the same as multiplying by 1. Therefore, the value of 50 m/s doesn't change.

$$\frac{1\text{ km}}{1000\text{ m}} = \frac{1\text{ km}}{1\text{ km}} = 1$$

$$\frac{3600\text{ s}}{1\text{ h}} = \frac{1\text{ h}}{1\text{ h}} = 1$$

Step 2 Multiply the resulting rate by $\frac{3600\text{ s}}{1\text{ h}}$ to get kilometers per hour.

$$\frac{1\text{ km}}{20\text{ s}} \bullet \frac{3600\text{ s}}{1\text{ h}} = \frac{1\text{ km}}{\cancel{20}^{1}\,\cancel{\text{s}}} \bullet \frac{\cancel{3600}^{180}\,\cancel{\text{s}}}{1\text{ h}}$$ Divide common factors and units.

$$= \frac{1 \bullet 180\text{ km}}{1\text{ h}}$$ Simplify.

$$= \frac{180\text{ km}}{1\text{ h}}$$ Multiply.

$$= 180\text{ km/h}$$ Simplify.

Follow the same process when values are expressed in scientific notation.

EXAMPLE 2

Convert 5.2×10^4 mL/s to liters per minute.

SOLUTION

Step 1 Multiply the rate by $\frac{1\text{ L}}{1000\text{ mL}}$, or $\frac{1\text{ L}}{1 \times 10^3\text{ mL}}$, to get liters per second.

$$\frac{5.2 \times 10^4\text{ mL}}{1\text{ s}} \bullet \frac{1\text{ L}}{1000\text{ mL}} = \frac{5.2 \times 10^4\ \cancel{\text{mL}}}{1\text{ s}} \bullet \frac{1\text{ L}}{1 \times 10^3\ \cancel{\text{mL}}}$$

$$= \frac{5.2 \times 10^4\text{ L}}{1 \times 10^3\text{ s}}$$

$$= 5.2 \times 10^1\text{ L/s}$$

Step 2 Multiply the resulting rate by $\frac{60 \text{ s}}{1 \text{ min}}$, or $\frac{6 \times 10^1 \text{ s}}{1 \text{ min}}$, to get liters per minute.

$$\frac{5.2 \times 10^1 \text{ L}}{1 \text{ s}} \bullet \frac{60 \text{ s}}{1 \text{ min}} = \frac{5.2 \times 10^1 \text{ L}}{1 \cancel{\text{s}}} \bullet \frac{6 \times 10^1 \cancel{\text{s}}}{1 \text{ min}}$$

$$= \frac{(5.2 \text{ L} \times 6) \bullet (10^1 \times 10^1)}{1 \text{ min}}$$

$$= \frac{31.2 \times 10^2 \text{ L}}{1 \text{ min}}$$

$$= 3.12 \times 10^3 \text{ L/min}$$ ■

You can use dimensional analysis in many everyday situations.

EXAMPLE 3

On average, a highway-registered car emits about 1.4×10^3 g of carbon dioxide each day. In 2010, there were about 1.35×10^8 highway-registered cars in the United States.

A About how many grams of carbon dioxide did highway-registered cars in the United States emit on a single day in 2010?

SOLUTION

Multiply the number of grams emitted per car by the number of cars.

$$\frac{1.4 \times 10^3 \text{ g}}{1 \text{ car}} \bullet \frac{1.35 \times 10^8 \text{ cars}}{1} = \frac{1.4 \times 10^3 \text{ g}}{1 \cancel{\text{car}}} \bullet \frac{1.35 \times 10^8 \cancel{\text{cars}}}{1}$$

$$= (1.4 \times 1.35 \text{ g})(10^3 \times 10^8)$$

$$= 1.89 \times 10^{11} \text{ g}$$

In 2010, highway-registered cars in the United States emitted about 1.89×10^{11} g of carbon dioxide in a single day.

B About how many kilograms of carbon dioxide did highway-registered cars in the United States emit in 2010?

SOLUTION

Step 1 Find the number of grams emitted per year. Multiply the number of grams emitted per day by 365 days.

$$\frac{1.89 \times 10^{11}\text{ g}}{1\text{ day}} \bullet \frac{365\text{ days}}{1\text{ year}} = \frac{1.89 \times 10^{11}\text{ g}}{1\text{ }\cancel{\text{day}}} \bullet \frac{365\text{ }\cancel{\text{days}}}{1\text{ year}}$$

$$= \frac{689.85 \times 10^{11}\text{ g}}{1\text{ year}}$$

$$\approx 6.9 \times 10^{13}\text{ g/year}$$

Step 2 Convert grams per year to kilograms per year. There are 1000, or 1×10^3, g in 1 kg.

$$\frac{6.9 \times 10^{13}\text{ g}}{1\text{ year}} \bullet \frac{1\text{ kg}}{1 \times 10^3\text{ g}} = \frac{6.9 \times 10^{13}\text{ }\cancel{\text{g}}}{1\text{ year}} \bullet \frac{1\text{ kg}}{1 \times 10^3\text{ }\cancel{\text{g}}}$$

$$= \frac{6.9 \times 10^{13}\text{ kg}}{1 \times 10^3\text{ year}}$$

$$= 6.9 \times 10^{10}\text{ kg/year}$$

In 2010, highway-registered cars in the United States emitted about 6.9×10^{10} kg of carbon dioxide.

Choosing Appropriate Units

You can determine which units of measure are an appropriate size for very large or very small real-world measurements by using scientific notation.

▶ **Remember** It is easy to convert measurements in the metric system, since metric measurements are all based on powers of 10. Here are some basic metric prefixes and their orders of magnitude.

Prefix	*milli–*	*centi–*	*deci–*	Unit (meter, liter, gram)	*deca–*	*hecto–*	*kilo–*
Order of magnitude	10^{-3}	10^{-2}	10^{-1}	1	10	10^2	10^3

EXAMPLE 4

Determine a more appropriate unit of measure than the one given.

A Human hair grows approximately 1.25×10^{-5} km/month.

SOLUTION

Determine which measurement equals 1 km when it is multiplied by 10^5. Start at *kilo–* in the metric system table. Move 5 columns to the left, which is *centi–*. Convert 1.25×10^{-5} km/month to centimeters per month.

$$\frac{1.25 \times 10^{-5}\ \cancel{\text{km}}}{1\ \text{month}} \bullet \frac{1 \times 10^{5}\ \text{cm}}{1\ \cancel{\text{km}}} = \frac{1.25\ \text{cm}}{1\ \text{month}}$$

Human hair grows approximately 1.25 cm/month.

B Earth spins approximately 1.68×10^{9} mm/h at the equator.

SOLUTION

Determine which measurement equals 1 mm when it is multiplied by 10^{-9}. Start at *milli–* in the metric system table. You can only move 6 columns to the right, so convert 1.68×10^{9} mm/h to kilometers per hour.

$$\frac{1.68 \times 10^{9}\ \cancel{\text{mm}}}{1\ \text{h}} \bullet \frac{1\ \text{km}}{1 \times 10^{6}\ \cancel{\text{mm}}} = \frac{1.68 \times 10^{3}\ \text{km}}{1\ \text{h}}$$

Earth spins approximately 1.68×10^{3} km/h.

C Trudy is going to use a hose to fill a 5000 gal pool. The hose will fill up the pool at a rate of 1.2 pt/s. Trudy wants to determine how long it will take for the hose to fill the pool.

SOLUTION

Determine which units of measure would be the most appropriate for Trudy to use. Pints should be converted to gallons. And since there are thousands of gallons, seconds should be converted to hours. So the rate for filling the pool should be expressed in gallons per hour.

Remember 8 pt = 1 gal

Convert pints to gallons.

$$\frac{1.2\ \cancel{pt}}{1\ s} \bullet \frac{1\ gal}{8\ \cancel{pt}} = \frac{0.15\ gal}{1\ s} = 1.5 \times 10^{-1}\ gal/s$$

Convert seconds to hours.

$$\frac{1.5 \times 10^{-1}\ gal}{1\ \cancel{s}} \bullet \frac{3.6 \times 10^{3}\ \cancel{s}}{1\ h} = \frac{5.4 \times 10^{2}\ gal}{1\ h}$$

The hose fills the pool with water at a rate of 5.4×10^{2} gal/h. ■

Scientific Notation on a Calculator

When a number has too many digits for a calculator's display, the calculator expresses the number in scientific notation.

Think About It The number of digits that a calculator can display varies from calculator to calculator.

EXAMPLE 5

Use a calculator to multiply or divide. Write the answer in scientific notation.

A 2000^{10}

SOLUTION

Enter the expression on a calculator.

2000 [x^y] 10 [=]

```
1.024e+33
```

The calculator's answer is in scientific notation, where **1.024** is the decimal part, and **e+33** is the power of 10 part, which means 10^{33}. Therefore, **1.024 e+33** represents 1.024×10^{33}.

B 0.00002^{20}

SOLUTION

Enter the expression on a calculator.

0.00002 [x^y] 20 [=]

```
1.048576e−94
```

Once again, the calculator expresses the answer in scientific notation, where **1.048576** is the decimal part and **e–94** is the power of 10 part, which means 10^{-94}. Therefore, **1.048576 e–94** represents 1.048576×10^{-94}. ■

▶ **Think About It** There can be slight variations in the way different calculators display scientific notation. For instance, on some calculators 1.024×10^{33} is displayed as 1.024E33.

The [x^y] button is actually a [∧] button on some calculators.

Linear Equations

Topic List

- Addition and Subtraction Equations
- More Addition and Subtraction Equations
- Multiplication and Division Equations
- Tougher Equations
- Multiple Transformations
- Variables on Both Sides of an Equation
- Strange Solutions
- Problem Solving with Equations

If you add 3 kg to one side of a balanced load, you need to add the same amount to the other side as well. Otherwise, the load won't balance. Similarly, whatever you do to one side of an equation, you have to do to the other side too. You have to keep your equations balanced.

Addition and Subtraction Equations

Use properties of equality and what you know about inverse operations to solve addition and subtraction equations.

An equation is a number sentence indicating that two expressions have the same value. A **solution** of an equation is a value for the variable that makes the equation a true statement. To **solve** an equation, you need to find all the solutions of the equation. Some one-variable equations have more than one solution.

One way to solve an equation is to find a series of equivalent equations, each one simpler than the one before. **Equivalent equations** are equations with the same solution or solutions.

Properties of Equality

Addition Property of Equality If $a = b$, then $a + c = b + c$ and $c + a = c + b$.

Subtraction Property of Equality If $a = b$, then $a - c = b - c$.

Substitution Property of Equality If $a = b$, then a may be replaced with b in any expression or equation.

The addition property of equality tells you that you can add the same value to each side of an equation to create an equivalent equation. The subtraction property of equality tells you that you can subtract the same value from each side of an equation to create an equivalent equation.

▶ **Think About It** Use the addition and subtraction properties to solve an equation. Use the substitution property to check your solution.

Solving a Subtraction Equation

Remember that addition and subtraction are inverse operations, so use the addition property of equality to solve subtraction equations.

EXAMPLE 1

Solve $x - 12 = 8$.

SOLUTION

You need to isolate x. The expression $x - 12$ indicates that 12 is subtracted from x. To "undo" the subtraction, use the inverse operation, addition.

$x - 12 = 8$	
$x - 12 + \mathbf{12} = 8 + \mathbf{12}$	Add 12 to each side. (Addition Property of Equality)
$x = 20$	Simplify.

CHECK

$x - 12 = 8$	Write the original equation.
$\mathbf{20} - 12 \stackrel{?}{=} 8$	Substitute 20 for x. (Substitution Property of Equality)
$8 = 8$ ✓	The solution is correct because $8 = 8$ is a true statement.

▶ **Remember** The solution in Example 1 is 20, not 8.

Look back at Example 1. The equations $x - 12 = 8$ and $x = 20$ are equivalent equations. The equation $x = 20$ has the variable isolated on one side of the equals sign, so it names the solution, 20.

Solving an Addition Equation

Use the subtraction property of equality to solve addition equations.

EXAMPLE 2

Solve $21 = b + 9$.

SOLUTION

$21 = b + 9$	
$21 - \mathbf{9} = b + 9 - \mathbf{9}$	Subtract 9 from each side. (Subtraction Property of Equality)
$12 = b$	Simplify.

CHECK

$21 = b + 9$	Write the original equation.
$21 \stackrel{?}{=} \mathbf{12} + 9$	Substitute 12 for b. (Substitution Property of Equality)
$21 = 21$ ✓	The solution is correct because $21 = 21$ is a true statement. ■

Simplifying First

Sometimes it helps if you simplify each side of an equation before trying to solve it.

EXAMPLE 3

Solve.

A $5 + x - 14 = -15$

SOLUTION

$5 + x - 14 = -15$

$x + 5 - 14 = -15$ — Use the commutative property of addition to rewrite $5 + x$ as $x + 5$. Then simplify: $5 - 14 = -9$

$x - 9 = -15$

$x - 9 + \mathbf{9} = -15 + \mathbf{9}$ — $x - 9 = -15$ is a subtraction equation. The inverse of subtraction is addition, so add 9 to each side.

$x = -6$

CHECK

$5 + x - 14 = -15$ — Write the original equation.

$5 + (\mathbf{-6}) - 14 \stackrel{?}{=} -15$ — Substitute -6 for x.

$-15 = -15$ ✓ — The solution is correct.

▶ **Think About It** In Example 3A, these are all equivalent equations:

$$5 + x - 14 = -15$$
$$x + 5 - 14 = -15$$
$$x - 9 = -15$$
$$x - 9 + 9 = -15 + 9$$
$$x = -6$$

The last one, $x = -6$, names the solution.

B $17 - (8 - q) = 10$

SOLUTION

$17 - (8 - q) = 10$	
$17 - 8 + q = 10$	Distributive Property
$9 + q = 10$	Simplify.
$9 - \mathbf{9} + q = 10 - \mathbf{9}$	Subtract 9 from each side.
$q = 1$	

CHECK

$17 - (8 - q) = 10$	Write the original equation.
$17 - (8 - \mathbf{1}) \stackrel{?}{=} 10$	Substitute 1 for q.
$17 - 7 \stackrel{?}{=} 10$	Use the order of operations. Simplify $8 - 1$ first because it is inside grouping symbols.
$10 = 10$ ✓	

▶ **Think About It** In Example 3B, the distributive property is used as follows:

$$\begin{aligned} &17 - (8 - q) \\ &= 17 + (-1)(8 - q) \\ &= 17 + (-1) \bullet 8 + (-1) \bullet (-q) \\ &= 17 - 8 + q \end{aligned}$$

Application: Change in Elevation

You can use an addition or subtraction equation to solve many real-world problems, including problems with changing altitude.

EXAMPLE 4

A hot-air balloon descended (went down) 150 ft to a height of 3500 ft. How high was the hot-air balloon before its descent?

SOLUTION

Step 1 Write an equation. Let x represent the height of the balloon before its descent.

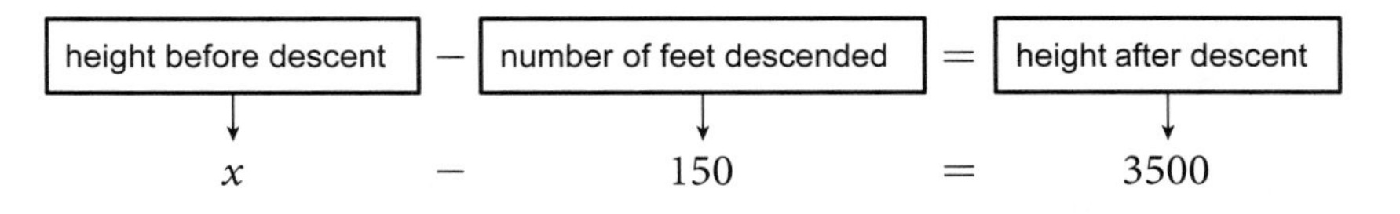

Step 2 Solve the equation.

$x - 150 = 3500$	
$x - 150 + \mathbf{150} = 3500 + \mathbf{150}$	Add 150 to each side.
$x = 3650$	Simplify.

Step 3 Check the solution.

$x - 150 = 3500$	Write the original equation.
$\mathbf{3650} - 150 \stackrel{?}{=} 3500$	Substitute 3650 for x.
$3500 = 3500$ ✓	Simplify.

The height of the hot-air balloon before its descent was 3650 ft.

More Addition and Subtraction Equations

You can apply the distributive property and combine like terms to simplify one or both sides of an equation before you solve it.

Simplifying Equations Before Solving

An equation may have two or more variable terms or two or more constant terms on one side of the equals sign. Combine any like terms before solving for the variable.

EXAMPLE 1

Solve.

A $\frac{3}{4}x - 3 + \frac{1}{4}x = 2\frac{1}{2} - \frac{1}{4}$

SOLUTION

There are two like variable terms on the left side of the equation and two constant terms on the right side. Collect the variable terms on the left side and collect the constants on the right side. Then simplify and solve for x.

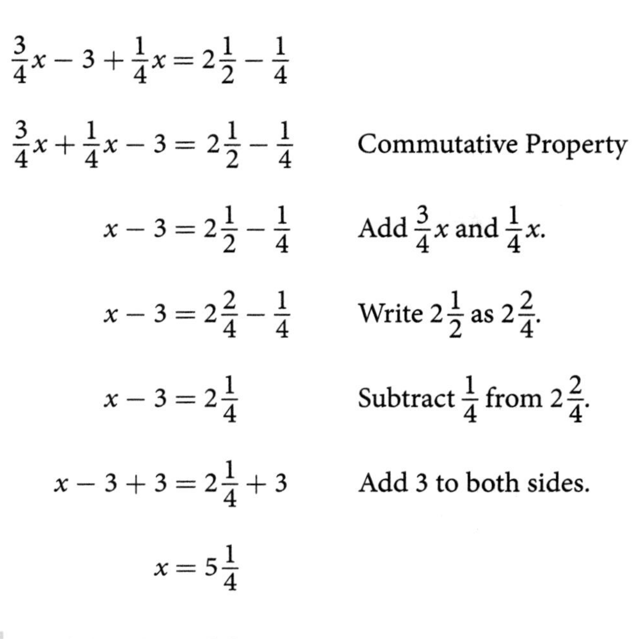

$\frac{3}{4}x - 3 + \frac{1}{4}x = 2\frac{1}{2} - \frac{1}{4}$

$\frac{3}{4}x + \frac{1}{4}x - 3 = 2\frac{1}{2} - \frac{1}{4}$ Commutative Property

$x - 3 = 2\frac{1}{2} - \frac{1}{4}$ Add $\frac{3}{4}x$ and $\frac{1}{4}x$.

$x - 3 = 2\frac{2}{4} - \frac{1}{4}$ Write $2\frac{1}{2}$ as $2\frac{2}{4}$.

$x - 3 = 2\frac{1}{4}$ Subtract $\frac{1}{4}$ from $2\frac{2}{4}$.

$x - 3 + 3 = 2\frac{1}{4} + 3$ Add 3 to both sides.

$x = 5\frac{1}{4}$

B $x + 3.2 - 6.5 = 8.3$

SOLUTION

There are two constant terms on the left side of the equation. Combine the constant terms and then solve for x.

$x + 3.2 - 6.5 = 8.3$

$x - 3.3 = 8.3$ Simplify the left side.

$x - 3.3 + 3.3 = 8.3 + 3.3$ Add 3.3 to both sides.

$x = 11.6$ Simplify. ■

To simplfy equations that include parentheses, apply the distributive property.

EXAMPLE 2

Solve.

A $4(x+2)-3x=15$

SOLUTION

Use the distributive property to eliminate the parentheses. Then simplify the equation by collecting like terms on the left side.

$4(x+2)-3x=15$	
$4x+8-3x=15$	Distributive Property
$4x-3x+8=15$	Commutative Property
$x+8=15$	Subtract $3x$ from $4x$.
$x+8-8=15-8$	Subtract 8 from both sides.
$x=7$	

B $\frac{5}{3}x-\frac{2}{3}\left(x+\frac{3}{4}\right)=-4$

SOLUTION

Apply the distributive property before collecting like terms on the left side. Then solve for x.

▶ **Think About It**

$$-\frac{2}{3}\left(x+\frac{3}{4}\right)=-\frac{2}{3}\cdot x-\frac{2}{3}\cdot\frac{3}{4}$$
$$=-\frac{2}{3}x-\frac{6}{12}$$
$$=-\frac{2}{3}x-\frac{1}{2}$$

$$\frac{5}{3}x - \frac{2}{3}\left(x + \frac{3}{4}\right) = -4$$

$$\frac{5}{3}x - \frac{2}{3}x - \frac{1}{2} = -4$$ Distributive Property

$$x - \frac{1}{2} = -4$$ Combine like terms. Subtract $\frac{2}{3}x$ from $\frac{5}{3}x$.

$$x - \frac{1}{2} + \frac{1}{2} = -4 + \frac{1}{2}$$ Add $\frac{1}{2}$ to both sides.

$$x = -3\frac{1}{2}$$ ■

Multiplication and Division Equations

You can use properties of equality to solve equations involving multiplication and division.

(More) Properties of Equality	
Multiplication Property of Equality	If $a = b$, then $ca = cb$ and $ac = bc$.
Division Property of Equality	If $a = b$ and $c \neq 0$, then $\frac{a}{c} = \frac{b}{c}$.

The multiplication property of equality tells you that you can multiply each side of an equation by the same value to create an equivalent equation. The division property of equality tells you that you can divide each side of an equation by the same nonzero value to create an equivalent equation.

Solving a Division Equation

Recall that you use inverse operations to solve equations. So use the multiplication property of equality to solve division equations.

EXAMPLE 1

Solve $\frac{x}{4} = 8$.

SOLUTION

You need to isolate x. The expression $\frac{x}{4}$ indicates that x is divided by 4. To "undo" the division, use the inverse operation, multiplication.

$$\frac{x}{4} = 8$$

$4 \cdot \frac{x}{4} = 4 \cdot 8$ Multiply each side by 4. (Multiplication Property of Equality)

$x = 32$ Simplify.

CHECK

$\frac{x}{4} = 8$ Write the original equation.

$\frac{32}{4} \stackrel{?}{=} 8$ Substitute 32 for x. (Substitution Property of Equality)

$8 = 8$ ✓ Simplify. The solution is correct because $8 = 8$ is a true statement.

The solution is 32. You can also say the solution set is $\{32\}$. ■

Solving a Multiplication Equation

Use the division property of equality to solve multiplication equations.

EXAMPLE 2

Solve $15 = -3n$.

SOLUTION

The expression $-3n$ indicates multiplication. Use division to "undo" the operation.

$$15 = -3n$$

$\frac{15}{-3} = \frac{-3n}{-3}$ Divide each side by -3. (Division Property of Equality)

$-5 = n$ Simplify. ■

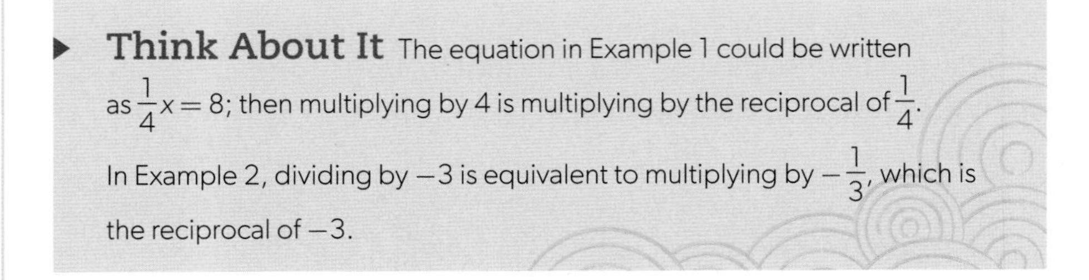

▶ **Think About It** The equation in Example 1 could be written as $\frac{1}{4}x = 8$; then multiplying by 4 is multiplying by the reciprocal of $\frac{1}{4}$.

In Example 2, dividing by -3 is equivalent to multiplying by $-\frac{1}{3}$, which is the reciprocal of -3.

Using a Reciprocal Property for Multiplication to Solve Equations

You don't really need the division property of equality. Instead of dividing, you could always multiply by the reciprocal. Still, the division property of equality can be convenient.

When an equation shows a variable multiplied by a fraction, use a reciprocal property for multiplication.

EXAMPLE 3

Solve.

A $\frac{1}{6}b = 12$

▶ **Remember** One of the reciprocal properties for multiplication says that for all $a \in \mathbb{R}$, $a \bullet \frac{1}{a} = 1$ if $a \neq 0$.

SOLUTION

$\frac{1}{6}b = 12$

$6 \cdot \frac{1}{6}b = 6 \cdot 12$ Multiply each side by 6, which is the reciprocal of $\frac{1}{6}$.

$1 \cdot b = 72$ Simplify. $6 \cdot \frac{1}{6} = 1$ by a reciprocal property for multiplication.

$b = 72$ Simplify. $1 \cdot b = b$ by the multiplicative identity property.

B $\frac{2t}{5} = 14$

SOLUTION

$\frac{2t}{5} = 14$

$\frac{2}{5}t = 14$ Rewrite the equation as a multiplication equation.

$\frac{5}{2} \cdot \frac{2}{5}t = \frac{5}{2} \cdot 14$ Multiply each side by $\frac{5}{2}$, which is the reciprocal of $\frac{2}{5}$.

$t = 35$ Simplify. ■

Application: Unit Price

Multiplication and division equations are useful for solving certain types of real-world problems such as unit price, which is a type of unit rate.

EXAMPLE 4

Mr. Boswell buys a package of 150 file folders for $6.00. What is the unit price per file folder?

SOLUTION

Step 1 Write an equation. Let f represent the unit price per file folder in dollars.

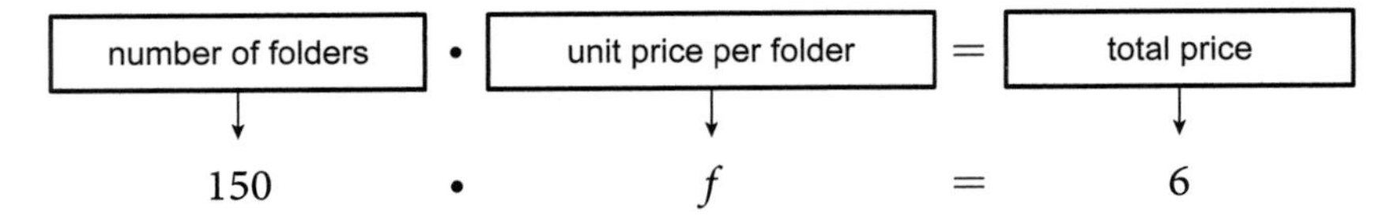

Step 2 Solve the equation.

$150f = 6$

$\frac{150f}{\mathbf{150}} = \frac{6}{\mathbf{150}}$ Divide each side by 150.

$f = 0.04$ Simplify.

Step 3 Check the solution.

$150f = 6$ Write the original equation.

$150 \cdot \mathbf{0.04} \stackrel{?}{=} 6$ Substitute 0.04 for f.

$6 = 6$ ✓ Simplify. The solution is correct.

The unit price is $0.04 = 4¢ per folder. ■

Tougher Equations

Equations can include all forms of rational numbers.

Solving Equations Involving Rational Numbers

Use transformations to solve an equation involving fractions and decimals just as you would to solve an equation involving only integers.

EXAMPLE

Solve.

A $\frac{2}{3}x - 6 = 14$

SOLUTION

$$\frac{2}{3}x - 6 = 14$$

$\frac{2}{3}x - 6 + \mathbf{6} = 14 + \mathbf{6}$ — Add 6 to both sides.

$\frac{2}{3}x = 20$ — Simplify.

$\frac{\overset{1}{\cancel{3}}}{\underset{1}{\cancel{2}}} \cdot \frac{\overset{1}{\cancel{2}}}{\underset{1}{\cancel{3}}}x = \overset{10}{\cancel{20}} \cdot \frac{3}{\underset{1}{\cancel{2}}}$ — Multiply both sides by $\frac{3}{2}$.

$x = 30$ — Simplify.

B $\frac{3}{4}(4x + 16) = 3$

SOLUTION

$$\frac{3}{4}(4x + 16) = 3$$

$\frac{3}{\cancel{4}_1} \cdot \cancel{4}^1 x + \frac{3}{\cancel{4}_1} \cdot \cancel{16}^4 = 3$	Distributive Property
$3x + 12 = 3$	Simplify.
$3x + 12 - \mathbf{12} = 3 - \mathbf{12}$	Subtract 12 from both sides.
$3x = -9$	Simplify.
$\frac{3x}{\mathbf{3}} = \frac{-9}{\mathbf{3}}$	Divide both sides by 3.
$x = -3$	Simplify.

C $1.4x - 5 = 4.2x + 13.2$

SOLUTION

$$1.4x - 5 = 4.2x + 13.2$$

$1.4x - \mathbf{4.2x} - 5 = 4.2x - \mathbf{4.2x} + 13.2$	Subtract $4.2x$ from both sides.
$-2.8x - 5 = 13.2$	Simplify.
$-2.8x - 5 + \mathbf{5} = 13.2 + \mathbf{5}$	Add 5 to both sides.
$-2.8x = 18.2$	Simplify.
$\frac{-2.8x}{\mathbf{-2.8}} = \frac{18.2}{\mathbf{-2.8}}$	Divide both sides by -2.8.
$x = -6.5$	Simplify. ■

Think About It You could have also solved this equation by subtracting $1.4x$ from both sides instead of subtracting $4.2x$.

$$\begin{aligned} 1.4x - 5 &= 4.2x + 13.2 \\ 1.4x - 1.4x - 5 &= 4.2x - 1.4x + 13.2 \\ -5 &= 2.8x + 13.2 \\ -5 - 13.2 &= 2.8x + 13.2 - 13.2 \\ -18.2 &= 2.8x \\ \frac{-18.2}{2.8} &= \frac{2.8x}{2.8} \\ -6.5 &= x \end{aligned}$$

Multiple Transformations

Solving an equation involves using the properties of equality and inverse operations to transform the original equation into a series of equivalent equations.

For example, $x - 12 = 8$ is transformed into $x = 20$ by the addition property of equality, and $\frac{x}{4} = 8$ is transformed into $x = 32$ by the multiplication property of equality.

Solving a Division-Subtraction Equation

To solve an equation such as $\frac{x}{4} - 12 = 8$, you need to make multiple transformations, using various properties and inverse operations.

EXAMPLE 1

Solve $\frac{x}{4} - 12 = 8$.

SOLUTION
Using the correct order of operations, take note of the order in which operations are applied to x.

$\frac{x}{4} - 12 = 8$ First, x is divided by 4. Second, 12 is subtracted from the quotient $\frac{x}{4}$.

Now use the properties of equality and inverse operations to "undo" these operations in reverse order.

$$\frac{x}{4} - 12 = 8$$

$\frac{x}{4} - 12 + \mathbf{12} = 8 + \mathbf{12}$ First, add 12 to each side to "undo" the subtraction. (Addition Property of Equality)

$\frac{x}{4} = 20$ Simplify.

$\mathbf{4} \bullet \frac{x}{4} = \mathbf{4} \bullet 20$ Second, multiply each side by 4 to "undo" the division. (Multiplication Property of Equality)

$x = 80$ Simplify.

CHECK

$\frac{x}{4} - 12 = 8$ Write the original equation.

$\frac{\mathbf{80}}{4} - 12 \stackrel{?}{=} 8$ Substitute 80 for x. (Substitution Property of Equality)

$20 - 12 \stackrel{?}{=} 8$ Use the order of operations to simplify.

$8 = 8$ ✓ The solution is correct.

The solution is 80, and the solution set is $\{80\}$. ■

Using Multiple Transformations to Solve an Equation

Multiple-transformation equations are not limited to subtraction and division, nor are they limited to two operations.

EXAMPLE 2

Solve.

A $3x + 18 = -39$

SOLUTION

Here x is multiplied by 3 and then 18 is added.

$3x + 18 = -39$	
$3x + 18 - 18 = -39 - 18$	Subtract 18 from each side to "undo" the addition. (Subtraction Property of Equality)
$3x = -57$	Simplify.
$\frac{3x}{3} = -\frac{57}{3}$	Divide each side by 3 to "undo" the multiplication. (Division Property of Equality)
$x = -19$	Simplify.

▶ **Think About It** To solve for a variable in an equation, use the reverse order of operations.

B $3 = \frac{1 - 7n}{5}$

SOLUTION

Here n is multiplied by -7, 1 is added to the product, and then the sum is divided by 5.

▶ **Think About It** If you prefer, use the commutative property of addition to rewrite the difference $1 - 7n$ as the sum $-7n + 1$.

$$3 = \frac{1 - 7n}{5}$$

$5 \cdot 3 = 5 \cdot \frac{1 - 7n}{5}$	Multiply each side by 5.
$15 = 1 - 7n$	Simplify.
$15 - 1 = 1 - 7n - 1$	Subtract 1 from each side.
$15 - 1 = (1 - 1) - 7n$	Combine like terms. (Commutative and Associative Properties of Addition)
$14 = -7n$	Simplify.
$\frac{14}{-7} = \frac{-7n}{-7}$	Divide each side by -7.
$-2 = n$	Simplify. ■

Simplifying First

It is helpful to simplify each side of an equation before trying to solve it.

EXAMPLE 3

Solve $3(g - 7) + g = 3$.

SOLUTION

You can solve this equation in two ways.

Strategy 1

$3(g - 7) + g = 3$

$3g - 21 + g = 3$ Distribute.

$(3g + g) - 21 = 3$ Combine like terms.

$4g - 21 = 3$ Simplify.

$4g - 21 + \mathbf{21} = 3 + \mathbf{21}$ Add 21 to each side.

$\frac{4g}{\mathbf{4}} = \frac{24}{\mathbf{4}}$ Divide each side by 4.

$g = 6$ Simplify.

Strategy 2

$3(g - 7) + g = 3$

$\frac{3(g - 7) + g}{\mathbf{3}} = \frac{3}{\mathbf{3}}$ Divide each side by 3.

$\frac{3(g - 7)}{3} + \frac{g}{3} = \frac{3}{3}$ Simplify.

$g - 7 + \frac{1}{3}g = 1$ Simplify.

$\left(g + \frac{1}{3g}\right) - 7 = 1$ Combine like terms.

$\frac{4}{3}g - 7 = 1$ Simplify.

$\frac{4}{3}g - 7 + \mathbf{7} = 1 + \mathbf{7}$ Add 7 to each side.

$\frac{4}{3}g = 8$ Simplify.

$\frac{\mathbf{3}}{\mathbf{4}} \cdot \frac{4}{3}g = \frac{\mathbf{3}}{\mathbf{4}} \cdot 8$ Multiply each side by $\frac{3}{4}$.

$g = 6$ Simplify. ■

Simplifying first can make solving a complicated equation easier.

Application: Perimeter

EXAMPLE 4

The width of a rectangle is 2 in. less than its length. The perimeter of the rectangle is 40 in. What are the length and width of the rectangle?

Problem-Solving Plan

Step 1 ***Identify*** Read the problem and identify the unknowns.

Step 2 ***Strategize*** Select and define the variables and variable expressions to represent the unknowns.

Step 3 ***Set Up*** Write an equation, inequality, or whatever tools you need to model the problem.

Step 4 ***Solve*** Solve the equation (or inequality or other model) and answer the question.

Step 5 ***Check*** Check your answer for reasonableness and accuracy with the original problem statement.

SOLUTION

Step 1 ***Identify*** Find the length and width of the rectangle, given the perimeter.

Step 2 ***Strategize*** Let l represent the length in inches. The width is 2 in. less than the length, or $l - 2$.

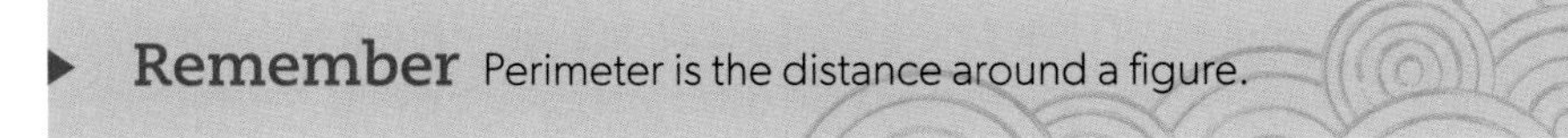

Step 3 ***Set Up*** Write an equation.

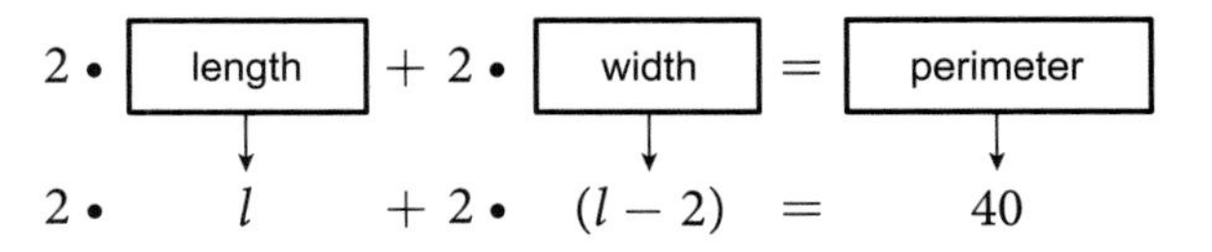

Step 4 ***Solve***

$$2l + 2(l - 2) = 40$$

$2l + 2l - 4 = 40$	Distribute.
$4l - 4 = 40$	Combine like terms.
$4l - 4 + 4 = 40 + 4$	Add 4 to each side.
$\frac{4l}{4} = \frac{44}{4}$	Divide each side by 4.
$l = 11$	Simplify.

If $l = 11$, then $l - 2 = 11 - 2 = 9$. The length of the rectangle is 11 in. and the width is 9 in.

Step 5 ***Check*** An informal way to check your work is to sketch the rectangle and find its perimeter.

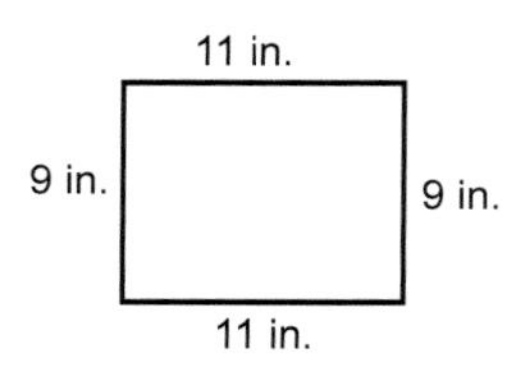

$$\text{perimeter} = 9 \text{ in.} + 11 \text{ in.} + 9 \text{ in.} + 11 \text{ in.} = 40 \text{ in.} \checkmark$$

The perimeter is 40 in. ■

Variables on Both Sides of an Equation

Some equations have variable terms on both sides of the equals sign.

When an equation has variables on both sides of the equals sign, use the properties of equality and inverse operations to isolate the variable terms on one side of the equation and isolate the constant terms on the other side.

Collecting Variables on One Side

In general, it does not matter on which side you isolate the variable terms. However, these two guidelines can help make your solutions easier:

- If one side of the equation contains only a variable term, isolate the variable terms on that side.
- If both sides of the equation contain both variable and constant terms, isolate the variable terms on the side with the greater variable coefficient.

EXAMPLE 1

Solve.

A $5x = 3x - 18$

SOLUTION

Because $5x$ is already isolated on the left side, it is best to isolate all of the variable terms on the left and isolate the constants on the right. Use the subtraction property of equality to "undo" the $3x$ that is currently added to -18 on the right side.

$5x = 3x - 18$	
$5x - \mathbf{3x} = 3x - 18 - \mathbf{3x}$	Subtract $3x$ from each side.
$5x - 3x = (3x - 3x) - 18$	Combine like terms.
$2x = -18$	Simplify.
$\frac{2x}{2} = \frac{-18}{2}$	Divide each side by 2.
$x = -9$	Simplify.

CHECK

$5x = 3x - 18$	
$5 \cdot (\mathbf{-9}) \stackrel{?}{=} 3 \cdot (\mathbf{-9}) - 18$	Substitute -9 for each x in the original equation and simplify.
$-45 \stackrel{?}{=} -27 - 18$	
$-45 = -45$ ✓	

The solution set is $\{-9\}$.

B $n - 4 = \frac{5n + 1}{2}$

SOLUTION

$n - 4 = \frac{5n + 1}{2}$	
$2 \cdot (n - 4) = 2 \cdot \frac{5n + 1}{2}$	Multiply each side by 2.
$2n - 8 = 5n + 1$	Simplify.
$2n - 8 - \mathbf{2n} = 5n + 1 - \mathbf{2n}$	Subtract $2n$ from each side to isolate the variable terms on the right.
$(2n - 2n) - 8 = (5n - 2n) + 1$	Combine like terms.
$-8 = 3n + 1$	Simplify.
$-8 - \mathbf{1} = 3n + 1 - \mathbf{1}$	Subtract 1 from each side to isolate the constant terms on the left.
$-9 = 3n$	Simplify.
$\frac{-9}{\mathbf{3}} = \frac{3n}{\mathbf{3}}$	Divide each side by 3.
$-3 = n$	Simplify.

The solution set is $\{-3\}$. ■

Simplifying First

As with any equation, it helps if you simplify each side first.

EXAMPLE 2

Solve $8(d + 2) - 36 = 2 + 6(1 - d)$.

▶ **Think About It** To shorten your solutions, you can combine consecutive steps of addition and subtraction or consecutive steps of multiplication and division.

SOLUTION

$$8(d+2)-36=2+6(1-d)$$

$8d+16-36=2+6-6d$	Distribute.
$8d-20=8-6d$	Simplify.
$8d-20+\mathbf{6d}+\mathbf{20}=8-6d+\mathbf{6d}+\mathbf{20}$	Add $6d$ and 20 to each side.
$(8d+6d)+(-20+20)=(-6d+6d)+(8+20)$	Combine like terms.
$14d=28$	Simplify.
$\frac{14d}{\mathbf{14}}=\frac{28}{\mathbf{14}}$	Divide each side by 14.
$d=2$	Simplify.

The solution set is $\{2\}$. ■

Application: Number Problem

EXAMPLE 3

Twice a number is 5 more than 3 times the number. Find the number.

SOLUTION

Step 1 Write an equation. Let n represent the number. Here, "more than" implies addition.

Twice a number	is	5 more than 3 times the number.
↓	↓	↓
$2n$	$=$	$5+3n$

Step 2 Solve the equation.

$$2n = 5 + 3n$$

$2n - \mathbf{3n} = 5 + 3n - \mathbf{3n}$ Subtract $3n$ from each side to isolate the variable terms on the left.

$\frac{-1n}{\mathbf{-1}} = \frac{5}{\mathbf{-1}}$ Divide each side by -1.

$n = -5$ Simplify.

Step 3 Check the solution.

$$2n = 5 + 3n$$

$2 \cdot (-5) \stackrel{?}{=} 5 + 3 \cdot (-5)$ Substitute -5 for each n in the original equation and simplify.

$$-10 \stackrel{?}{=} 5 + (-15)$$

$$-10 = -10 \checkmark$$

The number is -5. ■

Strange Solutions

Equations can have one solution, no solution, or infinitely many solutions.

Identifying Identities and Contradictions

Most of the equations that you have solved so far have had one or two solutions that make the equation true. But, it is possible for an equation to be true for any value of the variable or no value of the variable.

Definitions

An **identity** is an equation that is true for all values of the variable. An identity has infinitely many solutions, often represented as $\{x \mid x \in \mathbb{R}\}$.

A **contradiction** is an equation that is true for no values of the variable. A contradiction has no solutions, represented by the null set: $\{\}$ or $\varnothing$.

You can recognize identities and contradictions after solving a given equation. An identity has no variables and the same constant on both sides of the equals sign. A contradiction has no variables and different constants on each side of the equals sign.

EXAMPLE 1

Identify whether the equation has zero, one, or infinitely many solutions.

A $5x + 3 = 2(x + 3) - 3(1 - x)$

SOLUTION

Simplify each side. Then compare variables and constants.

$5x + 3 = 2(x + 3) - 3(1 - x)$	
$5x + 3 = 2x + 6 - 3 + 3x$	Distributive Property
$5x + 3 = 5x + 3$	Combine like terms and simplify.
$3 = 3$	Subtract $5x$ from each side.

This equation is an identity. There are infinitely many solutions.

B $5x + 3 = 2(x + 3) - 3(2 - x)$

SOLUTION

$5x + 3 = 2(x + 3) - 3(2 - x)$	
$5x + 3 = 2x + 6 - 6 + 3x$	Distributive Property
$5x + 3 = 5x$	Combine like terms and simplify.
$3 = 0$	Subtract $5x$ from each side.

This equation is a contradiction. There are zero solutions.

C $5x + 3 = 2(x + 3) - 3(2 - 2x)$

SOLUTION

$5x + 3 = 2(x + 3) - 3(2 - 2x)$	
$5x + 3 = 2x + 6 - 6 + 6x$	Distributive Property
$5x + 3 = 8x$	Combine like terms and simplify.
$3 = 3x$	Subtract $5x$ from each side.

Both sides have different quantities of x. This equation has one solution. (If you finish the solution, you'll find $x = 1$.)

Think About It Example 1C is often called a conditional equation because it is true only for the condition that x is 1.

Determining the Number of Solutions by Inspection

Without solving it, you can determine whether an equation in one variable has zero, one, or infinitely many solutions.

Think About It The left and right sides of an equation must be in simplest form before you can determine how many solutions the equation has. If the left or right side of an equation is not in simplest form, simplify it before applying the rules in this table.

How to Determine the Number of Solutions by Inspection

Number of solutions	Criteria	Example
zero	Variable terms on each side of the equals sign have the same coefficients but the constant terms are different.	$4x + 3 = 4x - 5$
one	Variable terms on each side of the equals sign have different coefficients.	$2 + x = 1 - 6x$
infinitely many	Variable terms on each side of the equals sign have the same coefficients and the constant terms are also the same.	$2x + 4 = 2x + 4$

EXAMPLE 2

By inspection, identify whether the equation has zero, one, or infinitely many solutions.

A $x + 3 = x + 2$

SOLUTION

The variable term is x on both sides of the equals sign. However, the constant term on the left side is 3, and the constant term on the right is 2. Since the variable terms on both sides are the same but the constant terms are different, the equation has no solution.

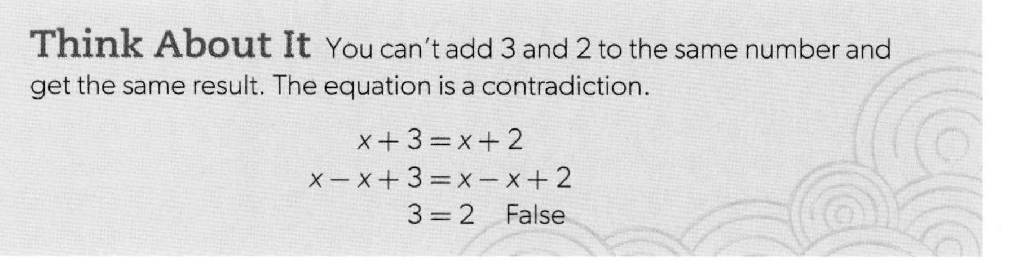

▶ **Think About It** You can't add 3 and 2 to the same number and get the same result. The equation is a contradiction.

$$\begin{aligned} x + 3 &= x + 2 \\ x - x + 3 &= x - x + 2 \\ 3 &= 2 \quad \text{False} \end{aligned}$$

CHECK

Substitute several values for x into the original equation.

$$x + 3 = x + 2$$

Let $x = 1$.	Let $x = -1$	Let $x = 0$
$1 + 3 \stackrel{?}{=} 1 + 2$	$-1 + 3 \stackrel{?}{=} -1 + 2$	$0 + 3 \stackrel{?}{=} 0 + 2$
$4 \neq 3$	$2 \neq 1$	$3 \neq 2$

The equation is false for every value of x we chose. The left side is always 1 greater than the right side.

B $2x + 10 = 2(x + 5)$

SOLUTION

Before comparing the left and right sides of an equation with variables on both sides, each side must be in simplest form. For this equation, use the distributive property on the right side to remove the parentheses.

$2x + 10 = 2(x + 5)$

$2x + 10 = 2x + 10$ Distributive Property

Notice that the expressions on both sides of the equals sign are identical. Since the variable terms and the constant terms are the same on both sides, the equation has an infinite number of solutions.

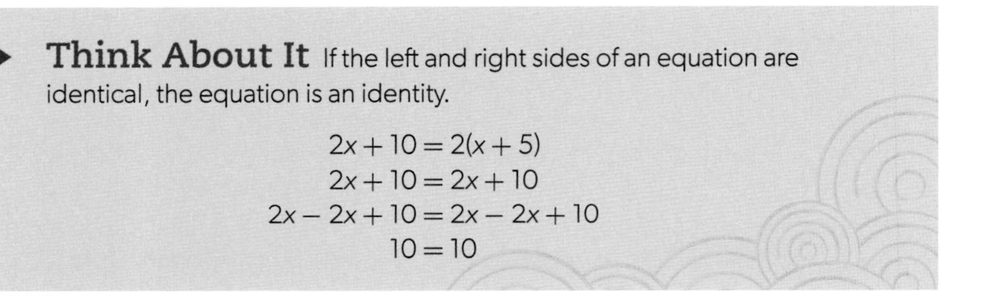

▶ **Think About It** If the left and right sides of an equation are identical, the equation is an identity.

$$\begin{aligned} 2x + 10 &= 2(x + 5) \\ 2x + 10 &= 2x + 10 \\ 2x - 2x + 10 &= 2x - 2x + 10 \\ 10 &= 10 \end{aligned}$$

CHECK

Substitute several values for x into the original equation.

$$2x + 10 = 2(x + 5)$$

Let $x = 2$.

$$\begin{aligned} 2(2) + 10 &\stackrel{?}{=} 2(2 + 5) \\ 4 + 10 &\stackrel{?}{=} 2 \bullet 7 \\ 14 &= 14 \checkmark \end{aligned}$$

Let $x = -1$.

$$\begin{aligned} 2(-1) + 10 &\stackrel{?}{=} 2(-1 + 5) \\ -2 + 10 &\stackrel{?}{=} 2 \bullet 4 \\ 8 &= 8 \checkmark \end{aligned}$$

Let $x = 0$.

$$\begin{aligned} 2(0) + 10 &\stackrel{?}{=} 2(0 + 5) \\ 0 + 10 &\stackrel{?}{=} 2 \bullet 5 \\ 10 &= 10 \checkmark \end{aligned}$$

Since the expressions on both sides of the equals sign are equivalent, the value of the left and right sides of the equation will always be the same for any value of x. Therefore, all numbers are solutions to the equation.

C $6x - 3(x - 1) = 4(x + 2) - 5$

SOLUTION

Simplify both sides of the equation.

$$\begin{aligned} 6x - 3(x - 1) &= 4(x + 2) - 5 \\ 6x - 3x + 3 &= 4x + 8 - 5 \\ 3x + 3 &= 4x + 3 \end{aligned}$$

In the simplified equation, the variable term on the left side is $3x$, and the variable term on the right side is $4x$. Since the variable terms on both sides of the equation are different, the equation has exactly one solution. ■

▶ **Think About It** When the coefficients of the variable terms on both sides of the equation are different, the variable terms will never combine to be zero. Therefore, the variable will remain in the equation.

Writing Equations with Strange Solutions

You can use the criteria for determining the number of solutions to write equations with zero, one, and infinitely many solutions.

EXAMPLE 3

Write an equation with the given number of solutions.

A zero

SOLUTION

Use the criteria for zero solutions to write an equation.

- Variable terms on each side of the equals sign have the same coefficients.

$$7x = 7x$$

- But the constant terms are different.

$$7x + 5 = 7x - 8$$

The equation $7x + 5 = 7x - 8$ has zero solutions.

CHECK

$7x + 5 \stackrel{?}{=} 7x - 8$

$5 \neq -8$ Subtract $7x$ from each side.

Since $5 \neq -8$ is a contradiction, the equation $7x + 5 = 7x - 8$ has zero solutions.

▶ **Think About It** Once you have found a basic equation with zero, one, or infinitely many solutions, you can use the properties of equality to write an equivalent equation that would have the same number of solutions.

$$7x + 5 = 7x - 8$$
$$7x + 5 + 2 = 7x - 8 + 2$$
$$7x + 7 = 7x - 6$$

$7x + 7 = 7x - 6$ also has zero solutions.

B infinitely many

SOLUTION

Use the criteria for infinitely many solutions to write an equation.

- Variable terms on each side of the equals sign have the same coefficients.

$$\mathbf{-3x} = \mathbf{-3x}$$

- And the constant terms are also the same.

$$-3x + \mathbf{4} = -3x + \mathbf{4}$$

The equation $-3x + 4 = -3x + 4$ has infinitely many solutions.

CHECK

$-3x + 4 \stackrel{?}{=} -3x + 4$

$4 = 4$ ✓ Add $3x$ to each side.

Since $4 = 4$ is an identity, the equation $-3x + 4 = -3x + 4$ has infinitely many solutions.

C one

SOLUTION

Use the criteria for one solution to write an equation.

- Variable terms on each side of the equals sign have different coefficients.

$$\mathbf{9}x - 3 = \mathbf{5}x + 17$$

The equation $9x - 3 = 5x + 17$ has one solution.

CHECK

$9x - 3 \stackrel{?}{=} 5x + 17$

$9x \stackrel{?}{=} 5x + 20$	Add 3 to each side.
$4x \stackrel{?}{=} 20$	Subtract $5x$ from each side.
$x = 5$ ✓	Divide each side by 4.

Since $x = 5$, the equation $9x - 3 = 5x + 17$ has one solution. ■

Problem Solving with Equations

Following a problem-solving plan can help you write and solve equations that model real-world problems.

Using Equations and a Plan to Solve Word Problems

When you solve a real-world problem, the first step is to identify the unknown quantities. In other words, ask yourself, "What am I trying to find?" Once you have identified the unknown quantities, you can follow this process.

Problem-Solving Plan

Step 1 *Identify* Read the problem and identify the unknowns.

Step 2 *Strategize* Select and define the variables and variable expressions to represent the unknowns.

Step 3 *Set Up* Write an equation, inequality, or whatever tools you need to model the problem.

Step 4 *Solve* Solve the equation (or inequality or other model) and answer the question.

Step 5 *Check* Check your answer for reasonableness and accuracy with the original problem statement.

EXAMPLE

Cindy and Melissa carried books from one room to another. Cindy carried 4 books per trip. Melissa carried 2 books per trip. When they were finished, they realized that they had both carried the same number of books; however, Cindy had made 7 fewer trips than Melissa did. How many trips did each girl make?

SOLUTION

To begin, identify the unknown quantities. The problem asks, "How many trips did each girl make?" Therefore, there are two unknowns: the number of trips Cindy made and the number of trips Melissa made. Since we've identified the unknowns, we can now follow the problem-solving plan.

Step 1 ***Identify*** Find the number of trips Cindy and Melissa made.

Step 2 ***Strategize*** Let m equal the number of trips that Melissa made.

Cindy made 7 fewer trips than Melissa did, so the expression $m - 7$ represents the number of trips Cindy made.

Step 3 ***Set Up*** Write an equation to model the problem.

Melissa carried 2 books per trip. Therefore, the total number of books she carried is $2m$.

Cindy carried 4 books per trip. Therefore, the total number of books Cindy carried is $4(m - 7)$.

Since both girls carried the same number of books, the total number of books Melissa carried equals the total number of books Cindy carried.

$$\text{number of books Melissa carried} = \text{number of books Cindy carried}$$
$$2m = 4(m - 7)$$

Step 4 ***Solve*** Use transformations to solve for m.

$2m = 4(m - 7)$	
$2m = 4m - 28$	Distributive Property
$2m - \mathbf{4m} = 4m - \mathbf{4m} - 28$	Subtract $4m$ from both sides.
$-2m = -28$	Simplfy.
$\frac{-2m}{\mathbf{-2}} = \frac{-28}{\mathbf{-2}}$	Divide both sides by -2.
$m = 14$	

The question asks how many trips each girl made. Since m equals 14, Melissa made 14 trips. Cindy made $m - 7$ trips. Replace m with 14 in the expression $m - 7$ to find the number of trips Cindy made. Cindy made $14 - 7 = 7$ trips.

Step 5 ***Check*** Check your results. Give your answer.

The problem states that Cindy made 7 fewer trips than Melissa. Since 7 is 7 fewer than 14, the answer makes sense. ■

Think About It After you solve an equation, it's always a good idea to check that your solution is correct.

Check Replace m with 14 in the original equation.

Let $m = 14$.

$$2m = 4(m - 7)$$
$$2 \cdot 14 \stackrel{?}{=} 4(14 - 7)$$
$$28 \stackrel{?}{=} 4(7)$$
$$28 = 28 \checkmark$$

Linear Relationships and Slope

Topic List

- Equations in Two Variables
- Lines and Intercepts
- Slope
- Slope and Similar Triangles
- Simple Linear Graphs
- Slope-Intercept Form
- Using Slope as a Rate
- Comparing Proportional Relationships

Some mountains are steeper than others. Just like mountains, lines can be steep and can slant upward or downward. A single number can describe the steepness and direction of a line.

Equations in Two Variables

An equation in the form $Ax + By = C$ is a linear equation in two variables.

Checking Solutions to Equations in Two Variables

A solution to a linear equation in two variables is an ordered pair (x, y). You can determine whether an ordered pair is a solution to an equation by substituting the values of x and y into the equation. If the equation simplifies to an identity (a statement such as $1 = 1$ that is always true), the ordered pair is a solution to the equation.

EXAMPLE 1

Determine whether the ordered pair is a solution to the equation $4x - y = 8$.

A $(0, 8)$

SOLUTION

Substitute 0 for x and 8 for y in the equation.

$$\begin{aligned} 4x - y &= 8 \\ 4 \bullet \mathbf{0} - \mathbf{8} &\stackrel{?}{=} 8 \\ 0 - 8 &\stackrel{?}{=} 8 \\ -8 &\neq 8 \end{aligned}$$

The ordered pair $(0, 8)$ is not a solution to the equation.

B $(-1, -12)$

SOLUTION

Substitute -1 for x and -12 for y in the equation.

$$\begin{aligned} 4x - y &= 8 \\ 4 \cdot (-1) - (-12) &\stackrel{?}{=} 8 \\ -4 + 12 &\stackrel{?}{=} 8 \\ 8 &= 8 \end{aligned}$$

The ordered pair $(-1, -12)$ is a solution to the equation. ■

Finding Solutions to an Equation in Two Variables

To find solutions to an equation in two variables, first solve the equation for y in terms of x. Once you have the equation solved for y, choose some values of x and substitute them to find values of y.

EXAMPLE 2

Find four solutions of the equation $6x + 3y = 9$.

SOLUTION

Step 1 Solve the equation for y.

$$6x + 3y = 9$$

$6x + 3y - 6x = 9 - 6x$	Subtract $6x$ from each side.
$3y = 9 - 6x$	Simplify.
$\frac{3y}{3} = \frac{9 - 6x}{3}$	Divide each side by 3.
$y = \frac{9}{3} - \frac{6x}{3}$	Simplify.
$y = 3 - 2x$	Simplify.

Step 2 Using the values for x in the table, find each value of y.

x	-2	0	4	8
y				

When $x = -2$:

$$y = 3 - 2x$$
$$= 3 - 2 \cdot (-2)$$
$$= 3 + 4$$
$$= 7$$

When $x = 0$:

$$y = 3 - 2x$$
$$= 3 - 2 \cdot 0$$
$$= 3 - 0$$
$$= 3$$

When $x = 4$:

$$y = 3 - 2x$$
$$= 3 - 2 \cdot 4$$
$$= 3 - 8$$
$$= -5$$

When $x = 8$:

$$y = 3 - 2x$$
$$= 3 - 2 \cdot 8$$
$$= 3 - 16$$
$$= -13$$

The completed table shows the values for y.

x	-2	0	4	8
y	7	3	-5	-13

Four solutions are $(-2, 7)$, $(0, 3)$, $(4, -5)$, and $(8, -13)$. There are infinitely many other solutions to this equation. ■

Application: Admission Prices

You can use equations in two variables to solve real-world applications.

EXAMPLE 3

At an art museum, admission tickets cost $12 for adults and $8 for children. On Sunday, 65 child tickets were sold and a total of $1780 was collected for admission. How many adult tickets were sold?

SOLUTION

Step 1 ***Identify*** Find the number of adult tickets sold.

Step 2 ***Strategize*** Let a represent the number of adult tickets sold and let c represent the number of child tickets sold.

Step 3 ***Set Up*** Write an equation to model the problem.

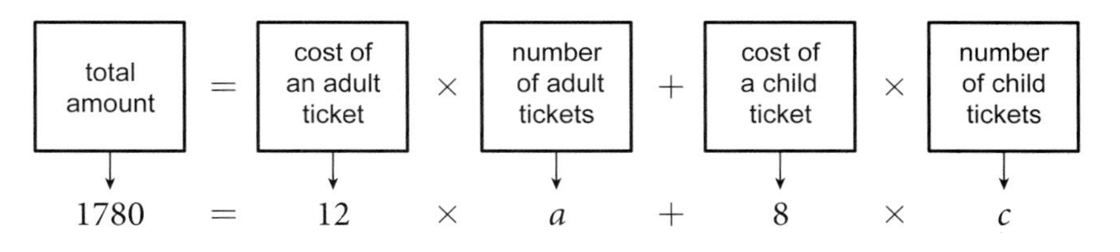

The problem is modeled by the equation $1780 = 12a + 8c$.

Step 4 ***Solve*** Substitute 65 into the equation for c.

$$1780 = 12a + 8c$$
$$1780 = 12a + 8 \bullet \mathbf{65}$$

Solve the equation for a.

$1780 = 12a + 8 \bullet 65$	Write the equation.
$1780 = 12a + 520$	Multiply.
$1260 = 12a$	Subtract 520 from each side.
$105 = a$	Divide each side by 12.

The art museum sold 105 adult tickets.

Step 5 ***Check***

$1780 = 12a + 8c$	Write the original equation.
$1780 \stackrel{?}{=} 12 \bullet \mathbf{105} + 8 \bullet \mathbf{65}$	Substitute 105 for a and 65 for c.
$1780 \stackrel{?}{=} 1260 + 520$	Multiply.
$1780 = 1780$ ✓	Add.

The solution is correct. ■

Lines and Intercepts

The graph of a linear equation is a line.

Definition

The **standard form** of a linear equation is $Ax + By = C$, where A, B, and C are numbers and A and B are not both zero.

Writing Equations in Standard Form

EXAMPLE 1

Write the equation in standard form.

A $4x = y + 12$

SOLUTION

Subtract y from both sides.

$$\begin{aligned} 4x &= y + 12 \\ 4x - y &= y + 12 - y \\ 4x - y &= 12 \end{aligned}$$

The equation in standard form is $4x - y = 12$.

B $y = 3x - 18$

SOLUTION

Subtract $3x$ from both sides.

$$\begin{aligned} y &= 3x - 18 \\ y - 3x &= 3x - 18 - 3x \\ y - 3x &= -18 \\ -3x + y &= -18 \end{aligned}$$

The equation in standard form is $-3x + y = -18$. ■

Graphing Lines on the Coordinate Plane

You can use ordered pairs to graph a line on the coordinate plane. If you graph any two points on the plane, there is exactly one line that passes through both points. So to graph a line, you need to know at least two points on the line.

▶ **Think About It** Although two points determine a line, it is often helpful to graph three points as a way of checking your work.

EXAMPLE 2

Graph the line containing the points $(0, 2)$, $(1, 5)$, and $(-2, -4)$.

SOLUTION

Graph each point. Then draw the line connecting the three points.

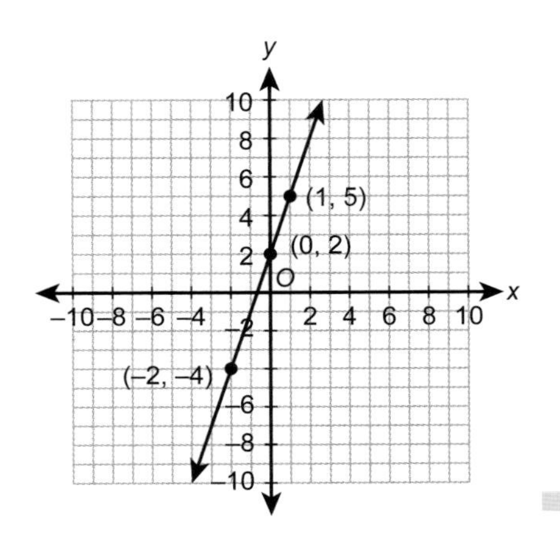

■

Graphing Collinear Points

Points are **collinear** if they lie on the same line.

EXAMPLE 3

Determine whether the points $(4, 0)$, $(6, 2)$, and $(-1, -1)$ are collinear.

SOLUTION

Graph each point. Then try to draw a line connecting the three points.

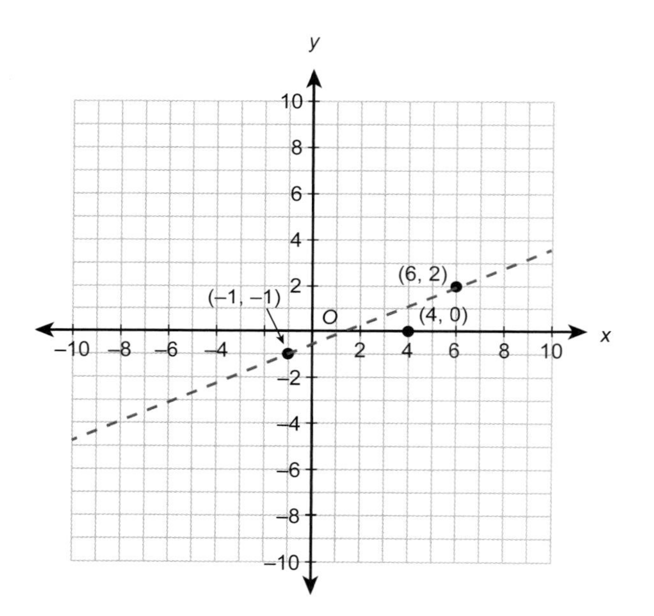

A single line cannot be drawn connecting the three points. The points are not collinear. ■

Graphing a Line Using a Table

You can use a table to graph an equation of a line. Use values for x in the table and find corresponding values of y. Graph the set of ordered pairs created by the table. Connect the points to draw the line.

EXAMPLE 4

Graph the equation of the line $y = -\frac{1}{2}x - 5$ from a table of values.

SOLUTION

Step 1 Using the values for x in the table, find each value of y.

x	−4	−2	0	2	4
y					

▶ **Remember** You may have to choose your own values for x. An equation of a line is defined for all values of x, so you can choose any x. Pick your x-values so that it is easy to find each y-value.

When $x = -4$:

$$\begin{aligned} y &= -\frac{1}{2}x - 5 \\ &= -\frac{1}{2}(-4) - 5 \\ &= 2 - 5 \\ &= -3 \end{aligned}$$

When $x = -2$:

$$\begin{aligned} y &= -\frac{1}{2}x - 5 \\ &= -\frac{1}{2}(-2) - 5 \\ &= 1 - 5 \\ &= -4 \end{aligned}$$

When $x = 0$:

$$\begin{aligned} y &= -\frac{1}{2}x - 5 \\ &= -\frac{1}{2}(0) - 5 \\ &= 0 - 5 \\ &= -5 \end{aligned}$$

When $x = 2$:

$$\begin{aligned} y &= -\frac{1}{2}x - 5 \\ &= -\frac{1}{2}(2) - 5 \\ &= -1 - 5 \\ &= -6 \end{aligned}$$

When $x = 4$:

$$\begin{aligned} y &= -\frac{1}{2}x - 5 \\ &= -\frac{1}{2}(4) - 5 \\ &= -2 - 5 \\ &= -7 \end{aligned}$$

The completed table shows the values for y.

x	−4	−2	0	2	4
y	−3	−4	−5	−6	−7

Step 2 Write each ordered pair from the table.

$$(-4, -3), (-2, -4), (0, -5), (2, -6), (4, -7)$$

Step 3 Graph each ordered pair on the coordinate plane, and connect the points to draw the line.

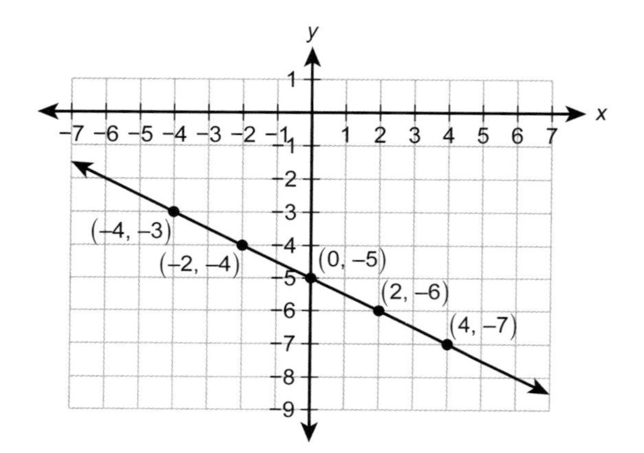

The equation $y = -\frac{1}{2}x - 5$ is shown by the graph of the line. ■

Using Intercepts to Graph Lines

When the equation of a line is in standard form, it is convenient to use the x- and y-intercepts to graph the line.

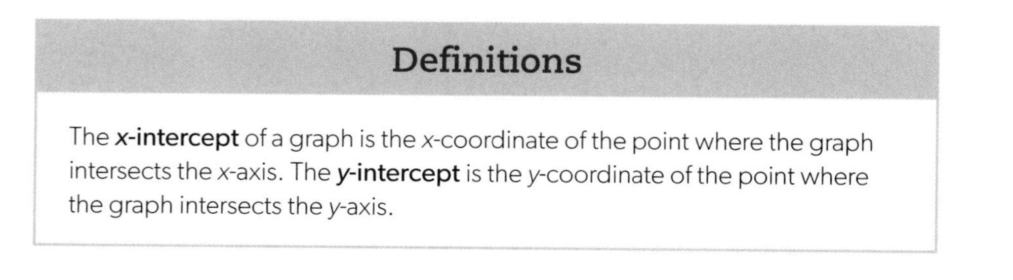

Definitions

The ***x*-intercept** of a graph is the x-coordinate of the point where the graph intersects the x-axis. The ***y*-intercept** is the y-coordinate of the point where the graph intersects the y-axis.

Any point that lies on the x-axis has a y-coordinate of 0 and any point that lies on the y-axis has an x-coordinate of 0. So to find the x-intercept of a line, find the value of x when $y = 0$, and to find the y-intercept, find the value of y when $x = 0$.

EXAMPLE 5

Graph the line $5x - 4y = 20$ by finding its x- and y-intercepts.

SOLUTION

Step 1 Find the x- and y-intercepts.

To find the x-intercept, substitute 0 for y. Then solve for x.

$$5x - 4y = 20$$

$$5x - 4 \bullet \mathbf{0} = 20 \qquad \text{Substitute 0 for } y.$$

$$5x - 0 = 20$$

$$5x = 20 \qquad \text{Solve for } x.$$

$$\frac{5x}{5} = \frac{20}{5}$$

$$x = 4$$

The x-intercept is 4, so the line intersects the x-axis at the point $(4, 0)$.

To find the y-intercept, substitute 0 for x. Then solve for y.

$$5x - 4y = 20$$

$$5 \bullet \mathbf{0} - 4y = 20 \qquad \text{Substitute 0 for } x.$$

$$0 - 4y = 20$$

$$-4y = 20 \qquad \text{Solve for } y.$$

$$\frac{-4y}{-4} = \frac{20}{-4}$$

$$y = -5$$

The y-intercept is -5, so the line intersects the y-axis at the point $(0, -5)$.

Step 2 Graph the x- and y-intercepts, and connect the points to draw the line.

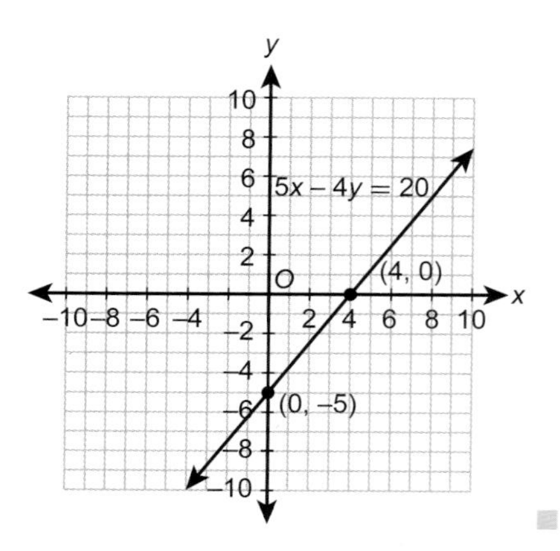

Application: Purchase

EXAMPLE 6

You are buying food for a family reunion and have purchased 120 hot dogs. Hot dog rolls come in packages of 8 and packages of 10. The situation can be modeled by the linear equation

$$8x + 10y = 120$$

where x is the number of packages containing 8 rolls and y is the number of packages containing 10 rolls.

A Find the x- and y-intercepts and graph the equation $8x + 10y = 120$.

SOLUTION

To find the x-intercept, substitute 0 for y. Then solve for x.

$$\begin{aligned} 8x + 10y &= 120 \\ 8x + 10 \bullet \mathbf{0} &= 120 \\ 8x &= 120 \\ x &= 15 \end{aligned}$$

The x-intercept is 15.

To find the y-intercept, substitute 0 for x. Then solve for y.

$$\begin{aligned} 8x + 10y &= 120 \\ 8 \bullet \mathbf{0} + 10y &= 120 \\ 10y &= 120 \\ y &= 12 \end{aligned}$$

The y-intercept is 12.

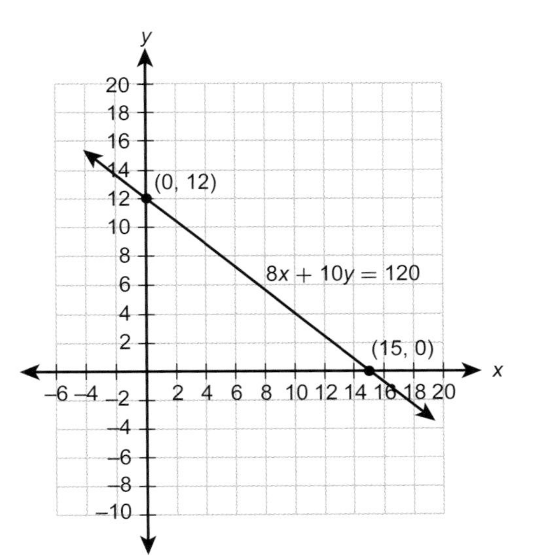

B What is the domain for this problem?

SOLUTION

Since only a whole number of packages can be purchased, only the whole number solutions are meaningful. The domain is all whole numbers greater than or equal to 0 and less than or equal to 15.

C Name all possible choices for the number of packages of each quantity of hot dog rolls you could buy.

SOLUTION

Use a table to list all the whole number coordinates the line passes through.

x	0	5	10	15
y	12	8	4	0

From the table, read the four possible choices: 0 packages of 8 rolls and 12 packages of 10 rolls, 5 packages of 8 rolls and 8 packages of 10 rolls, 10 packages of 8 rolls and 4 packages of 10 rolls, and 15 packages of 8 rolls and 0 packages of 10 rolls. ■

Slope

The steepness of a line can be described with the slope ratio.

The **slope** of a line is the ratio of the vertical change, or **rise**, between any two points on the line to the horizontal change, or **run**, between the same two points.

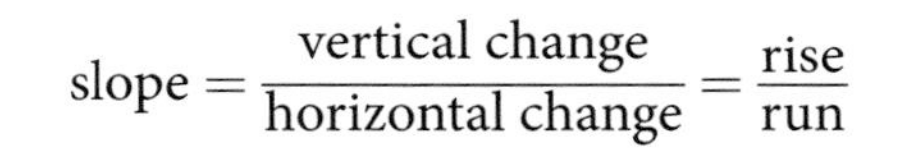

$$\text{slope} = \frac{\text{vertical change}}{\text{horizontal change}} = \frac{\text{rise}}{\text{run}}$$

Slope Formula

The slope, m, of a line containing the two points (x_1, y_1) and (x_2, y_2) can be found using the formula

$$m = \frac{y_2 - y_1}{x_2 - x_1}.$$

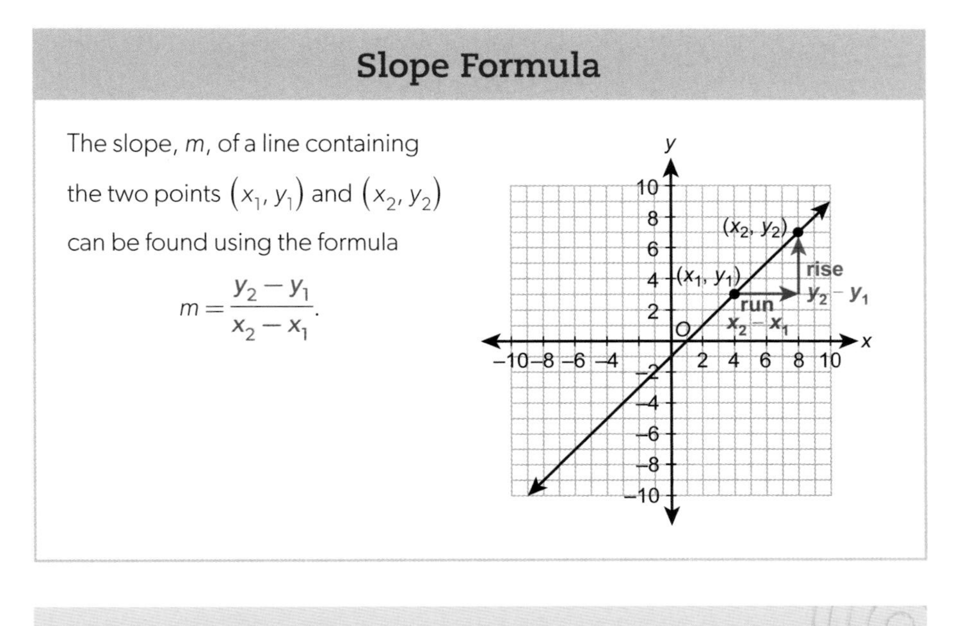

▶ **Think About It** $y_2 - y_1$ is the vertical change and $x_2 - x_1$ is the horizontal change.

Finding the Slope of a Line

To find the slope of a line, you can use the graph of the line to find the rise and run or you can use the slope formula if you know two points that lie on the line.

EXAMPLE 1

A Find the slope of the line shown in the graph using the ratio of rise to run.

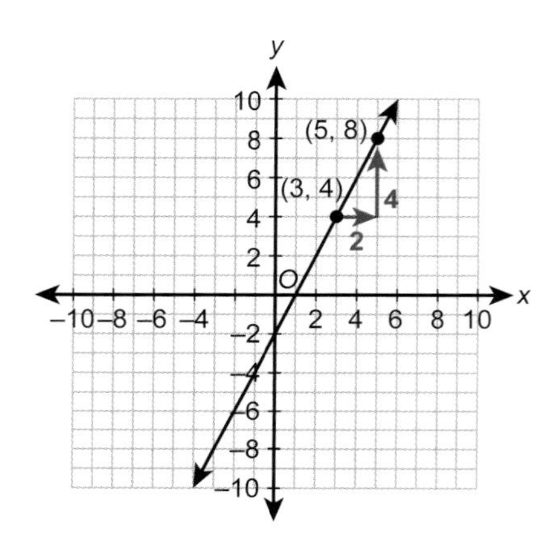

SOLUTION

The vertical change between the two points is 4 units. The horizontal change between the two points is 2 units.

$$\text{slope} = \frac{\text{rise}}{\text{run}} = \frac{4}{2} = 2$$

The slope of the line is 2.

B Find the slope of the line passing through the points $(-3, 7)$ and $(1, 2)$.

SOLUTION

Use the slope formula. Choose either point to be x_1, y_1.

Substitute values into the slope formula for x_1, x_2, y_1, and y_2.

$(1,\ 2) \rightarrow x_1, y_1$ $\qquad$ $(-3,\ 7) \rightarrow x_2, y_2$

$$m = \frac{y_2 - y_1}{x_2 - x_1} = \frac{7 - 2}{-3 - 1} = \frac{5}{-4} = -\frac{5}{4}$$

The slope of the line is $-\frac{5}{4}$. ■

Finding the Slope of Horizontal and Vertical Lines

EXAMPLE 2

Find the slope of the line.

A

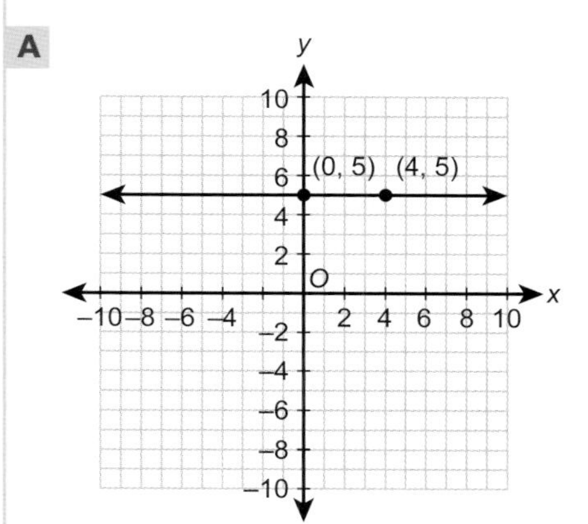

SOLUTION

The points (0, 5) and (4, 5) lie on the line. Use the slope formula.

(0, 5) → x_1, y_1 (4, 5) → x_2, y_2

Substitute values into the slope formula for x_1, x_2, y_1, and y_2.

$$m = \frac{y_2 - y_1}{x_2 - x_1} = \frac{5 - 5}{4 - 0} = \frac{0}{4} = 0$$

The slope of the line is 0. All horizontal lines have a slope of 0.

B

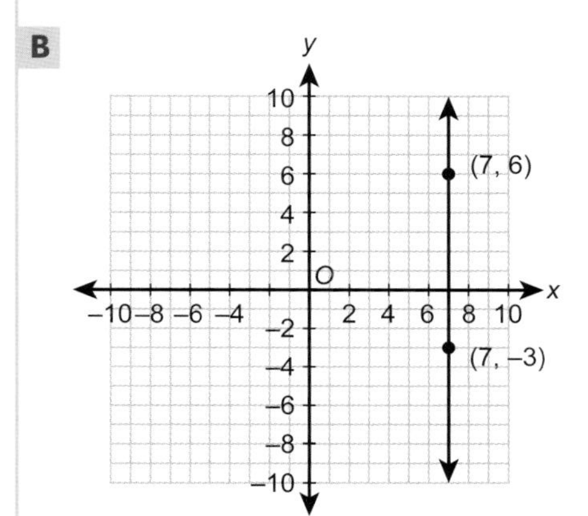

SOLUTION

The points $(7, 6)$ and $(7, -3)$ lie on the line. Use the slope formula. Substitute values into the slope formula for x_1, x_2, y_1, and y_2.

$(7, 6)$ → x_1, y_1 $(7, -3)$ → x_2, y_2

$$m = \frac{y_2 - y_1}{x_2 - x_1} = \frac{-3 - 6}{7 - 7} = \frac{-9}{0} \quad \textbf{undefined}$$

Division by zero is undefined, so the slope of the line is undefined. All vertical lines have undefined slope. ■

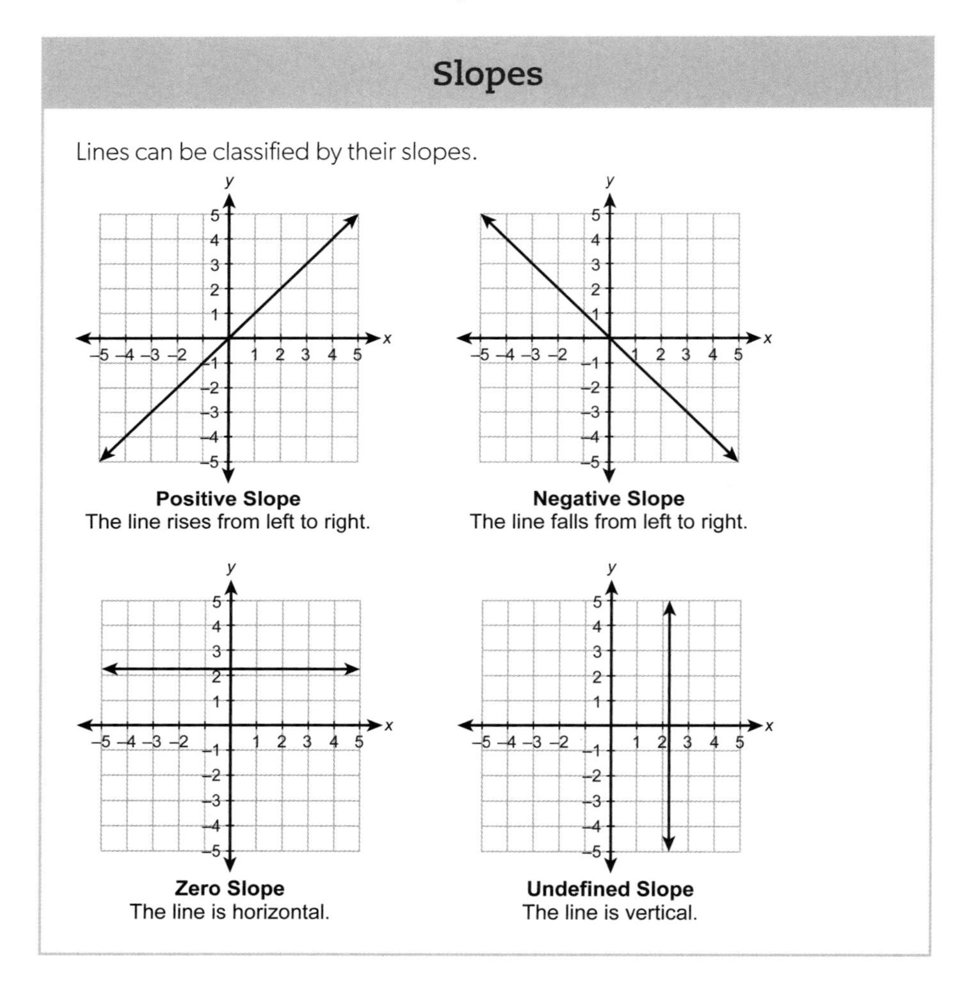

Using the Equation of a Line to Determine the Slope

EXAMPLE 3

Find the slope of the line $3x + 5y = 30$.

SOLUTION

Step 1 You need two points to find the slope of the line. Intercepts are easy points to find, so use them to compute the slope.

Find the x- and y-intercepts of the line.

To find the x-intercept, substitute 0 into the equation for y. Then solve for x.

$$\begin{aligned} 3x + 5y &= 30 \\ 3x + 5 \bullet \mathbf{0} &= 30 \\ 3x &= 30 \\ x &= 10 \end{aligned}$$

The x-intercept is 10.

To find the y-intercept, substitute 0 into the equation for x. Then solve for y.

$$\begin{aligned} 3x + 5y &= 30 \\ 3 \bullet \mathbf{0} + 5y &= 30 \\ 5y &= 30 \\ y &= 6 \end{aligned}$$

The y-intercept is 6.

The points $(10, 0)$ and $(0, 6)$ lie on the line $3x + 5y = 30$.

Step 2 Use the intercepts to find the slope of the line.

$$m = \frac{y_2 - y_1}{x_2 - x_1} = \frac{6 - 0}{0 - 10} = \frac{6}{-10} = -\frac{3}{5}$$

The slope of the line $3x + 5y = 30$ is $-\frac{3}{5}$. ■

Graphing a Line Using a Point on the Line and the Slope

EXAMPLE 4

Graph the line that contains the point (1, 6) and has a slope of $\frac{2}{3}$.

SOLUTION

The slope of the line is $\frac{2}{3}$, so the vertical change, $y_2 - y_1$, is 2 and the horizontal change, $x_2 - x_1$, is 3. Since you know **(1, 6)** is a point on the line, you can set up and solve the two equations.

$$\begin{aligned} y_2 - y_1 &= 2 \\ y_2 - \mathbf{6} &= 2 \\ y_2 - 6 + 6 &= 2 + 6 \\ y_2 &= 8 \end{aligned} \qquad \begin{aligned} x_2 - x_1 &= 3 \\ x_2 - \mathbf{1} &= 3 \\ x_2 - 1 + 1 &= 3 + 1 \\ x_2 &= 4 \end{aligned}$$

A second point on the line is (4, 8). Now plot the two points, (1, 6) and (4, 8), and draw the line.

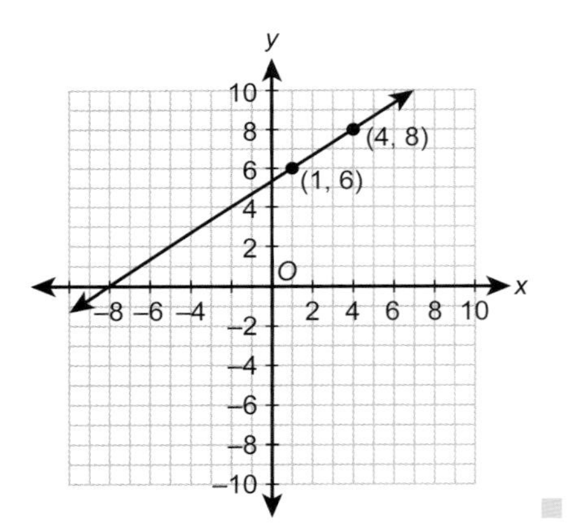

Application: Rate of Change

A **rate of change** is the ratio of a change in one quantity to a change in a second quantity. A linear equation models a constant rate of change.

EXAMPLE 5

The table shows the total late fee for a movie rental. Find the rate of change of late fee to time.

Time (days late)	2	4	6
Total late fee ($)	1.50	3	4.50

SOLUTION

Write the rate of change as a ratio. Start by picking two ordered pairs.

$$\text{rate of change} = \frac{\text{change in late fee}}{\text{change in time}} = \frac{3 - 1.50}{4 - 2} = \frac{1.50}{2} = 0.75$$

Choose two more ordered pairs to see that the rate of change is constant.

$$\text{rate of change} = \frac{\text{change in late fee}}{\text{change in time}} = \frac{4.50 - 3}{6 - 4} = \frac{1.50}{2} = 0.75$$

The rate of change is 75¢ per day. ■

Slope and Similar Triangles

Similar right triangles lying along a line can show that the slope of the line is constant.

Slope and Similar Right Triangles

Any two points on a line form the hypotenuse of a right triangle. The slope of the hypotenuse is the ratio of the rise to the run. The rise is equal to the length of the vertical leg of the triangle, and the run is equal to the length of the horizontal leg of the triangle.

EXAMPLE 1

Show that the slope of the line is constant.

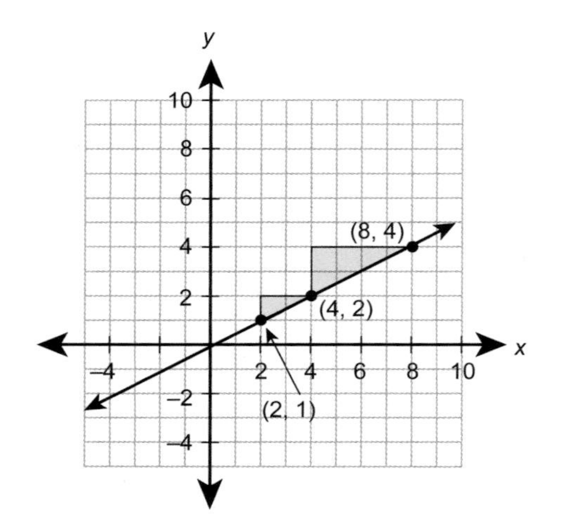

SOLUTION

For the smaller triangle, $\frac{\text{rise}}{\text{run}} = \frac{2-1}{4-2} = \frac{1}{2}$. For the larger triangle, $\frac{\text{rise}}{\text{run}} = \frac{4-2}{8-4} = \frac{2}{4} = \frac{1}{2}$. Since the ratio of $\frac{\text{rise}}{\text{run}}$ represents the slope of the line, the hypotenuse of each triangle has the same slope, a constant value of $\frac{1}{2}$. ■

EXAMPLE 2

The points $(0, -4)$, $(2, 2)$, and $(6, 14)$ lie on the same graph. Show that each pair of points defines a line with the same slope.

SOLUTION

To help visualize the pairs of points, use the rise and the run from $(0, -4)$ to $(2, 2)$, from $(2, 2)$ to $(6, 14)$, and from $(0, -4)$ to $(6, 14)$ to draw right triangles with the line as the hypotenuse.

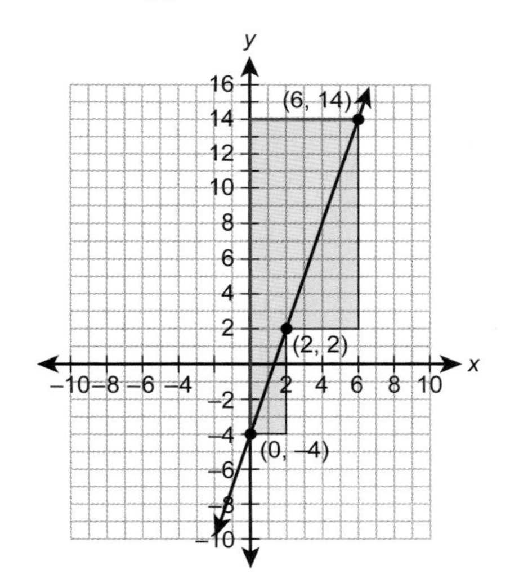

For the triangle defined by $(0, -4)$ and $(2, 2)$, $\frac{\text{rise}}{\text{run}} = \frac{2 - (-4)}{2 - 0} = \frac{6}{2} = 3$.

For the triangle defined by $(2, 2)$ and $(6, 14)$, $\frac{\text{rise}}{\text{run}} = \frac{14 - 2}{6 - 2} = \frac{12}{4} = 3$.

For the triangle defined by $(0, -4)$ and $(6, 14)$, $\frac{\text{rise}}{\text{run}} = \frac{14 - (-4)}{6 - 0} = \frac{18}{6} = 3$.

Since ratio of $\frac{\text{rise}}{\text{run}}$ represents the slope of the line, the hypotenuse of each triangle has the same slope, a constant value of 3. ■

▶ Q&A

Q What is the *y*-intercept of the line?

A −4

When you are computing the slope of a line, you can choose any two points on the line and you will always get the same slope. That means that you can choose two points that are convenient because of the context, data, or ease of calculation.

Simple Linear Graphs

The graph of a linear equation is a straight line.

Deriving the Equation of a Line That Passes Through the Origin

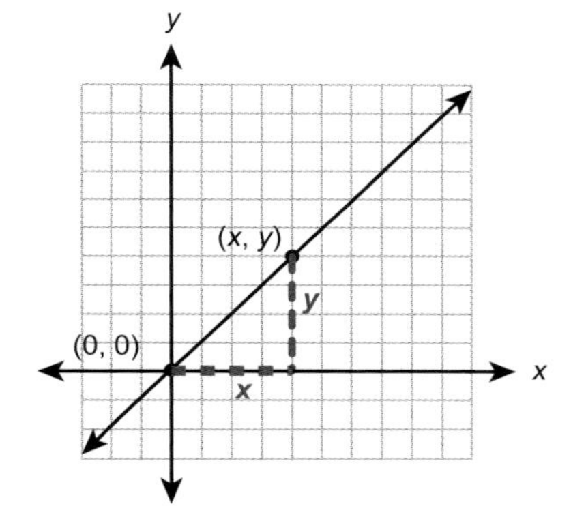

Use the slope formula to show that the slope of any line through a point (x, y) and the origin $(0, 0)$ is $\frac{y}{x}$.

$$m = \frac{y_2 - y_1}{x_2 - x_1}$$

$$m = \frac{y - 0}{x - 0} \qquad \text{Let } (x_1, y_1) = (0, 0) \text{ and } (x_2, y_2) = (x, y).$$

$$m = \frac{y}{x}$$

Multiplication equations are easier to work with than division equations, so solve the equation $m = \frac{y}{x}$ for y.

$$m = \frac{y}{x}$$

$$x \bullet m = \frac{y}{x} \bullet x \qquad \text{Multiply both sides by } x.$$

$$mx = y$$

$$y = mx \qquad \text{Symmetric Property}$$

Equation for a Line That Passes Through the Origin

The equation of any line with slope m that passes through the origin and the point (x, y) can be written as

$$y = mx.$$

Graphing a Line from Its Equation by Plotting Points

EXAMPLE 1

Graph $y = 2x$.

SOLUTION

Use the equation to find ordered pairs of points that lie on the line. Choose values for x and substitute them into the equation. Then simplify the corresponding y-values.

x	$y = 2x$	(x, y)
-3	$y = 2 \bullet (-3) = -6$	$(-3, -6)$
-1	$y = 2 \bullet (-1) = -2$	$(-1, -2)$
0	$y = 2 \bullet 0 = 0$	$(0, 0)$
1	$y = 2 \bullet 1 = 2$	$(1, 2)$
3	$y = 2 \bullet 3 = 6$	$(3, 6)$

Plot points for the ordered pairs, and then connect them with a line.

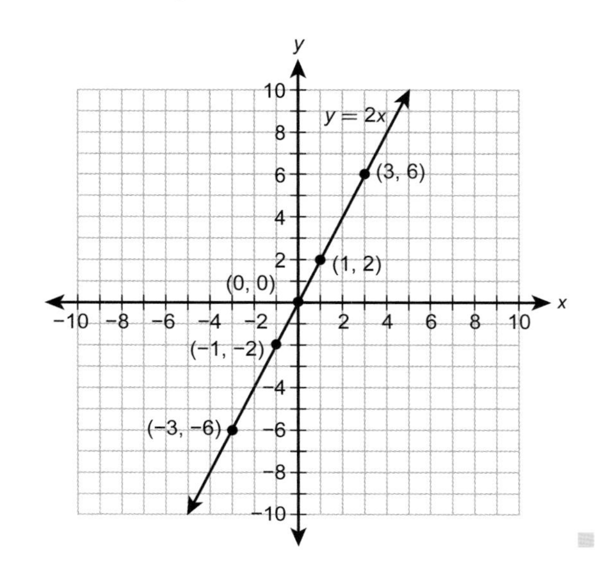

▸ **Think About It** The equation of any line that passes through the origin is $y = mx$. The equation of this line is $y = 2x$, so the slope, m, is 2. Choose any two points on this line, and you will find that the slope is 2.

Let $(x_1, y_1) = (1, 2)$ and let $(x_2, y_2) = (3, 6)$.

$$m = \frac{y_2 - y_1}{x_2 - x_1} = \frac{6 - 2}{3 - 1} = \frac{4}{2} = 2$$

Graphing a Line from Its Equation Using the Origin and the Slope

EXAMPLE 2

Graph $y = -\frac{1}{3}x$.

SOLUTION

The equation is in the form $y = mx$, which means that the graph of the equation is a straight line that passes through the origin and has a slope of $-\frac{1}{3}$. To graph the line, plot the point (0, 0), and use the slope to find other points on the line.

Step 1 Plot the point (0, 0).

Step 2 Since the slope is $-\frac{1}{3}$, move 1 unit up and 3 units to the left from the origin. Plot the point $(-3, 1)$.

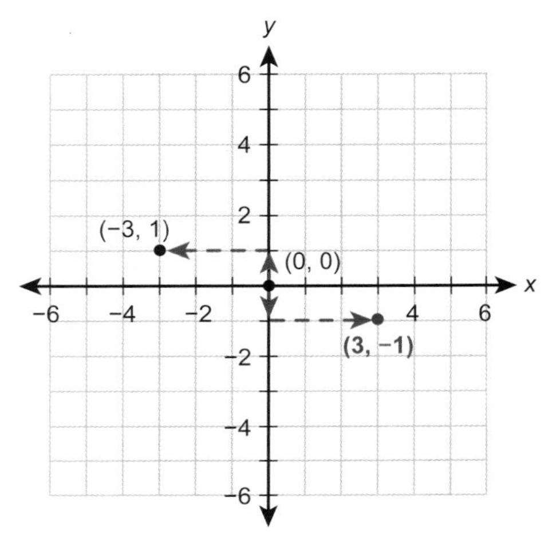

Step 3 Beginning at the origin again, move 1 unit down and 3 units to the right. Plot the point $(3, -1)$.

Step 4 Draw a line through the points.

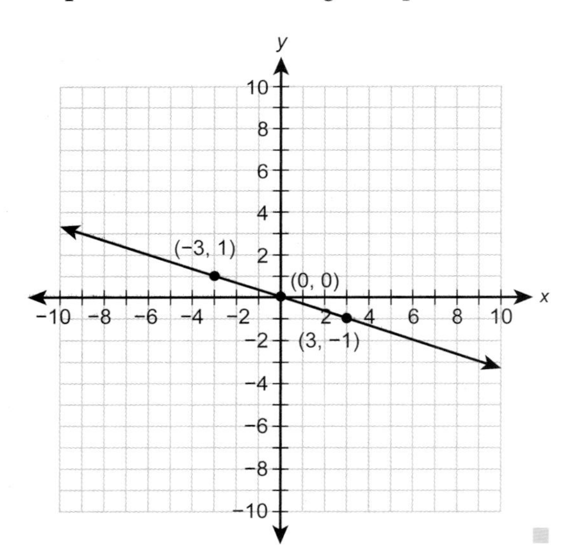

Writing an Equation from Its Graph

EXAMPLE 3

Write an equation from the graph.

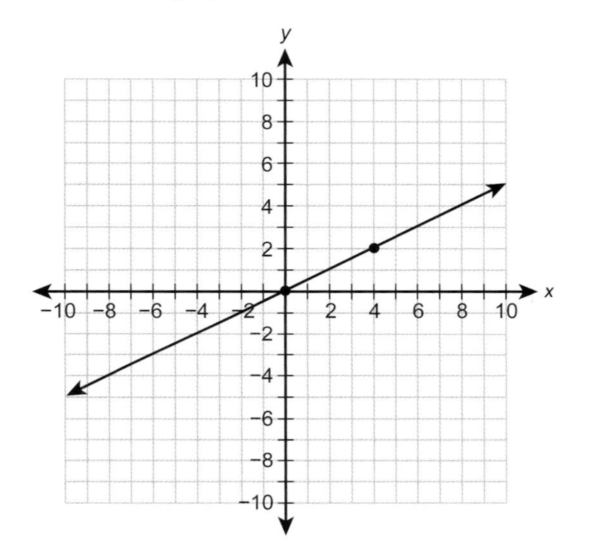

Step 1 Find the slope. Choose two points on the line, and use the slope formula. Let $(x_1, y_1) = (0, 0)$ and let $(x_2, y_2) = (4, 2)$.

$$m = \frac{y_2 - y_1}{x_2 - x_1} = \frac{2 - 0}{4 - 0} = \frac{2}{4} = \frac{1}{2}$$

The slope m is $\frac{1}{2}$.

Step 2 Substitute $\frac{1}{2}$ for m in the equation $y = mx$. The equation shown in the graph is $y = \frac{1}{2}x$. ■

Slope-Intercept Form

You can write the equation of a line in various forms, including standard form and slope-intercept form.

The different forms of the equation of a particular line are equivalent. That is, even though they are written differently, they represent the same line, so they will have the same graph and the same solutions.

The different forms can help identify characteristics of a line more easily. For example, the slope-intercept form of a linear equation can help you identify the slope and y-intercept, while the slope may not be easily identifiable from the same equation written in standard form.

Definition

The **slope-intercept form** of a linear equation is

$$y = mx + b,$$

where m is the slope of the line and b is the y-intercept.

Identifying the Slope and y-Intercept

EXAMPLE 1

Identify the slope and y-intercept.

A $y = 3x + 4$

SOLUTION

The equation of the line is in slope-intercept form. m is the slope of the line and b is the y-intercept.

$$\begin{array}{c} y = mx + b \\ \downarrow \quad \downarrow \\ y = 3x + 4 \end{array}$$

The slope of the line is 3 and the y-intercept is 4.

B $y = -5x - \frac{1}{2}$

SOLUTION

Write the equation as $y = -5x + \left(-\frac{1}{2}\right)$.

$$\begin{array}{c} y = mx + b \\ \downarrow \quad \downarrow \\ y = -5x + \left(-\frac{1}{2}\right) \end{array}$$

The slope of the line is -5 and the y-intercept is $-\frac{1}{2}$. ■

Converting a Line from Standard to Slope-Intercept Form

EXAMPLE 2

Write the equation of the line $2x + 5y = 15$ in slope-intercept form.

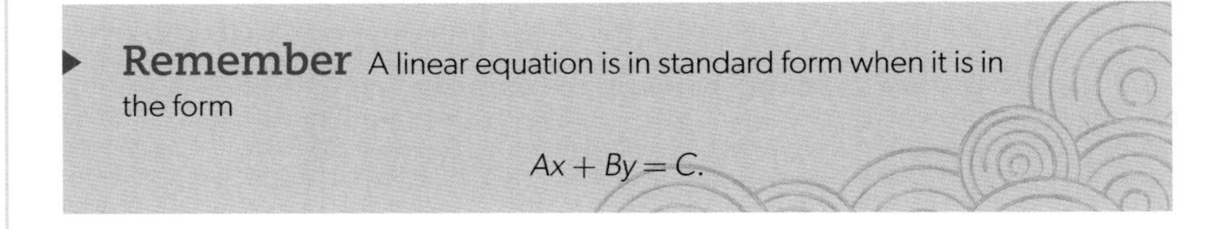

▶ **Remember** A linear equation is in standard form when it is in the form

$$Ax + By = C.$$

SOLUTION

Solve the equation for y.

$2x + 5y = 15$

$5y = -2x + 15$	Subtract $2x$ from each side of the equation.
$y = -\frac{2}{5}x + 3$	Divide each side by 5.

The equation in slope-intercept form is $y = -\frac{2}{5}x + 3$. ■

Using Slope-Intercept Form to Graph a Line

EXAMPLE 3

Graph the line $3x + y = 5$.

SOLUTION

Step 1 Write the equation in slope-intercept form.

$3x + y = 5$

$y = -3x + 5$	Subtract $3x$ from each side of the equation.

Step 2 Use the equation to identify the slope and y-intercept of the line.

$$\begin{array}{c} y = mx + b \\ \downarrow \quad \downarrow \\ y = -3x + 5 \end{array}$$

The slope of the line is -3 and the y-intercept is 5.

Step 3 Use the y-intercept to graph a point on the line. The line intersects the y-axis at the point (0, 5).

Step 4 Use the slope of the line to graph a second point on the line. The slope of the line is -3 or $\frac{-3}{1}$. The rise is -3 and the run is 1.

Start at the point (0, 5). Move 3 units down and 1 unit to the right. A second point on the line is (1, 2). Draw a line through the points (0, 5) and (1, 2).

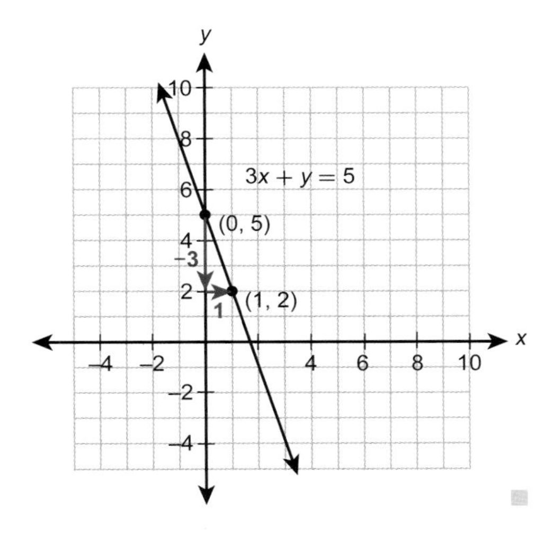

Application: Profit

EXAMPLE 4

You are selling items on an online auction site. Each item sells for \$2.50 and there is a one-time listing fee of \$8.

A Write an equation to model your profit, P.

SOLUTION

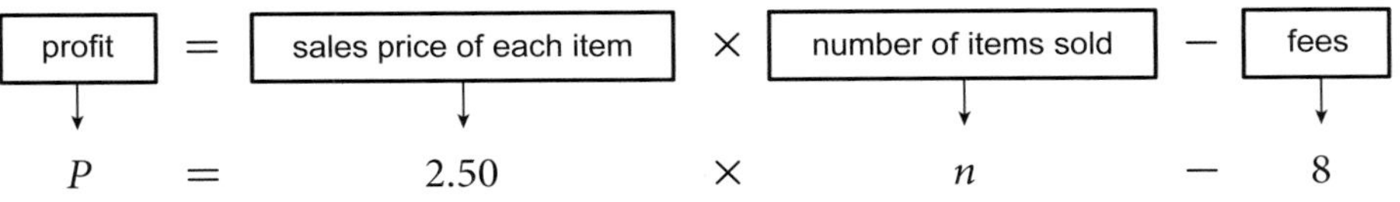

The problem is modeled by the equation $P = 2.5n - 8$.

B Graph the equation.

SOLUTION

Find the slope and y-intercept of the line.

$$y = mx + b$$

$$P = 2.5n + (-8)$$

The slope of the line is 2.5 and the y-intercept is -8. Use the slope of the line to graph a second point on the line. Write the slope of the line as $\frac{2.5}{1}$.

The rise is 2.5 and the run is 1. Start at the point $(0, -8)$. Move 2.5 units up and 1 unit to the right. A second point on the line is $(1, -5.5)$. Draw a line through the points $(0, -8)$ and $(1, -5.5)$.

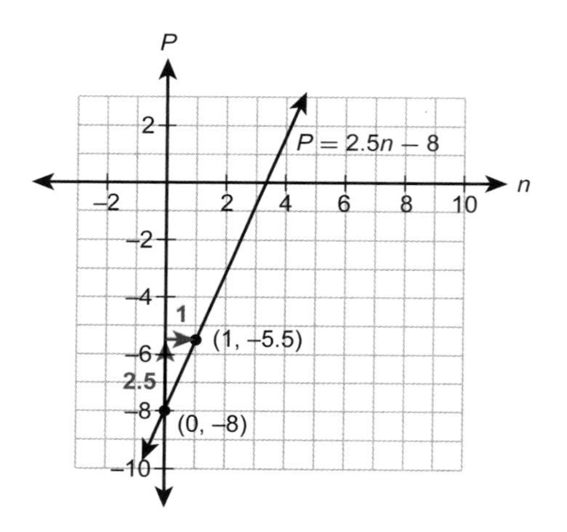

C What does each intercept represent?

SOLUTION

The vertical axis represents P, the dollar amount of your profit. The P-intercept, $(0, -8)$ represents the greatest amount of money you can lose, or the greatest negative profit amount. If you sell **0** items, you will still have to pay the listing fee of \$8. Your profit will be **−\$8**. The horizontal axis represents n, the number of items sold. The line crosses the n-axis between 3 and 4, at the point $(3.2, 0)$. If you sold 3.2 items, you would break even. Any n-value greater than that number signifies a positive profit amount. Since you can sell only whole items, you must sell 4 items to make a profit.

D What is the domain of the problem?

SOLUTION

Since you can only sell whole items, the domain of the problem is all whole numbers. ■

Using Slope as a Rate

The slope of a line that models a real-world situation can be interpreted as a rate.

Proportional Relationships

Definitions

A **proportional relationship** is a relationship that can be modeled by an equation in the form $y = kx$, where k is the **constant of proportionality**.

The graph of any proportional relationship is a line that passes through the origin. You can decide whether or not a relationship is proportional by looking at its graph. If the graph is a line passing through the origin, the relationship is proportional.

EXAMPLE 1

A Use a graph to show that the relationship between x and y is proportional.

x	0	1	2	3	4
y	0	4	8	12	16

SOLUTION

Use the values in the table to plot the points (x, y).

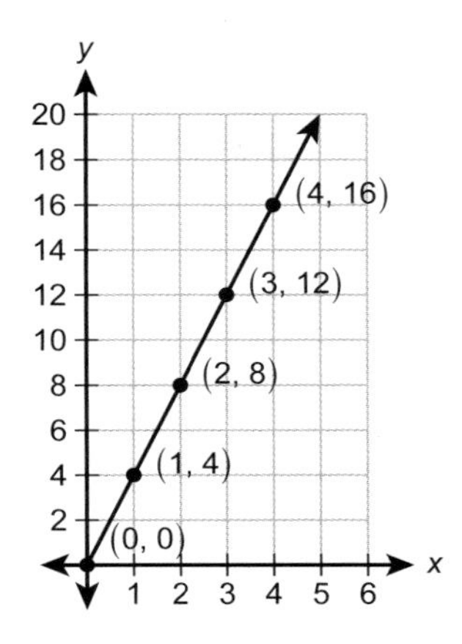

The points fall on a line passing through the origin, so the relationship is proportional. For each point, the y-value is 4 times the x-value, so the equation relating x and y is $y = 4x$. The equation has the form $y = kx$, with $k = 4$, so the constant of proportionality is 4.

B The equation $y = 0.2x$ models a proportional relationship. Complete the table and graph the data.

x	0	5	10	15	20
y					

SOLUTION

To complete the table, multiply each x-value by 0.2.

When $x = 0$:

$$\begin{aligned} y &= 0.2x \\ &= 0.2(0) \\ &= 0 \end{aligned}$$

When $x = 5$:

$$\begin{aligned} y &= 0.2x \\ &= 0.2(5) \\ &= 1 \end{aligned}$$

When $x = 10$:

$$\begin{aligned} y &= 0.2x \\ &= 0.2(10) \\ &= 2 \end{aligned}$$

When $x = 15$:

$$\begin{aligned} y &= 0.2x \\ &= 0.2(15) \\ &= 3 \end{aligned}$$

When $x = 20$:

$$\begin{aligned} y &= 0.2x \\ &= 0.2(20) \\ &= 4 \end{aligned}$$

x	0	5	10	15	20
y	0	1	2	3	4

Graph the ordered pairs.

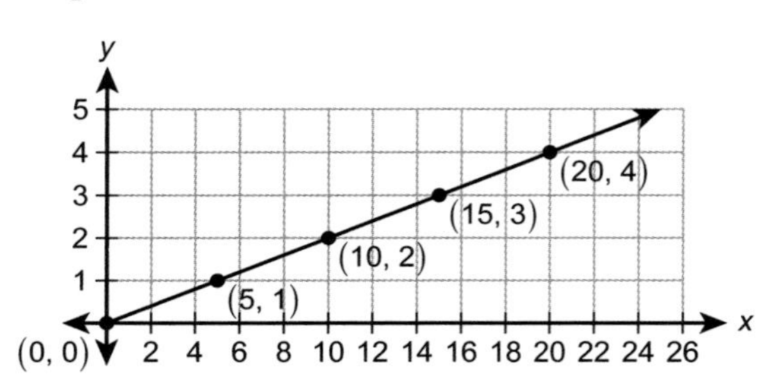

For each point, the y-value is 0.2 times the x-value. The equation has the form $y = kx$, with $k = 0.2$, so the constant of proportionality is 0.2.

EXAMPLE 2

State whether the relationship modeled by the graph is proportional or not proportional. Explain your answer.

A

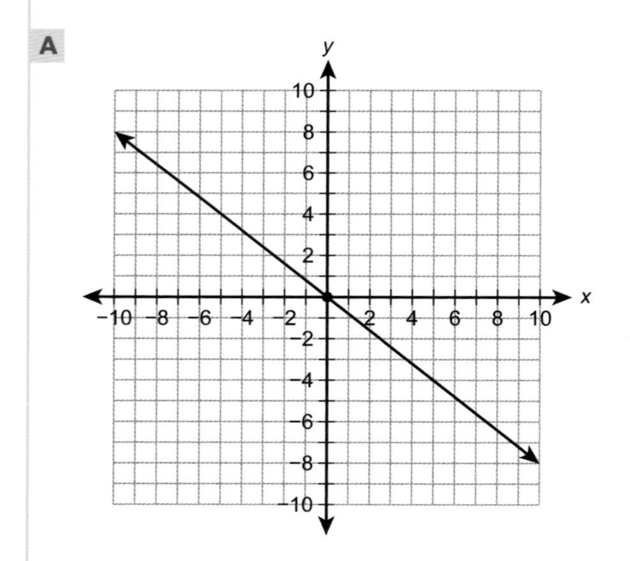

SOLUTION

The graph is a line that passes through the origin, so the relationship is proportional.

B

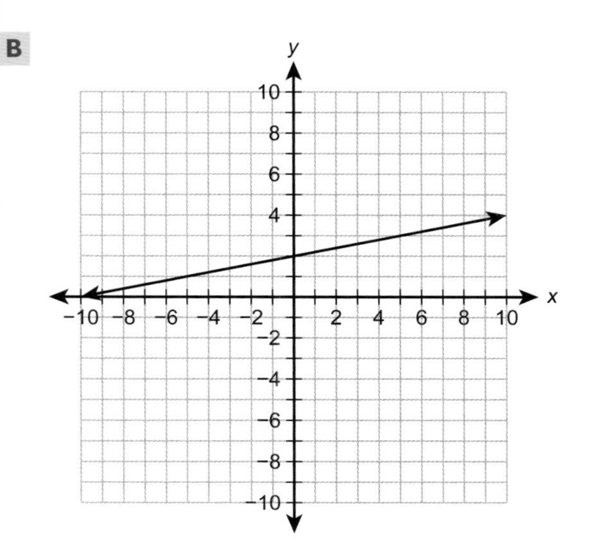

SOLUTION

The graph is a line, but the line does not pass through the origin. The relationship is not proportional.

Unit Rates

A proportional relationship can be modeled by an equation in the form $y = mx$. When an equation is written in this form, the constant of proportionality is the slope, m, of the line and expresses the rate at which y is changing in relation to x. The value of y when $x = 1$ is the unit rate for the relationship.

Definitions

A **rate** is a ratio of two quantities measured in different units.

A **unit rate** is a rate in which the second quantity in the ratio is 1. When a unit rate is expressed as a fraction, the denominator is 1.

When a problem involves the change in a quantity per 1 unit change in another quantity, the problem involves a unit rate.

EXAMPLE 3

Andrea can swim 1.5 laps per minute. How many laps can she swim in 12 min?

SOLUTION

Andrea's swimming speed is an example of a unit rate. For every 1 min she swims, she completes 1.5 laps. To find the number of laps she swims in 12 min, multiply her rate by the number of minutes.

$$1.5 \cdot 12 = 18$$

Andrea can swim 18 laps in 12 min. ■

EXAMPLE 4

A school's enrollment in 2005 was 690 students. In 2010, the school's enrollment was 810. What was the average annual rate of increase in enrollment?

SOLUTION

The school's enrollment increased by 810 − 690, or 120 students in 5 years. Divide 120 by 5.

$$120 \div 5 = 24$$

The school's enrollment increased at an average rate of 24 students per year. ■

▶ **Think About It** An annual rate of increase in enrollment is a unit rate because it describes the amount the enrollment increases in 1 year.

Interpreting Slope as a Rate

The graph shows the cost of buying different amounts of apples. Notice that the slope is $\frac{5}{2}$. By dividing 5 by 2, you can express this slope as 2.5, or $\frac{2.5}{1}$. When the slope has a denominator of 1, you can interpret the slope as a unit rate. The slope of 2.5 tells you that apples cost $2.50/lb.

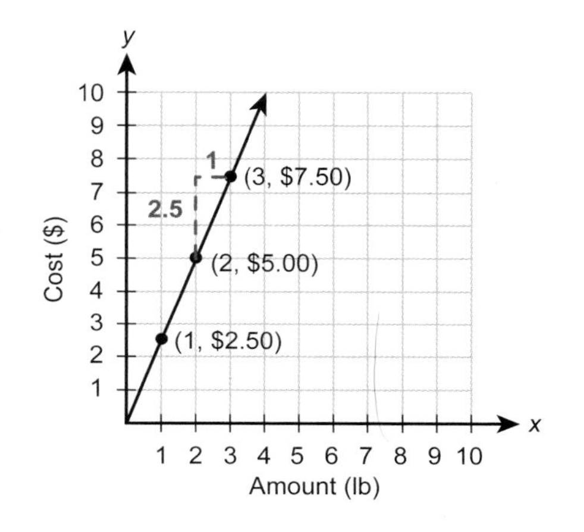

EXAMPLE 5

The graph shows the altitude of an aircraft over time.

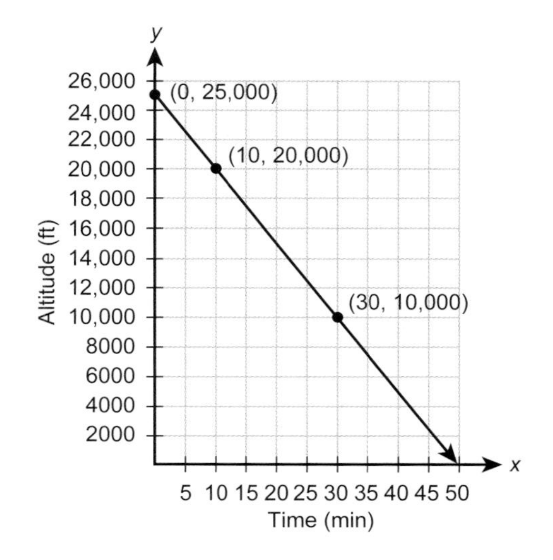

A What is the slope of the line?

SOLUTION

Choose any two points on the line, such as $(10, 20{,}000)$ and $(30, 10{,}000)$. Use the slope formula.

$$\begin{aligned} m &= \frac{y_2 - y_1}{x_2 - x_1} \\ &= \frac{10{,}000 - 20{,}000}{30 - 10} \\ &= -\frac{10{,}000}{20} \\ &= -500 \end{aligned}$$

The slope is -500.

B Interpret the slope as a rate.

SOLUTION

The rate is -500 ft/min. Since the rate is negative, the airplane is descending, which means that its altitude decreases by 500 ft/min. The airplane descends 500 ft each minute.

Finding Rates and Drawing Graphs

EXAMPLE 6

The table shows snow totals at different times during a snowstorm that began at 9:00 p.m.

Time	9:00 p.m.	11:00 p.m.	12:00 a.m.	3:00 a.m.	4:00 a.m.
Amount of snow (in.)	2	4.4	5.6	9.2	10.4

A Draw the graph that represents the situation.

SOLUTION

Step 1 Create a list of ordered pairs in which x is the number of hours that have elapsed since 9:00 p.m. and y is the number of inches of snow that has fallen. Set up a table.

Time	Hours since 9:00 p.m. x	Amount of snow (in.) y	Ordered pair (x, y)
9:00 p.m.	0	2	(0, 2)
11:00 p.m.	2	4.4	(2, 4.4)
12:00 a.m.	3	5.6	(3, 5.6)
3:00 a.m.	6	9.2	(6, 9.2)
4:00 a.m.	7	10.4	(7, 10.4)

Step 2 Plot points for the ordered pairs, and connect them with a line.

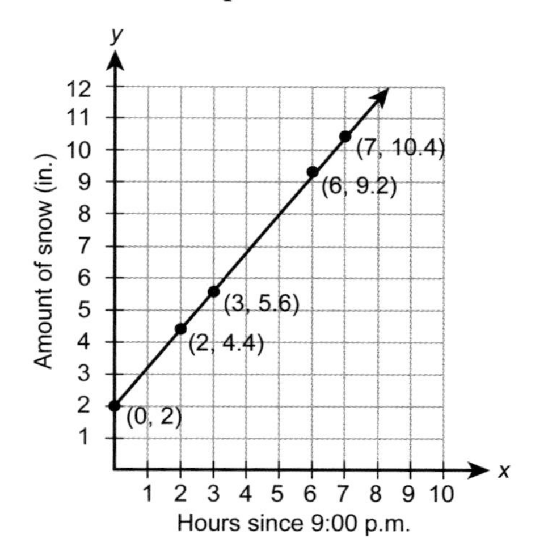

B What is the slope of the line?

SOLUTION

Use the slope formula. Let $(x_1, y_1) = (3, 5.6)$ and let $(x_2, y_2) = (6, 9.2)$.

$$m = \frac{y_2 - y_1}{x_2 - x_1} = \frac{9.2 - 5.6}{6 - 3} = \frac{3.6}{3} = 1.2$$

The slope is 1.2.

C Interpret the slope as a rate.

SOLUTION

The rate is 1.2 in./h, which means that 1.2 in. of snow fell every hour. The amount of snow on the ground increases by 1.2 in./h. ■

EXAMPLE 7

Mariah reads 7 books every 4 months. Graph the line that represents this situation.

SOLUTION

Step 1 Calculate the rate at which Mariah reads per month. Divide 7 books by 4 months.

$$\frac{7 \text{ books}}{4 \text{ months}} = 1.75 \text{ books/month}$$

Mariah reads 1.75 books each month.

Step 2 Write an equation to represent the situation. Let x represent the number of months and let y represent the number of books read.

$$y = 1.75x$$

Step 3 Create a table of ordered pairs. Choose values for x and solve for the corresponding y values.

Months x	Books read $y = 1.75x$	Ordered pair (x, y)
0	$y = 1.75 \bullet 0 = 0$	$(0, 0)$
1	$y = 1.75 \bullet 1 = 1.75$	$(1, 1.75)$
2	$y = 1.75 \bullet 2 = 3.5$	$(2, 3.5)$
3	$y = 1.75 \bullet 3 = 5.25$	$(3, 5.25)$

Step 4 Graph the ordered pairs.

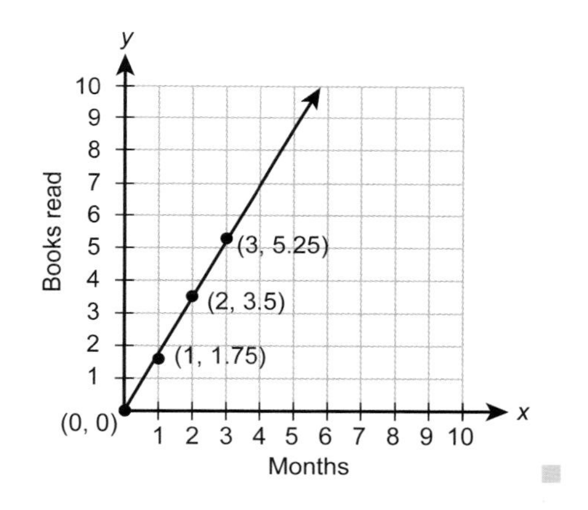

Comparing Proportional Relationships

You can use slope to compare proportional relationships.

Making Comparisons

When you're interpreting the slope of a line as a rate, the steepness of the slope is important. The steeper the slope, the greater the rate is. You can compare rates by comparing slopes.

▶ **Think About It** A proportional relationship is a relationship that can be described by an equation of the form $y = kx$, where k is the constant of proportionality. The constant, k, is also the slope. Therefore, any equation of the form $y = mx$ is a proportional relationship.

EXAMPLE 1

The graph shows the distances traveled by two bicyclists over several minutes.

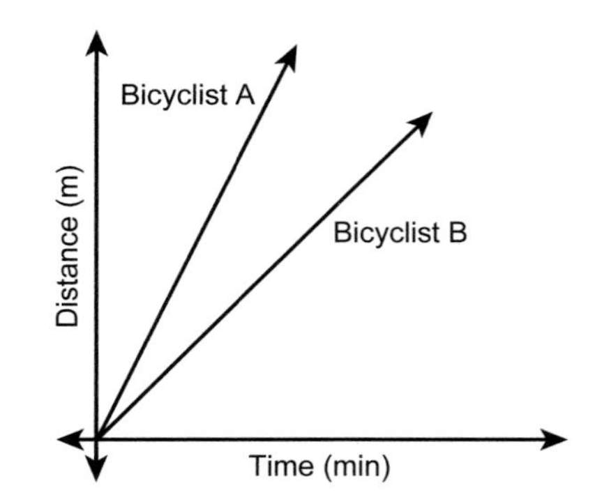

A Which bicyclist is moving at a faster rate?

SOLUTION

The line that represents the distance traveled by Bicyclist A has a steeper slope than the line that represents the distance traveled by Bicyclist B. Therefore, Bicyclist A is moving at a faster rate.

B If the equation $y = 18x$ represents the distance, y, Bicyclist A travels in x min, then which equation could represent the distance traveled by Bicyclist B?

A. $y = 14x$

B. $y = 19x$

C. $y = 21x$

D. $y = 24x$

SOLUTION

In the equation $y = 18x$, the slope is 18. Therefore, Bicyclist A is moving at a rate of 18 m/min. Bicyclist B is moving at a slower rate, so the slope of the line that represents Bicyclist B is less than 18. In answer choice A, the slope is 14, which is less than 18. The slopes of the equations in choices B, C, and D are all greater than 18. The correct answer is A. ■

EXAMPLE 2

In a laboratory experiment, Liquid A is heated at a rate given by the equation $y = 4x$ and Liquid B is heated at a rate given by the equation $y = 3x$. For both equations, x is the number of minutes since the experiment began and y is the temperature in degrees Celsius. Graph the two equations, and use the graphs to compare the heating rates for the two liquids.

SOLUTION

Step 1 Create a table of ordered pairs for each equation. Choose values for x and solve for corresponding y-values.

Liquid A

Time since experiment began x (min)	Temperature (°C) $y = 4x$	Ordered pair (x, y)
0	$y = 4 \bullet 0 = 0$	$(0, 0)$
2	$y = 4 \bullet 2 = 8$	$(2, 8)$
4	$y = 4 \bullet 4 = 16$	$(4, 16)$
6	$y = 4 \bullet 6 = 24$	$(6, 24)$
8	$y = 4 \bullet 8 = 32$	$(8, 32)$

Liquid B

Time since experiment began x (min)	Temperature (°C) $y = 3x$	Ordered pair (x, y)
0	$y = 3 \bullet 0 = 0$	$(0, 0)$
2	$y = 3 \bullet 2 = 6$	$(2, 6)$
4	$y = 3 \bullet 4 = 12$	$(4, 12)$
6	$y = 3 \bullet 6 = 18$	$(6, 18)$
8	$y = 3 \bullet 8 = 24$	$(8, 24)$

Step 2 Graph the ordered pairs from each table.

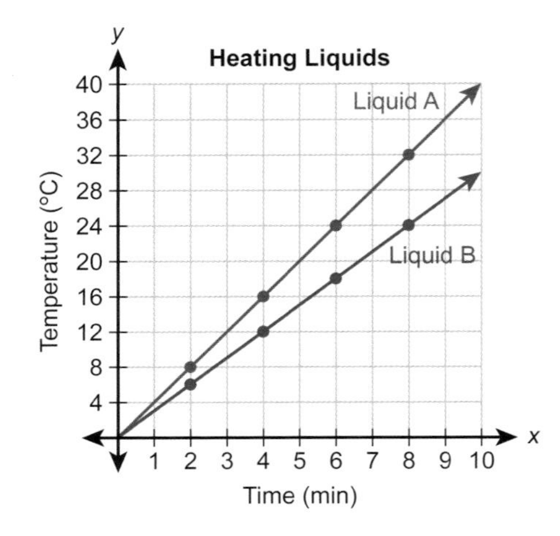

Step 3 Use the slope of each line to compare the heating rates for the two liquids.

The line representing Liquid A has a slope of 4—meaning that Liquid A is heating at a rate of 4°C/min. The line representing Liquid B has a slope of 3—meaning that Liquid B is heating at a rate of 3°C/min. Since 4°C/min is faster than 3°C/min, Liquid A is heating up faster than Liquid B. ■

▶ **Think About It** The line that represents Liquid A has a steeper slope than the line that represents Liquid B. Therefore, Liquid A has a faster heating rate than Liquid B.

Comparing Proportional Relationships Represented in Different Ways

In Example 1, the relationships between distance and time for both bicyclists were represented as lines. Sometimes you may need to compare relationships that are not represented in the same way. One relationship may be represented in a table and the other in an equation or a graph. How do you compare rates in those situations? Since slope can be interpreted as rate; find and compare the slopes.

EXAMPLE 3

A car's fuel efficiency is determined by the number of miles it can travel for every 1 gal of gas it uses. The table shows the number of miles Car A travels on different amounts of gas. The equation $y = 30x$ represents the number of miles Car B travels if it uses x gallon of gas. Which car is more fuel efficient?

Fuel used (gal)	0	12	16	20	22
Distance traveled (mi)	0	264	352	440	484

SOLUTION

Step 1 Determine Car A's fuel efficiency in miles per gallon.

Create ordered pairs from the data in the table by letting x represent the number of gallons used and letting y represent the number of miles traveled. Then choose two sets of ordered pairs. Substitute the x- and y-coordinates of those ordered pairs into the slope formula to find the slope.

Fuel used (gal)	0	12	16	20	22
Distance traveled (mi)	0	264	352	440	484
Ordered pair	$(0, 0)$	$(12, 264)$	$(16, 352)$	$(20, 440)$	$(22, 484)$

Choose ordered pairs $(0, 0)$ and $(12, 264)$.

$$m = \frac{y_2 - y_1}{x_2 - x_1} = \frac{264 - 0}{12 - 0} = \frac{264}{12} = 22$$

The slope is 22. Therefore, Car A's fuel efficiency is 22 mpg.

Step 2 Determine Car B's fuel efficiency in miles per gallon.

In the equation $y = 30x$, the slope is 30. The slope represents the number of miles Car B can travel per gallon of gas. Therefore, Car B's fuel efficiency is 30 mpg.

Step 3 Compare the rates.

Since $30 > 22$, Car B has greater fuel efficiency than Car A does. Car B is more fuel efficient than Car A is. ■

▶ **Think About It** The greater the distance a car can travel per gallon of gas, the more fuel efficient the car is.

EXAMPLE 4

The table shows sales of admission tickets to an amusement park in 1 wk. The graph show sales of admission tickets to a water park over the same week. Which admission ticket is more expensive?

Amusement Park Admission Revenue

Tickets sold	178	182	212	230	343	542	564
Sales ($)	4628	4732	5512	5980	8918	14,092	14,664

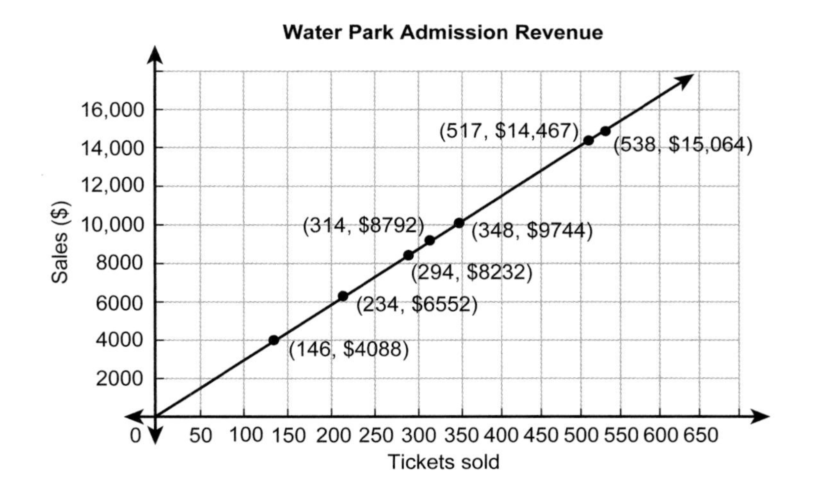

SOLUTION

Step 1 Determine the price per ticket for admission to the amusement park.

Let x represent the number of tickets sold and let y represent sales revenue. Choose $(230, \$5980)$ and $(182, \$4732)$ as a set of ordered pairs. Use the slope formula to find the slope.

$$m = \frac{y_2 - y_1}{x_2 - x_1} = \frac{\$5980 - \$4732}{230 - 182} = \frac{\$1248}{48} = \$26$$

The slope represents the price per ticket to the amusement park. Therefore, it costs \$26 per ticket for admission to the amusement park.

Step 2 Determine the price per ticket for admission to the water park.

Choose points $(146, \$4088)$ and $(234, \$6552)$ on the line, and use the slope formula to find the slope.

$$m = \frac{y_2 - y_1}{x_2 - x_1} = \frac{\$6552 - \$4088}{234 - 146} = \frac{\$2464}{88} = \$28$$

The slope represents the price per ticket to the water park. Therefore, it costs \$28 per ticket for admission to the water park.

Step 3 Compare the rates.

Admission to the water park is \$28 per ticket and admission to the amusement park is \$26 per ticket. Water park tickets are more expensive than amusement park tickets. ■

Lines

Topic List

- Point-Slope Form
- Forms of Linear Equations
- Equations from Graphs
- Linear Models
- Sketching Lines

You've probably heard the phrase, "That's where I draw the line." In algebra, you can take that expression literally. Linear equations and their graphs play an important role in the never-ending quest to model the real world.

Point-Slope Form

You can write the equation of a line in point-slope form if you know the slope of the line and the coordinates of any point that lies on the line.

Definition

The **point-slope form** of the equation of a line that passes through the point (x_1, y_1) and has a slope of m is $y - y_1 = m(x - x_1)$.

You can see how the point-slope form is derived using the slope formula.

$m = \dfrac{y_2 - y_1}{x_2 - x_1}$	Write the slope formula.
$m(x_2 - x_1) = \dfrac{y_2 - y_1}{x_2 - x_1}(x_2 - x_1)$	Multiply both sides by $x_2 - x_1$.
$m(x_2 - x_1) = y_2 - y_1$	Simplify.
$y_2 - y_1 = m(x_2 - x_1)$	Symmetric Property
$y - y_1 = m(x - x_1)$	Substitute y for y_2 and x for x_2.

Writing the Equation of a Line in Point-Slope Form

EXAMPLE 1

Use point-slope form to write an equation of the line that passes through the given point or points. Use the given slope or the slope formula when given two points.

A $(3, 5); m = -\frac{1}{2}$

SOLUTION

$(3, 5); m = -\frac{1}{2}$

$$\begin{aligned} y - y_1 &= m\,(x - x_1) \\ &\downarrow \quad \downarrow \quad \downarrow \\ y - 5 &= -\frac{1}{2}(x - 3) \end{aligned}$$

The equation of the line in point-slope form is

$$y - 5 = -\frac{1}{2}(x - 3).$$

B $(-1, -6); m = 5$

SOLUTION

$(-1, -6); m = 5$

$$\begin{aligned} y - y_1 &= m(x - x_1) \\ &\downarrow \quad \downarrow \quad \downarrow \\ y - (-6) &= 5[x - (-1)] \\ y + 6 &= 5(x + 1) \end{aligned}$$

The equation of the line in point-slope form is

$$y + 6 = 5(x + 1).$$

C Write an equation in point-slope form of the line that passes through $(1, -3)$ and $(-2, 3)$.

SOLUTION

Step 1 Find the slope of the line by using the slope formula and the two given points.

$$m = \frac{y_2 - y_1}{x_2 - x_1} = \frac{3 - (-3)}{-2 - 1} = \frac{6}{-3} = -2$$

Step 2 Write the equation in point-slope form. Use one of the given points and the slope in the point-slope equation.

Using point $(-2, 3)$:

$$\begin{aligned} y - y_1 &= m(x - x_1) \\ y - 3 &= -2[x - (-2)] \\ y - 3 &= -2(x + 2) \end{aligned}$$

The equation of the line in point-slope form is $y - 3 = -2(x + 2)$. ■

▶ **Think About It** If you use $(1, -3)$ to write the equation of the line in point-slope form, you get the equation $y + 3 = -2(x - 1)$. Although this equation looks different from the equation in the solution, you can see that they are equivalent when both are written in slope-intercept form.

$$\begin{aligned} y - 3 &= -2(x + 2) \\ y - 3 &= -2x - 4 \\ y &= -2x - 1 \end{aligned} \qquad \begin{aligned} y + 3 &= -2(x - 1) \\ y + 3 &= -2x + 2 \\ y &= -2x - 1 \end{aligned}$$

Using the Graph of a Line to Write the Equation in Point-Slope Form

EXAMPLE 2

Use the graph to solve.

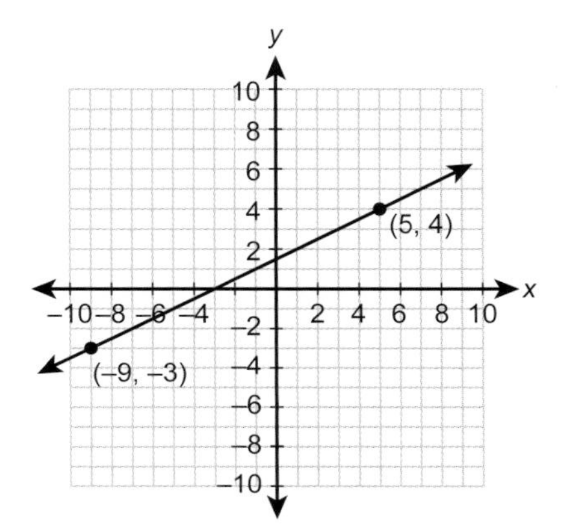

A Write an equation of the line shown in the graph using the coordinates $(5, 4)$.

SOLUTION

Step 1 Find the slope of the line using the slope formula.

$$m = \frac{y_2 - y_1}{x_2 - x_1} = \frac{4 - (-3)}{5 - (-9)} = \frac{4 + 3}{5 + 9} = \frac{7}{14} = \frac{1}{2}$$

Step 2 Write the equation in point-slope form. Use point $(5, 4)$ in the point-slope equation.

$$y - y_1 = m(x - x_1)$$

$$\downarrow \quad \downarrow \quad \downarrow$$

$$y - 4 = \frac{1}{2}(x - 5)$$

B Write an equation of the line shown in the graph using the coordinates $(-9, -3)$.

SOLUTION

Step 1 Use the slope found in Example 2A: $\frac{1}{2}$.

Step 2 Write the equation in point-slope form. Use the point $(-9, -3)$.

$$y - y_1 = m(x - x_1)$$

$$\downarrow \quad \downarrow \quad \downarrow$$

$$y - (-3) = \frac{1}{2}[x - (-9)]$$

$$y + 3 = \frac{1}{2}(x + 9)$$

C Determine whether the two equations are equivalent.

SOLUTION

Show that the equations in Step 2 of Examples 2A and 2B are equivalent by writing each in slope-intercept form.

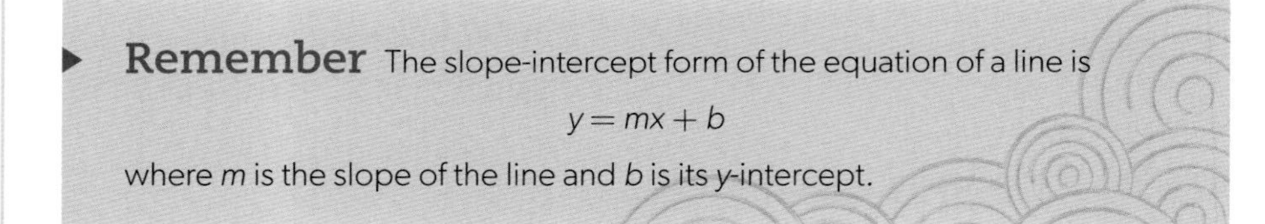
▶ **Remember** The slope-intercept form of the equation of a line is

$$y = mx + b$$

where m is the slope of the line and b is its y-intercept.

Solve the first equation for y.

$$y - 4 = \frac{1}{2}(x - 5)$$

$$y - 4 = \frac{1}{2}x - \frac{5}{2}$$

$$y = \frac{1}{2}x - \frac{5}{2} + 4$$

$$y = \frac{1}{2}x - \frac{5}{2} + \frac{8}{2}$$

$$y = \frac{1}{2}x + \frac{3}{2}$$

Solve the second equation for y.

$$y + 3 = \frac{1}{2}(x + 9)$$

$$y + 3 = \frac{1}{2}x + \frac{9}{2}$$

$$y = \frac{1}{2}x + \frac{9}{2} - 3$$

$$y = \frac{1}{2}x + \frac{9}{2} - \frac{6}{2}$$

$$y = \frac{1}{2}x + \frac{3}{2}$$

The equations are equivalent. ■

Application: Writing a Linear Equation

EXAMPLE 3

Corbin is buying concert tickets for some of his friends. The table shows the cost when purchasing different numbers of tickets. The total cost includes a parking fee of $12.

Number of tickets (x)	2	4	6	8
Total cost (y)	$29	$46	$63	$80

A Write the equation that gives the total cost, y, in terms of the number of tickets purchased, x, in point-slope form.

SOLUTION

Step 1 Use the table to find the slope of the line. Choose any two data pairs in the table.

Let $(x_1, y_1) = (2, 29)$ and $(x_2, y_2) = (4, 46)$.

$$m = \frac{y_2 - y_1}{x_2 - x_1} = \frac{46 - 29}{4 - 2} = \frac{17}{2}$$

The slope of the line is $\frac{17}{2}$.

Step 2 Write the equation in point-slope form, using the data point (2, 29).

$$y - y_1 = m(x - x_1)$$

$$y - 29 = \frac{17}{2}(x - 2)$$

B Convert the equation from Example 3A to slope-intercept form.

SOLUTION

Write the equation in slope-intercept form.

$y - 29 = \frac{17}{2}(x - 2)$	
$y - 29 = \frac{17}{2}x - 17$	Distributive Property
$y = \frac{17}{2}x - 17 + 29$	Add 29 to each side.
$y = \frac{17}{2}x + 12$	Simplify.

C What is the meaning of the y-intercept?

SOLUTION

The y-intercept represents the cost of parking.

D What is the meaning of the slope?

SOLUTION

The cost of each ticket is the slope of the line. Write $\frac{17}{2}$ as a decimal.

$$\frac{17}{2} = 8.5$$

The cost of each ticket is $8.50. ■

Forms of Linear Equations

You can write linear equations in different forms.

All linear equations have the following characteristics in common:

- There is no variable with an exponent other than 1 or zero.
- The variables are not multiplied together.
- It is possible to write the equation without any variable in the denominator of a fraction.
- The graph of the equation in a coordinate plane is a line.

Converting Between Forms of Linear Equations

Three forms of linear equations are most common.

Definitions

The **standard form** of a linear equation is $Ax + By = C$, where A, B, and C are numbers, and A and B are not both zero.

The **slope-intercept form** of a linear equation is $y = mx + b$, where m is the slope and b is the y-intercept of the corresponding line.

The **point-slope form** of a linear equation is $y - y_1 = m(x - x_1)$, where m is the slope and (x_1, y_1) is a point on the corresponding line.

EXAMPLE 1

A Write the equation $4x + 3y = 15$ in slope-intercept form.

SOLUTION

To convert to slope-intercept form, solve the equation for y.

$4x + 3y = 15$

$3y = -4x + 15$	Subtract $4x$ from both sides.
$y = -\frac{4}{3}x + 5$	Divide both sides by 3.

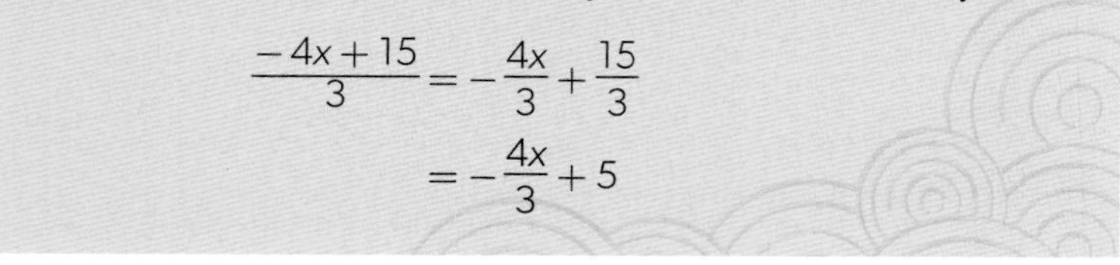

▶ **Think About It** To divide $-4x + 15$ by 3, divide each term by 3:

$$\frac{-4x + 15}{3} = -\frac{4x}{3} + \frac{15}{3}$$
$$= -\frac{4x}{3} + 5$$

B Write the equation $y - 4 = \frac{1}{5}(x + 7)$ in standard form.

SOLUTION

To convert to standard form, isolate the variables from the constants.

$y - 4 = \frac{1}{5}(x + 7)$	
$5y - 20 = x + 7$	Multiply both sides by 5 to clear the fraction.
$-x + 5y - 20 = 7$	Subtract x from both sides.
$-x + 5y = 27$	Add 20 to both sides.

▶ **Think About It** The final equation in Example 1B, $-x + 5y = 27$, is in standard form. An equivalent equation, also in standard form, is $x - 5y = -27$.

C Write the equation $y + 2 = 3(x - 4)$ in slope-intercept form.

SOLUTION

To convert to slope-intercept form, isolate the variable y.

$y + 2 = 3(x - 4)$

$y + 2 = 3x - 12$ Distribute 3.

$y = 3x - 14$ Subtract 2 from both sides.

Graphing a Linear Equation in Slope-Intercept Form

EXAMPLE 2

Graph $y = \frac{1}{2}x - 3$.

SOLUTION

This equation is in the form $y = mx + b$.

$$y = \frac{1}{2}x + (-3)$$

The slope is $\frac{1}{2}$. The y-intercept is -3, so the point $(0, -3)$ is on the line.

Plot the y-intercept at $(0, -3)$. From that point, count the vertical and horizontal change in the slope ratio to plot another point on the line.
As a good graphing habit, do this several times, plotting several more points.
Then draw a line through the points.

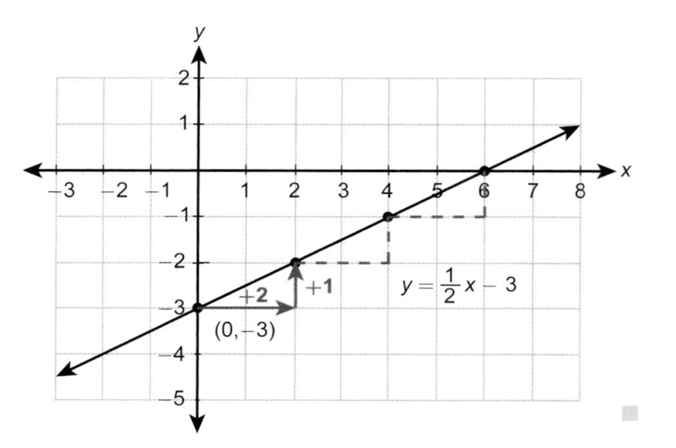

Graphing a Linear Equation in Standard Form

EXAMPLE 3

Graph $5x + 4y = 6$ using two different methods.

SOLUTION

Method 1 Convert the equation to slope-intercept form. Then use the graphing method shown in Example 2.

$5x + 4y = 6$

$4y = -5x + 6$	Subtract $5x$ from both sides.
$y = -\frac{5}{4}x + \frac{3}{2}$	Divide both sides by 4.

Plot the y-intercept at $\left(0, \frac{3}{2}\right)$. Then count, using the slope $-\frac{5}{4}$, to plot another point.

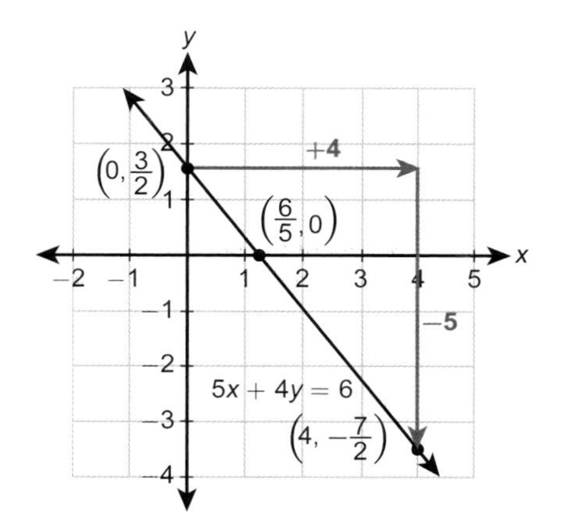

Method 2 Find both intercepts and use them to draw the line.

Find the x-intercept:	Find the y-intercept:
$5x + 4y = 6$	$5x + 4y = 6$
$5x + 4 \bullet \mathbf{0} = 6$	$5 \bullet \mathbf{0} + 4y = 6$
$5x = 6$	$4y = 6$
$x = \frac{6}{5}$	$y = \frac{3}{2}$
Plot the point $\left(\frac{6}{5}, 0\right)$.	Plot the point $\left(0, \frac{3}{2}\right)$.

Draw the line through these points. The line is the same as in Method 1. ■

Graphing a Linear Equation in Point-Slope Form

EXAMPLE 4

Graph $y - 2 = 4(x + 3)$.

SOLUTION

The slope is 4 and $(-3, 2)$ is a point on the corresponding line. Plot $(-3, 2)$. Then count, using the slope $\frac{4}{1}$, to plot another point. Another point on the line is $(-2, 6)$. Draw the line through the two points.

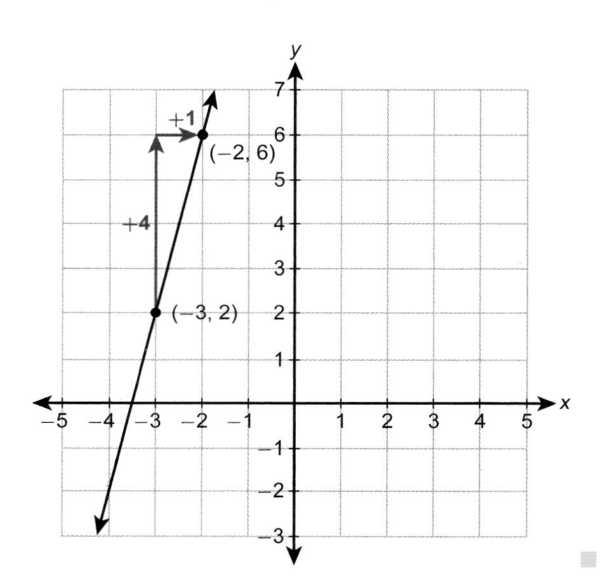

Linear Graph Family: $y = mx + b$

Any changes to the parameters m and b in equations of the form $y = mx + b$ will change the graphs of the lines.

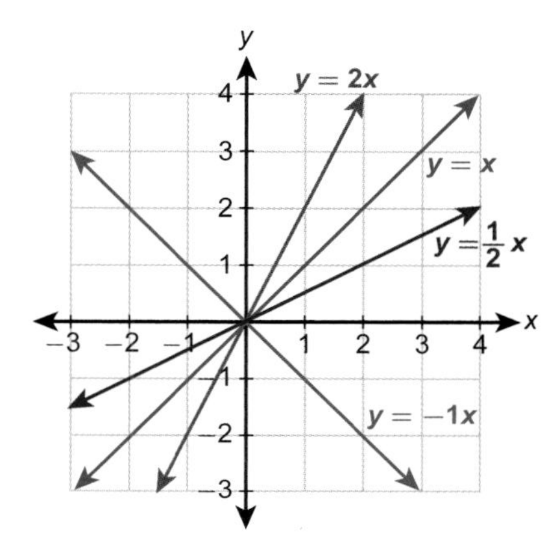

If you change only the parameter m, you get lines through the same y-intercept, but with different slopes.

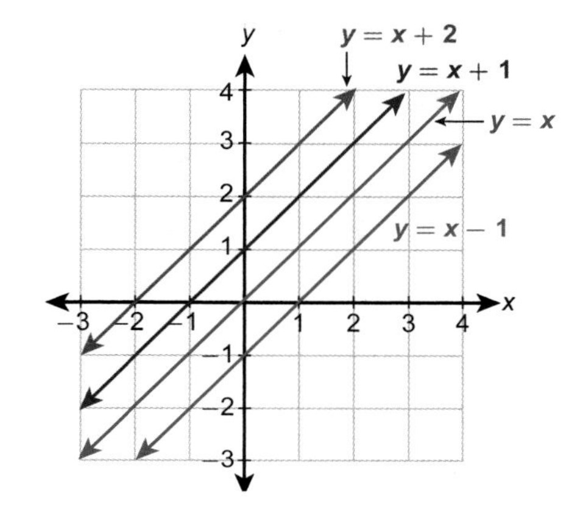

If you change only the parameter b, you get lines with the same slope but different y-intercepts.

Equations from Graphs

You know how to graph a line when given an equation. You can also use the graph of a line to determine the equation of the line.

Writing the Equation of a Line in Point-Slope Form Using a Graph

When you know two points that lie on a line, you can write the equation of the line using point-slope form.

EXAMPLE 1

Write the equation of the line in point-slope form.

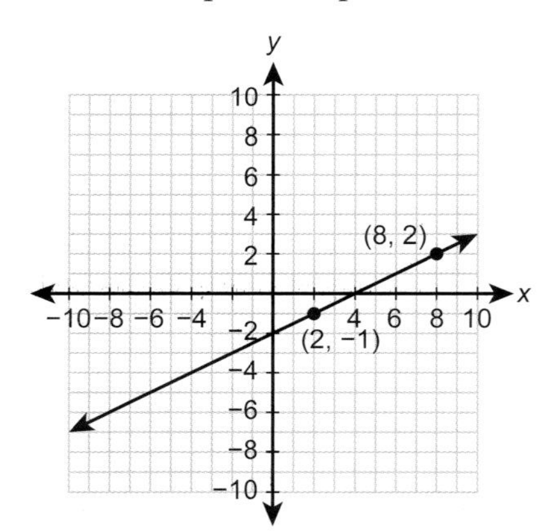

SOLUTION

Step 1 Use the slope formula to find the slope of the line.

$$m = \frac{y_2 - y_1}{x_2 - x_1} = \frac{2 - (-1)}{8 - 2} = \frac{3}{6} = \frac{1}{2}$$

Step 2 Write the equation in point-slope form. You can use either point in the point-slope equation. Using the point $(8, 2)$:

$y - y_1 = m(x - x_1)$ Point-slope form

$y - 2 = \frac{1}{2}(x - 8)$ Substitute 2 for y_1, $\frac{1}{2}$ for m, and 8 for x_1.

The equation of the line in point-slope form is $y - 2 = \frac{1}{2}(x - 8)$. ■

Using a Graph to Write the Equation of a Line in Standard Form

EXAMPLE 2

Write the equation of the line from Example 1 in standard form.

SOLUTION

$y - 2 = \frac{1}{2}(x - 8)$ Equation in point-slope form

$y - 2 = \frac{1}{2}x - 4$ Distributive Property

$y = \frac{1}{2}x - 2$ Add 2 to both sides of the equation.

$-\frac{1}{2}x + y = -2$ Subtract $\frac{1}{2}x$ from both sides.

$-2\left(-\frac{1}{2}x + y\right) = -2(-2)$ Multiply both sides by -2.

$x - 2y = 4$ Simplify.

The equation of the line in standard form is $x - 2y = 4$. ■

Using a Graph to Write the Equation of a Line in Slope-Intercept Form

When you know two points that lie on a line and one of those points is the y-intercept, you can write the equation of the line using slope-intercept form.

EXAMPLE 3

Write the equation of the line shown in the graph.

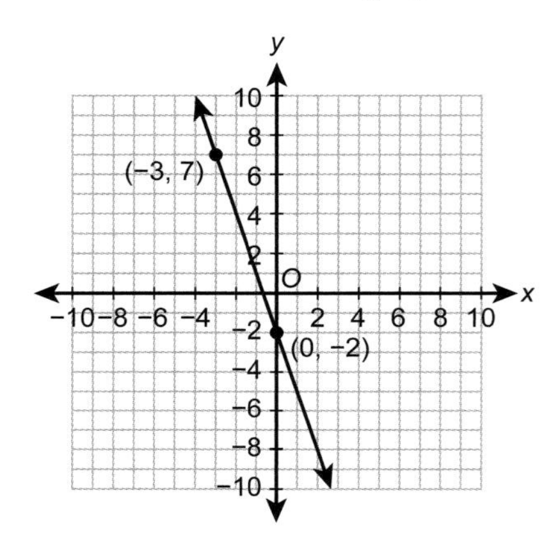

SOLUTION

Step 1 Use the slope formula to find the slope of the line.

$$m = \frac{y_2 - y_1}{x_2 - x_1} = \frac{7 - (-2)}{-3 - 0} = \frac{9}{-3} = \mathbf{-3}$$

Step 2 Write the equation in slope-intercept form. The line intersects the y-axis at the point $(0, -2)$ so the y-intercept is -2.

$y = mx + b$	Slope-intercept form
$y = \mathbf{-3}x + (-2)$	Substitute -3 for m and -2 for b.
$y = -3x - 2$	Simplify.

The equation of the line in slope-intercept form is $y = -3x - 2$. ■

Writing the Equation of a Horizontal and a Vertical Line

EXAMPLE 4

Write the equation of each line shown in the graph.

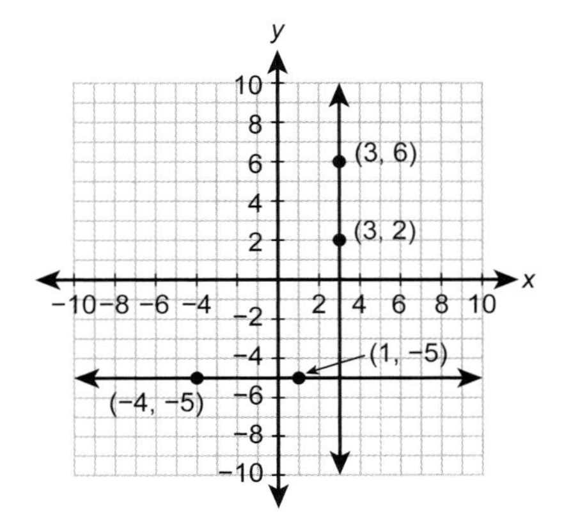

A the horizontal line

SOLUTION

The y-coordinate of every point on the horizontal line is -5. The equation of the line is $y = -5$.

Another way to solve the problem is to find the slope of the line and use slope-intercept form to write the equation of the line. The line crosses the y-axis at $(0, -5)$ so the y-intercept is -5.

$$m = \frac{y_2 - y_1}{x_2 - x_1} = \frac{-5 - (-5)}{1 - (-4)} = \frac{0}{5} = 0$$

$$y = mx + b$$
$$y = 0 \bullet x + (-5)$$
$$y = -5$$

B the vertical line

▶ **Remember** The slope of a vertical line is undefined, so you can't use the point-slope or slope-intercept formulas to find the equation.

SOLUTION

The x-coordinate of every point on the vertical line is 3. The equation of the line is $x = 3$.

Linear Models

Many real-world phenomena fit a linear model. Use your knowledge of lines to find the linear equation that models a situation.

Linear Models in Table Form

Represent table data with a linear model by writing a linear equation from the table data. Write each measurement in a data table as an ordered pair representing the coordinates of a point. Calculate the slope from any two points, and then write the linear equation using the point-slope formula.

EXAMPLE 1

The table shows the height of a certain plant at various times, in weeks, after it was planted. The growth of the plant follows a linear model.

Week	2	4	6	8
Plant height (cm)	12.6	16	19.4	22.8

▸ **Remember** When two quantities are related by a constant rate of change, the relationship between them can be modeled by the linear equation

$$y = mx + b.$$

The rate of change is the slope of the line, m.

A How can you use the table values to show that the rate of change in the plant's growth is constant? Explain your thinking and show your work.

SOLUTION

Write each pair of data values as an ordered pair.

$$(2, 12.6), (4, 16), (6, 19.4), \text{ and } (8, 22.8)$$

Because the plant's growth follows a linear model, the rate of change is just the slope of the line through the points. Find the rate of change between pairs of points. Use the formula $m = \frac{y_2 - y_1}{x_2 - x_1}$.

$$\frac{16 - 12.6}{4 - 2} = \frac{3.4}{2} = 1.7$$

$$\frac{19.4 - 16}{6 - 4} = \frac{3.4}{2} = 1.7$$

$$\frac{22.8 - 19.4}{8 - 6} = \frac{3.4}{2} = 1.7$$

The slope is 1.7 for all pairs of points, so the rate of change is constant.

B Write a linear equation in slope-intercept form to represent the height of the plant over time. Explain what the y-intercept of this equation represents.

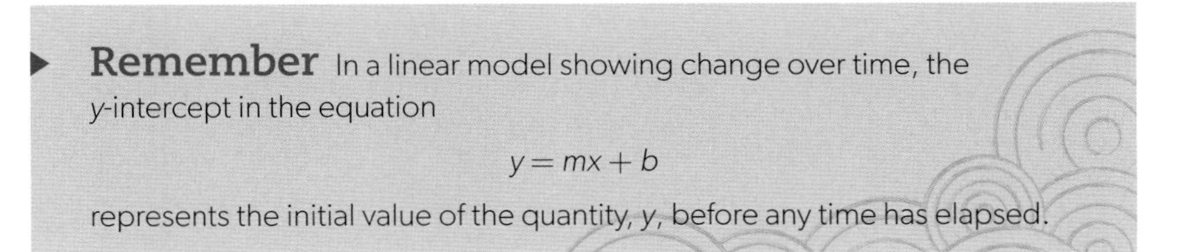

SOLUTION

The slope of the line is 1.7. Choose any pair of data values from the table to represent a point on the line, for example, $(4, 16)$. Write the equation of the line in point-slope form.

$$y - 16 = 1.7(x - 4)$$

Rewritten in slope-intercept form, this equation is

$$\begin{aligned} y - 16 &= 1.7x - 1.7 \bullet 4 \\ y - 16 &= 1.7x - 6.8 \\ y - 16 + 16 &= 1.7x - 6.8 + 16 \\ y &= 1.7x + 9.2 \end{aligned}$$

The y-intercept of this equation represents the height of the plant when x is 0, which is when it was planted. ■

EXAMPLE 2

The table shows the total pounds of fish fed to the sharks at an aquarium in a certain number of weeks. Write a linear equation in point-slope form to represent the pounds of fish fed to the sharks over time. Explain what the slope of this equation represents.

Weeks	4	8	12	16	20
Pounds of fish	1440	2880	4320	5760	7200

SOLUTION

The point-slope form of an equation is $y - y_1 = m(x - x_1)$, where (x_1, y_1) lies on the line and m is the slope.

Use any two ordered pairs from the table to find the slope.

Let $(x_1, y_1) = (4, 1440)$ and $(x_2, y_2) = (8, 2880)$.

$$m = \frac{2880 - 1440}{8 - 4} = \frac{1440}{4} = 360$$

The slope is 360, which means that the sharks are fed 360 lb of fish each week. Choose any pair of data values from the table to represent a point on the line. Write the linear equation in point-slope form.

$$y - 1440 = 360(x - 4)$$ ■

▶ **Think About It** If you chose a point other than $(4, 1440)$ to write the equation in point-slope form, the equations would look different. However, the two equations represent the same line. By writing the equations in slope-intercept form, you would find that the equations are equivalent.

EXAMPLE 3

The table shows the amount of money Beth will earn selling jars of honey at a farmers' market. Write a linear equation in standard form to represent the amount of money Beth earns selling x jars.

Jars sold	2	4	6	8	10
Amount earned ($)	14	38	62	86	110

SOLUTION

Write the linear equation in point-slope form first and then convert to standard form. Use any two ordered pairs from the table to find the slope.

Let $(x_1, y_1) = (2, 14)$ and $(x_2, y_2) = (4, 38)$.

$$m = \frac{38 - 14}{4 - 2} = \frac{24}{2} = 12$$

Write the linear equation in point-slope form using any point from the table. This example uses $(2, 14)$.

$$y - 14 = 12(x - 2)$$

Convert the equation to standard form.

▶ **Remember** The standard form of a linear equation is $Ax + By = C$, where A and B cannot both be zero.

$$\begin{aligned} y - 14 &= 12(x - 2) \\ y - 14 &= 12x - 24 \\ y &= 12x - 10 \\ -12x + y &= -10 \end{aligned}$$

The linear equation in standard form that represents the amount of money Beth earns selling x jars of honey is $-12x + y = -10$. ■

Linear Models in Graphical Form

You can also represent data with a linear model by writing a linear equation from the graph of the data. Plot each point on a coordinate grid, and then draw a line through the points. Find the slope and the y-intercept of the line, and then use the slope-intercept form to write the equation of the line.

EXAMPLE 4

A riding lawnmower has an 8 L capacity fuel tank. The graph models the lawnmower's fuel usage, which is the number of liters of fuel in the tank versus the number of hours the lawnmower is driven.

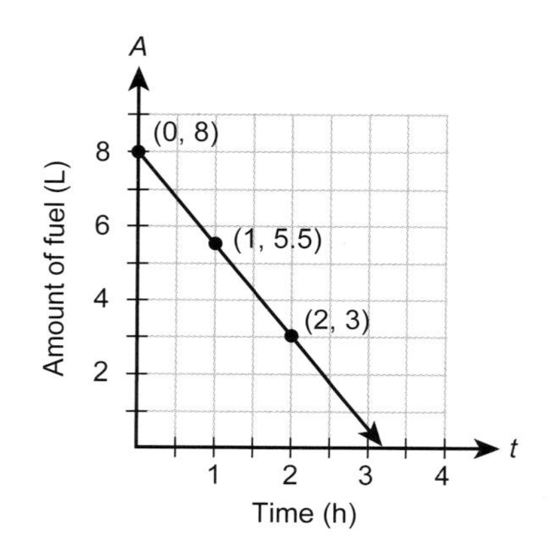

A Find the rate of change of the amount of fuel in the tank over time.

SOLUTION

The rate of change in the amount of fuel in the tank over time is the slope of the line. Use two points to find the slope of the line.

$$m = \frac{5.5 - 8}{1 - 0} = -\frac{2.5}{1} = -2.5$$

The slope of the line is -2.5, so the rate of change is -2.5 L/h.

▶ **Think About It** One gallon is equal to approximately 3.8 L.

B Write a linear equation in slope-intercept form that models the amount of fuel in the tank as time goes by. Find the value of the x-intercept and explain what its value means in this situation.

> ▶ **Remember** You can estimate the x-intercept of a graph by estimating the value of x where the line crosses the x-axis.

SOLUTION

The slope of the line is -2.5. The y-intercept of the graph is 8, so the equation of the line in slope-intercept form is $y = -2.5x + 8$. The x-intercept of this equation represents the time when the amount of fuel in the tank is 0 L—that is, when the lawnmower will run out of gas. Solve for the x-intercept by setting $y = 0$ in the equation and solving for x.

$$\begin{aligned} 0 &= -2.5x + 8 \\ 0 - 8 &= -2.5x + 8 - 8 \\ -8 &= -2.5x \\ \frac{-8}{-2.5} &= \frac{-2.5x}{-2.5} \\ 3.2 &= x \end{aligned}$$

The riding lawnmower will run out of gas after 3.2 h of mowing. ■

EXAMPLE 5

The graph shows the total cost a website charges for an annual membership and a fee for each movie its members download. Write a linear equation in point-slope form that models the total cost for the number of movies downloaded. Find the value of the slope and the value of the y-intercept and explain what each value means in this situation.

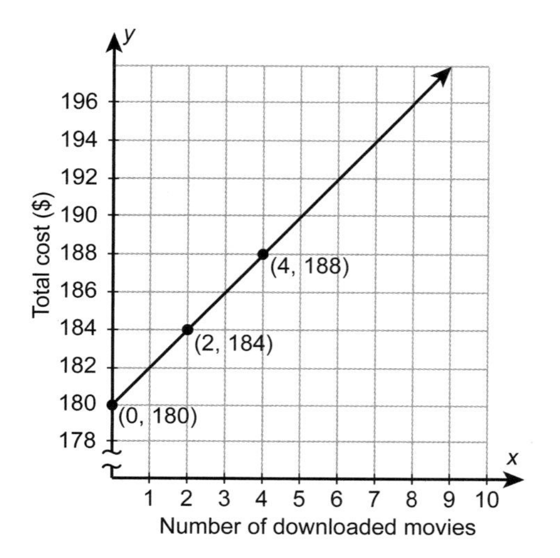

SOLUTION

Use two points to find the slope of the line.

$$m = \frac{184 - 180}{2 - 0} = \frac{4}{2} = 2$$

The slope represents the fee for downloading 1 movie. Therefore, the members of the website are charged \$2 to download a movie.

The y-intercept is 180 because $y = 180$ when $x = 0$. This intercept represents the annual membership charge the members pay in addition to the fee per downloaded movie.

Choose any point that lies on the line, for example, $(2, 184)$. Write the linear equation in point-slope form.

$$(y - 184) = 2(x - 2)$$ ■

EXAMPLE 6

Tony borrowed money from his parents to buy a computer. He is making monthly payments to pay them back, as shown in the graph. Write a linear equation in standard form that models the amount Tony still owed after he made any number of monthly payments. Explain what the slope and the x- and y-intercepts of this equation represent.

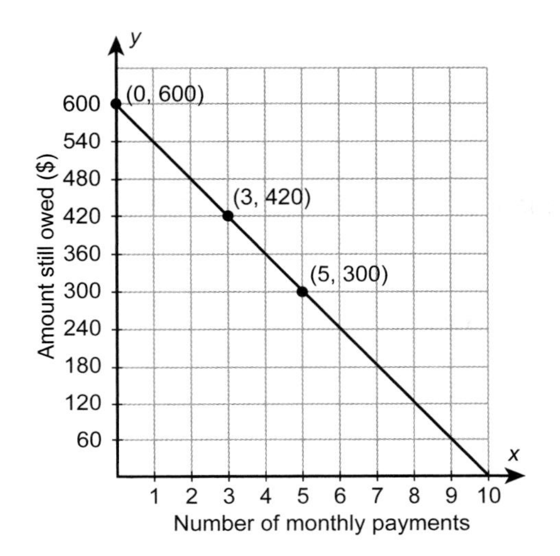

SOLUTION

Write the linear equation in slope-intercept form first and then convert to standard form. Use two points to find the slope of the line.

$$m = \frac{420 - 300}{3 - 5} = \frac{120}{-2} = -60$$

The y-intercept is 600 because $y = 600$ when $x = 0$. Write the equation in slope-intercept form.

$$y = -60x + 600$$

Rewrite the equation in standard form.

$$y = -60x + 600$$
$$60x + y = 600$$

The y-intercept is 600. Tony originally owed $600 to his parents for his computer. The slope is -60, which shows that Tony is paying his parents back $60 each month. The x-intercept is 10. It will take Tony 10 payments to pay his parents back all of the money he owes them.

Sketching Lines

In a linear model, data values lie along a line. You can sketch the graph of the line if you know either two points on the line or a point on the line and the line's slope.

Two Points on a Line

You can graph the line representing a linear model from two points on the line.

EXAMPLE 1

Fatima has 2.5 gal of gas in her car. A pump at the gas station adds gas to her car at a constant rate. After 70 s, the gas tank in Fatima's tank is full, holding 12.4 gal.

Graph the amount of gas in the car's tank versus time.

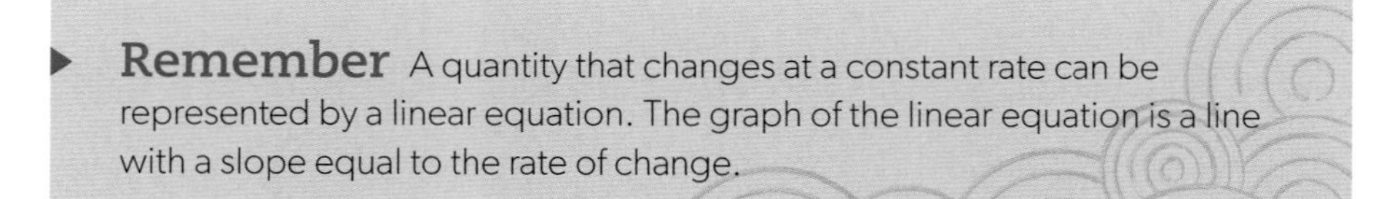

Remember A quantity that changes at a constant rate can be represented by a linear equation. The graph of the linear equation is a line with a slope equal to the rate of change.

SOLUTION

Let t represent the amount of time spent filling the tank and let A represent the amount of gas in the car's tank.

The pump fills the gas tank at a constant rate, so the graph of the amount, A, of gas in the car's tank versus time, t, is a line. The value of A depends on t, so plot t along the horizontal axis and A along the vertical axis.

Write the initial amount in the gas tank as a point with coordinates $(0, 2.5)$ and the final amount in the gas tank as a point with coordinates $(70, 12.4)$.

Draw a line through these two points.

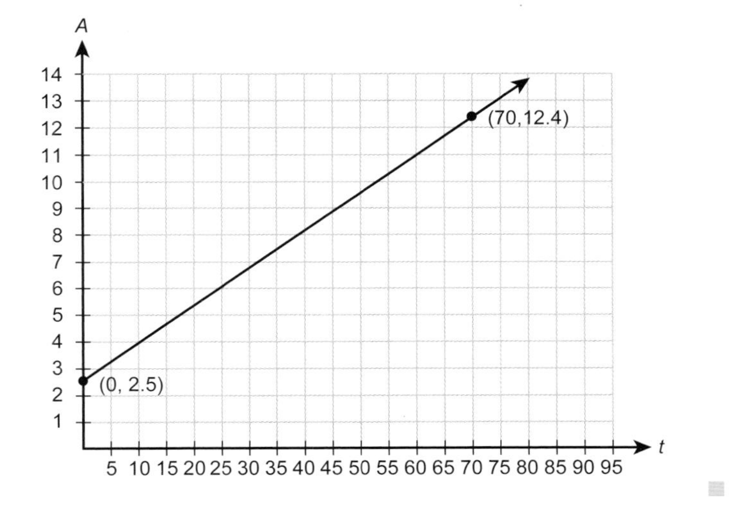

▸ **Think About It** Choose an appropriate scale for an axis by identifying the minimum and maximum values of the variable plotted along the axis.

A Point on a Line and the Line's Slope

You can also graph the line representing a linear model using one point on the line and the line's slope. Write the data value as an ordered pair. Plot the point using the ordered pair as the coordinates. Use the plotted point and slope to draw the line.

EXAMPLE 2

At the beginning of track season, Kamala finished a 400 m race in 75 s. Her finishing time decreases at a rate of 0.6 s/wk over the course of the 12 wk track season. Draw a graph representing Kamala's finishing times from the beginning of track season until 12 wk later. Choose an appropriate scale.

▶ **Think About It** If you know the slope of the line and a point on the line, you can find all other points on the line. Use the point-slope formula to write the equation of the line. Use the equation to find the coordinates of more points on the line.

SOLUTION

Let w represent the number of weeks from the beginning of track and let t represent Kamala's finishing time.

Kamala's finishing time decreases at a constant rate of 0.6 s/wk, so the graph of the finishing time, t versus w, is a line with a slope of -0.6. The value of t depends on w, so plot w along the horizontal axis and t along the vertical axis.

Write Kamala's finishing time at the beginning of track season as a point with coordinates $(0, 75)$. From this point, draw a line with a slope of -0.6, the rate of change. The value -0.6 is equivalent to a $\frac{\text{rise}}{\text{run}}$ of $-\frac{6}{10} = -\frac{3}{5}$.

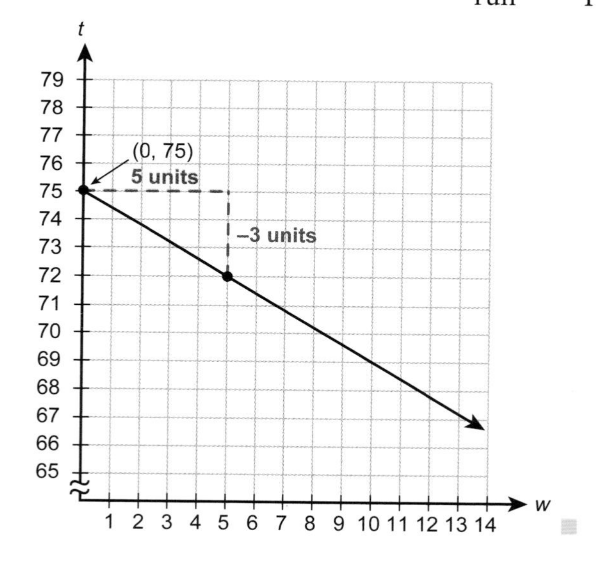

▶ **Q&A**

Q What is the equation of the line in Example 2 in slope-intercept form?

A $t = -0.6w + 75$

Systems of Equations

Topic List

- Systems of Linear Equations
- Using Graphs to Solve Systems
- Classifying Systems
- Substitution Method
- Linear Combination
- Applications: Systems of Linear Equations
- Applications of Linear Systems
- Mixture Problems

When two people meet, they often find that they have friends, tastes, or experiences in common. Whenever two lines meet, you know they have at least one point in common. Finding the point where the two lines meet can help you solve problems in the real world.

Systems of Linear Equations

You can use algebra to determine whether an ordered pair is a solution to a system of linear equations.

Solutions to a System of Equations

Definition

Two or more linear equations using the same variables make a **system of linear equations**.

Intersection Point of Equations

A system of linear equations can be represented by one or more lines in the coordinate plane. If the lines intersect, then the point of intersection (x, y) is the solution to the system.

▶ **Think About It** A system of equations need not be linear. For instance, in the system $xy = 6$, $x - y = 7$, the first equation is not linear.

Any point that makes both equations true is a solution to the system. Such a point satisfies the system.

EXAMPLE 1

Is the point a solution to the system of equations? Explain why or why not.

$$
\begin{aligned}
x + y &= -3 \\
2x - y &= 6
\end{aligned}
$$

A $(2, -5)$

SOLUTION

Substitute $x = 2$ and $y = -5$ into each equation.

$$
\begin{aligned}
x + y &= -3 \\
2 + (-5) &= -3 \\
-3 &= -3
\end{aligned}
\qquad
\begin{aligned}
2x - y &= 6 \\
2(2) - (-5) &= 6 \\
4 - (-5) &= 6 \\
4 + 5 &= 6 \\
9 &\neq 6
\end{aligned}
$$

The point $(2, -5)$ satisfies the first equation but not the second equation, so it is not a solution because it does not satisfy both equations.

B $(1, -4)$

SOLUTION

Substitute $x = 1$ and $y = -4$ into each equation.

$$
\begin{aligned}
x + y &= -3 \\
1 + (-4) &= -3 \\
-3 &= -3
\end{aligned}
\qquad
\begin{aligned}
2x - y &= 6 \\
2(1) - (-4) &= 6 \\
2 - (-4) &= 6 \\
2 + 4 &= 6 \\
6 &= 6
\end{aligned}
$$

The point $(1, -4)$ satisfies both equations, so it is a solution to the system of linear equations. ■

Application: Coin Problems

You can use substitution to test a possible solution to a system of linear equations.

EXAMPLE 2

Nell has a piggy bank full of dimes and nickels. She empties the bank and counts the coins. She counts 35 coins in all, with a total value of $2.85. Nell says she has 21 dimes and 14 nickels.

▶ **Think About It** In story problems, first identify the unknown quantities and assign each one a variable.

A Write a system of linear equations to represent the number of coins that Nell had in her piggy bank and the total value of the coins.

SOLUTION

Let d be the number of dimes and n be the number of nickels.

The equation $d + n = 35$ represents the total number of coins.

The equation $0.10d + 0.05n = 2.85$ represents the total value of the coins.

B Determine whether Nell could have counted the number of dimes and nickels correctly.

SOLUTION

If Nell counted correctly, then $(21, 14)$ is a solution to the system of equations. Substitute $d = 21$ and $n = 14$ into each equation.

$$\begin{aligned} d + n &= 35 \\ 21 + 14 &= 35 \\ 35 &= 35 \end{aligned}$$

$$\begin{aligned} 0.10d + 0.05n &= 2.85 \\ 0.10(21) + 0.05(14) &= 2.85 \\ 2.10 + 0.70 &= 2.85 \\ 2.80 &\neq 2.85 \end{aligned}$$

The point $(21, 14)$ satisfies the first equation but not the second equation, so it is not a solution to the system of equations.

Nell did not count the number of dimes and nickels correctly if the rest of the information is correct. ■

Using Graphs to Solve Systems

Graphing a system of equations is one way to find a solution to the system.

Using a Graph to Solve a System of Equations

A solution to a system is the point of intersection of the graphs in the system. Algebraically, a solution to a system is an ordered pair that is a solution to each equation in the system.

EXAMPLE 1

Solve the system by graphing. Then check the solution algebraically.

$$x + 2y = 4$$
$$4x - 2y = 16$$

SOLUTION

Graph each line in the coordinate plane. The intersection of the two lines appears to be the point $(4, 0)$.

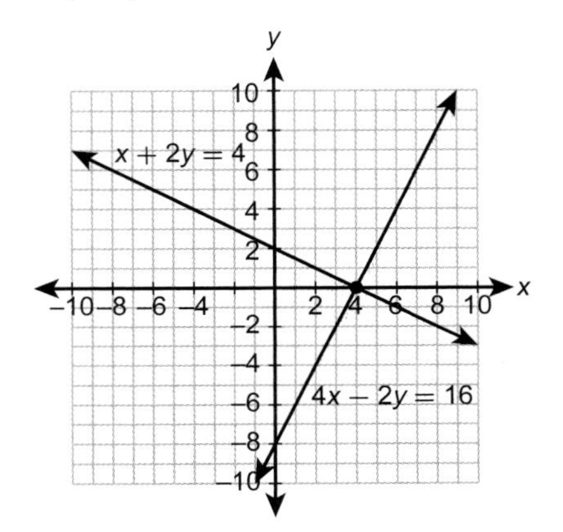

The point $(4, 0)$ is the solution to the system of equations.

CHECK

$$x + 2y = 4 \qquad\qquad 4x - 2y = 16$$
$$4 + 2 \bullet 0 \stackrel{?}{=} 4 \qquad\qquad 4 \bullet 4 - 2 \bullet 0 \stackrel{?}{=} 16$$
$$4 = 4 \checkmark \qquad\qquad 16 = 16 \checkmark$$

The solution $(4, 0)$ is correct. ■

Estimating Solutions Using Graphs

The solution to a system of equations may not be an ordered pair of integers. You can estimate the solution, to the nearest integer, by graphing the two equations, locating the intersection point, and then finding the point with integer coordinates nearest the intersection point.

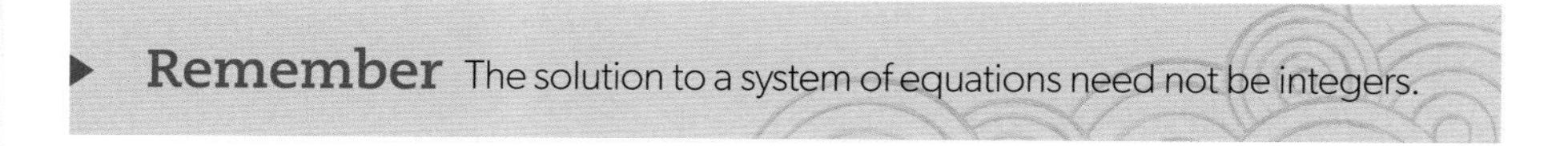

EXAMPLE 2

Find the solution to the system of equations. Round to the nearest integer values, if necessary.

$$2x + y = 9$$
$$x - 5y = 20$$

SOLUTION

Graph the equations and locate the point where the two graphs intersect.

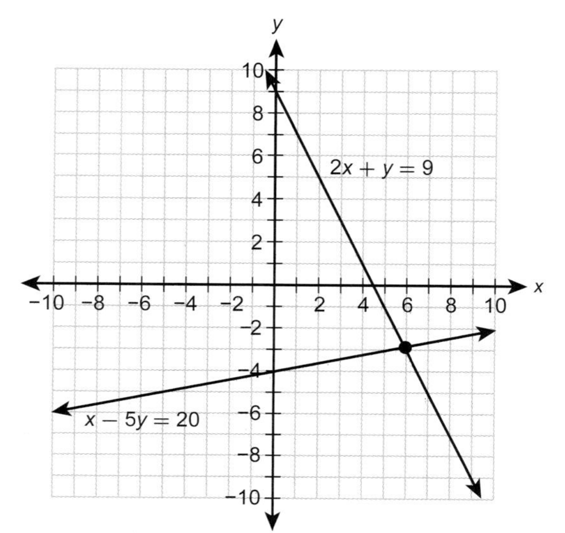

The coordinates of the intersection point are not integers. The nearest point with integer values is $(6, -3)$.

The point $(6, -3)$ is an approximate solution to the system of equations.

▸ **Think About It** You can use graphing to estimate the solution to any system of equations, not just linear systems.

CHECK

$$\begin{aligned} 2x + y &= 9 \\ 2(6) + (-3) &\stackrel{?}{=} 9 \\ 12 - 3 &\stackrel{?}{=} 9 \\ 9 &= 9 \checkmark \end{aligned}$$

$$\begin{aligned} x - 5y &= 20 \\ (6) - 5(-3) &\stackrel{?}{=} 20 \\ 6 + 15 &\stackrel{?}{=} 20 \\ 21 &\neq 20 \end{aligned}$$

Since 21 is close to 20, $(6, -3)$ is a good estimate for the solution. The ordered pair is on the first line and is pretty close to the second line. ■

Classifying Systems

In some situations, you can determine the number of solutions for a system of linear equations without solving the system.

Number of Solutions to a System

A system of linear equations can have exactly one solution, no solution, or infinitely many solutions. To determine how many solutions a system of linear equations has, write the equations in slope-intercept form, $y = mx + b$. Then compare the slopes and the y-intercepts.

- The linear equations of a system with exactly one solution will have different slopes.
- The linear equations of a system with no solutions will have the same slopes, but different y-intercepts.
- The linear equations of a system with infinitely many solutions will have the same slopes and the same y-intercepts.

EXAMPLE 1

Determine the number of solutions to the given system of linear equations.

A $y = -2x - 4$
$y = 5x + 5$

SOLUTION

The equations are already written in slope-intercept form. Notice that the equations have different slopes $(m = -2$ and $m = 5)$. If two lines have different slopes, they must intersect somewhere at a single point. Even without knowing where they intersect, you can conclude that this system has one solution.

B $-3x + y = 8$
$2y = 6x - 10$

SOLUTION

Write each equation in slope-intercept form.

$-3x + y = 8$

$y = 3x + 8$ Add $3x$ to both sides.

$2y = 6x - 10$

$y = 3x - 5$ Divide both sides by 2.

Notice that the equations have the same slope $(m = 3)$ but different y-intercepts $(b = 8$ and $b = -5)$, meaning that the lines represented by the equations are parallel. Therefore, the lines do not intersect. The system of equations has no solution.

C $2y = 4(x + 3)$
$y - 2x = 6$

SOLUTION

Write each equation in slope-intercept form.

$2y = 4(x + 3)$

$2y = 4x + 12$ Distributive Property

$y = 2x + 6$ Divide both sides by 2.

$y - 2x = 6$

$y = 2x + 6$ Add $2x$ to both sides.

Notice that the equations have the same slope $(m = 2)$ and the same y-intercept $(b = 6)$. If two lines have the same slope and y-intercept, they must be the same line. Each of the infinite number of points on one line is also on the other line. Therefore, the system has infinitely many solutions. ■

Classifying Systems of Linear Equations

A system of linear equations is **consistent** if it has exactly one solution or infinitely many solutions. A consistent system with exactly one solution is a **consistent independent** system. A consistent system with infinitely many solutions is a **consistent dependent** or a **coincident** system. Coincident linear systems contain equations whose graphs are the same line. When the lines of a system of linear equations are parallel there is no solution to the system. A system of equations with no solution is an **inconsistent** system.

EXAMPLE 2

Classify the system as consistent or inconsistent. If the system is consistent, determine whether it is coincident.

A

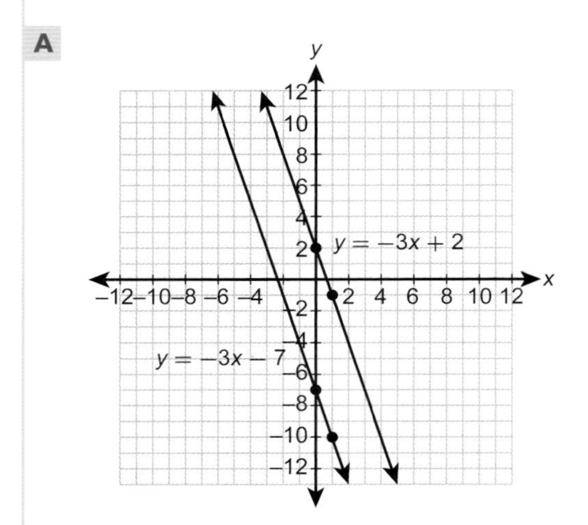

SOLUTION

The slope of both lines is -3, so the lines are parallel and do not intersect. The system is inconsistent.

B

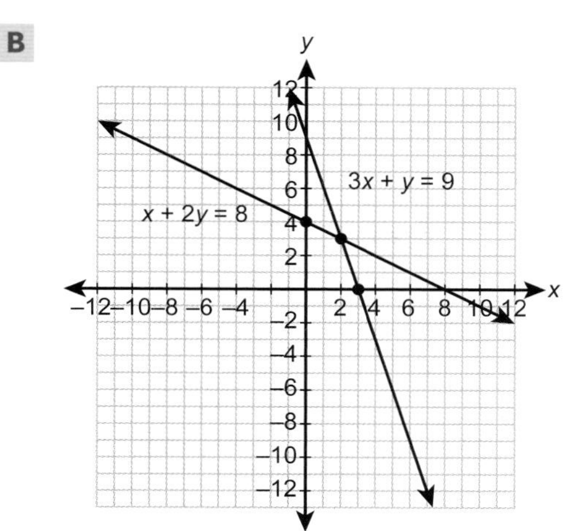

SOLUTION

The lines intersect at a single point. The system is consistent independent.

C

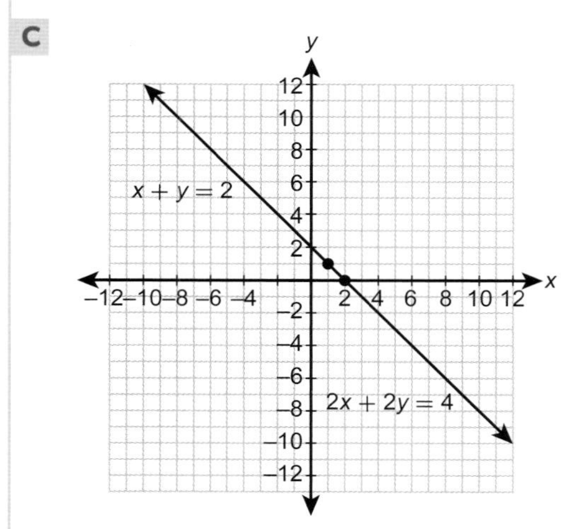

SOLUTION

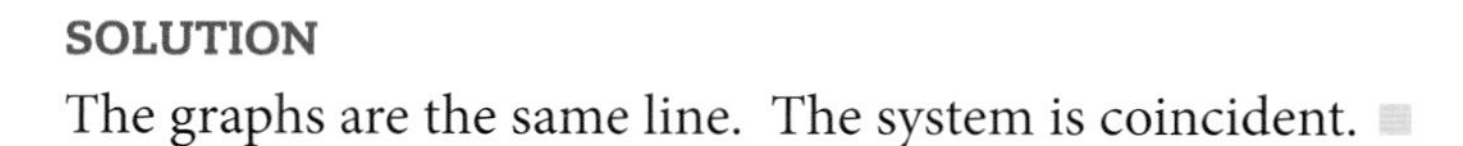

The graphs are the same line. The system is coincident.

Classifying Systems by Inspection

Sometimes you can determine the number of solutions to a system of linear equations simply by looking at the equations.

EXAMPLE 3

Determine the number of solutions to the system. State whether the system is inconsistent, consistent independent, or coincident.

A $x + 4y = 6$
$x + 4y = 15$

▶ **Think About It** It is easier to compare two linear equations if both are in the same form.

SOLUTION

The left hand side of both equations is the expression $x + 4y$. In the first equation, this expression is equal to 6. But in the second equation, this expression is equal to 14.

It is impossible for the expression $x + 4y$ to equal two different values simultaneously—that is, for the same (x, y) ordered pair. Therefore, this system has no solutions. The system is inconsistent.

B $x + 4y = 7$
$3x + 12y = 21$

SOLUTION

The second equation is equal to the first equation multiplied by 3.

$$\begin{aligned} 3(x + 4y) &= 3(7) \\ 3x + 3(4y) &= 21 \\ 3x + 12y &= 21 \end{aligned}$$

The two equations simplify to one equation with the same graph, so this system has infinitely many solutions. The system is coincident.

▶ **Think About It** If two linear equations have the same coefficients for x and y when in the same form, then the equations' slopes are equal, so their y-intercepts determine whether they are inconsistent or coincident.

C $x - y = 1$

$2x + y = 4$

SOLUTION

Check to see if the system has either infinitely many solutions or no solutions.

The second equation is not a multiple of the first equation, so the system does not have infinitely many solutions.

Also, the expression $x - y$ on the left side on the first equation is not equal to the expression $2x + y$ on the left side of the second equation. Therefore, it's not true that the system has no solutions.

By process of elimination, the system must have one solution. The system is consistent independent. ■

Substitution Method

The substitution method is a way to solve a system of linear equations algebraically.

How to Use the Substitution Method to Solve Systems of Equations

Step 1 Solve one of the equations for one of the variables.

Step 2 Substitute the expression obtained in Step 1 into the other equation. Solve the resulting equation.

Step 3 Substitute the value of the variable found in Step 2 into the equivalent equation from Step 1 and solve for the variable.

▶ **Remember** Equivalent equations have the same solution. Use the properties of equality to write equivalent equations.

Using the Substitution Method to Solve a System of Equations

EXAMPLE 1

Solve the system.

$$4x + y = 14$$
$$x - 2y = 8$$

> ▸ **Think About It** Whenever possible, solve for a variable with a coefficient of 1 or −1.

SOLUTION

Step 1 Solve the first equation for y. (You could also solve the second equation for x.)

$4x + y = 14$

$y = -4x + 14$ — Subtract $4x$ from each side of the equation.

Step 2 Substitute $-4x + 14$ for y in the second equation.

$x - 2y = 8$

$x - 2(\mathbf{-4x + 14}) = 8$ — Substitute $-4x + 14$ for y.

$x + 8x - 28 = 8$ — Distributive Property

$9x - 28 = 8$ — Combine like terms.

$9x = 36$ — Add 28 to each side.

$x = 4$ — Divide each side by 9.

Step 3 Substitute 4 for x in the equivalent equation from Step 1.

$y = -4x + 14$

$y = -4 \bullet \mathbf{4} + 14$ — Substitute 4 for x.

$y = -16 + 14$ — Simplify.

$y = -2$

The solution to the system is $(4, -2)$.

CHECK

Substitute 4 for x and -2 for y into each original equation in the system.

$$\begin{aligned} 4x + y &= 14 \\ 4 \bullet \mathbf{4} + (\mathbf{-2}) &\stackrel{?}{=} 14 \\ 16 - 2 &\stackrel{?}{=} 14 \\ 14 &= 14 \checkmark \end{aligned} \qquad \begin{aligned} x - 2y &= 8 \\ \mathbf{4} - 2 \bullet (\mathbf{-2}) &\stackrel{?}{=} 8 \\ 4 + 4 &\stackrel{?}{=} 8 \\ 8 &= 8 \checkmark \end{aligned}$$

The solution $(4, -2)$ is correct. ■

What Happens When the Variables Disappear?

You may sometimes eliminate a variable when using the substitution method, leaving either a statement that is always true (an identity) or a statement that is always false (a contradiction). If the statement is an identity, then the system is consistent and coincident. If the statement is a contradiction, then the system is inconsistent.

EXAMPLE 2

Solve the system.

A $-x + 5y = 3$
$-3x + 15y = 9$

SOLUTION

Step 1 Solve the first equation for x.

$-x + 5y = 3$

$-x = -5y + 3$ Subtract $5y$ from each side.

$x = 5y - 3$ Multiply each side by -1.

Step 2 Substitute $5y - 3$ for x in the second equation.

$-3x + 15y = 9$

$-3(5y - 3) + 15y = 9$ Substitute $5y - 3$ for x.

$-15y + 9 + 15y = 9$ Distributive Property

$9 = 9$ Simplify.

Since the statement is an identity, the system is consistent and coincident. There are infinitely many solutions to the system. If you graph these lines, you will see that they have the same graph.

B $y = -5x + 10$
$5x + y = 3$

SOLUTION

Step 1 The first equation is already solved for y.

Step 2 Substitute $-5x + 10$ for y in the second equation.

$$5x + y = 3$$

$$5x + (\mathbf{-5x + 10}) = 3 \quad \text{Substitute } -5x + 10 \text{ for } y.$$

$$5x - 5x + 10 = 3 \quad \text{Remove parentheses.}$$

$$10 = 3 \quad \text{Simplify.}$$

▶ **Remember** If a system of linear equations is inconsistent, then the lines are parallel.

The final statement is a contradiction. The system is inconsistent, so there is no solution. Graph the equations to see that they are parallel and thus never intersect. ■

Application: Solving a Mixture Problem

EXAMPLE 3

How many quarts of pure water should be combined with an unknown amount of solution containing 50% ammonia to obtain 5 qt of a solution that contains 10% ammonia?

SOLUTION

Use the problem-solving plan.

Step 1 ***Identify*** Find the number of quarts of pure water and the number of quarts of the 50% ammonia solution that would make 5 qt of a 10% ammonia solution.

Step 2 ***Strategize*** Let p equal the number of quarts of pure water and a equal the number of quarts of the 50% ammonia solution.

Step 3 ***Set Up*** Write a system of equations to model the problem.

Equation 1 The total number of quarts of the cleaning solution mixture is represented by the equation $p + a = 5$.

Equation 2 If you keep in mind that 50% ammonia is the same as 50% water and that 10% ammonia is the same as 90% water, then the total amount of water in the cleaning solution can be represented as follows.

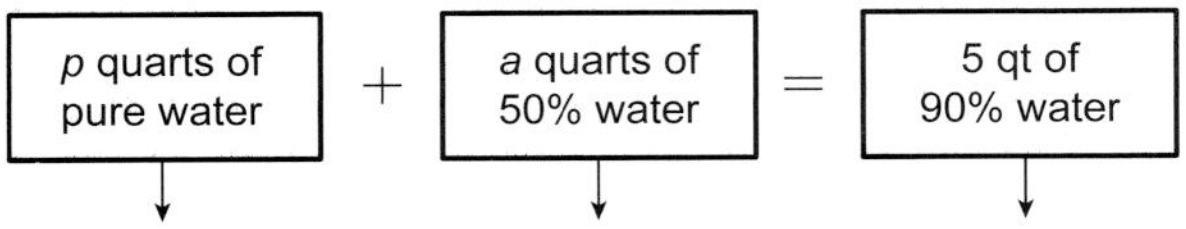

p quarts of pure water	+	*a* quarts of 50% water	=	5 qt of 90% water
↓		↓		↓
$1 \cdot p$	$+$	$0.5 \cdot a$	$=$	$0.9 \cdot 5$
p	$+$	$0.5a$	$=$	4.5

The system of equations is $\begin{array}{r} p + a = 5 \\ p + 0.5a = 4.5 \end{array}$.

Step 4 ***Solve*** Use the substitution method.
Solve Equation 1 for p.

$$\begin{aligned} p + a &= 5 \\ p &= 5 - a \end{aligned}$$

Substitute $5 - a$ into the second equation for p.

$$\begin{aligned} p + 0.5a &= 4.5 \\ (\mathbf{5 - a}) + 0.5a &= 4.5 \\ -0.5a &= -0.5 \\ a &= 1 \end{aligned}$$

Substitute 1 for a into the equation $p = 5 - a$.

$$\begin{aligned} p &= 5 - a \\ p &= 5 - \mathbf{1} \\ p &= 4 \end{aligned}$$

So 4 quarts of water should be mixed with 1 quart of 50% ammonia solution to make 5 qt of a 10% ammonia solution.

Step 5 ***Check*** Substitute 1 for a and 4 for p in the original equations.

$$p + a = 5$$
$$\mathbf{4} + \mathbf{1} \stackrel{?}{=} 5$$
$$5 = 5 \checkmark$$

$$p + 0.5a = 4.5$$
$$\mathbf{4} + 0.5 \bullet \mathbf{1} \stackrel{?}{=} 4.5$$
$$4 + 0.5 \stackrel{?}{=} 4.5$$
$$4.5 = 4.5 \checkmark$$

The answer is correct. ■

Linear Combination

You can use the linear combination method to solve a system of linear equations algebraically.

How to Use the Linear Combination Method to Solve Systems of Equations

Step 1 Add or subtract the equations to eliminate one of the variables.

Step 2 Solve the resulting equation for the remaining variable.

Step 3 Substitute the value of the variable found in Step 2 into either of the original equations to obtain the value of the other variable.

▶ **Think About It** The linear combination method is also called the elimination method.

Using the Linear Combination Method to Solve a System of Equations

EXAMPLE 1

Solve the system.

A $2x + y = 5$
$-2x - 7y = 13$

> **Think About It** When using the linear combination method, be sure to put both equations in standard form and line up like terms in the equations vertically.

SOLUTION

Step 1 Since the coefficients of the x terms, 2 and -2, are opposites, add the equations to eliminate x.

$$\begin{array}{r} 2x + y = 5 \\ +\,(-2x - 7y = 13) \\ \hline -6y = 18 \end{array}$$

Step 2 Solve the resulting equation for y.

$-6y = 18$

$y = -3$ Divide each side by -6.

Step 3 Substitute -3 for y in the first equation and solve for x. (You can use either of the original equations for this step.)

$2x + y = 5$

$2x + (-3) = 5$ Substitute -3 for y.

$2x = 8$ Add 3 to each side.

$x = 4$ Divide each side by 2.

The solution to the system is $(4, -3)$.

> **Think About It** When using subtraction, be sure to subtract every term in the second equation from the corresponding term in the first.

B $4x + 5y = -5$
$x + 5y = 10$

Step 1 Since the coefficients of the y terms are equal, you can subtract the equations to eliminate y.

$$\begin{array}{r} 4x + 5y = \ \ -5 \\ -(x + 5y = \ \ \ 10) \\ \hline 3x \qquad = -15 \end{array}$$

Step 2 Solve the resulting equation for x.

$3x = -15$

$x = -5$ Divide each side by 3.

Step 3 Substitute -5 for x in the second equation and solve for y. Remember that you can use either of the original equations for this step.

$x + 5y = 10$

$-5 + 5y = 10$ Substitute -5 for x.

$5y = 15$ Add 5 to each side.

$y = 3$ Divide each side by 5.

The solution to the system is $(-5, 3)$. ■

Application: Geometry

You can apply the linear combination method to solve systems of linear equations that model situations in geometry.

EXAMPLE 2

The perimeter of a rectangle is 44 ft. The length of the rectangle is 1 more than twice the width. Find the dimensions of the rectangle.

Step 1 Write a system of equations to model the problem.

Equation 1 This equation represents the perimeter of the rectangle. Use the formula $P = 2l + 2w$.

$$44 = 2l + 2w$$

Equation 2 The length of the rectangle is 1 more than twice the width. Write an equation to model this statement.

$$l = 2w + 1$$

Write this linear equation in standard form by subtracting $2w$ from each side.

$$l - 2w = 1$$

The system of equations is $\begin{array}{r} 2l + 2w = 44 \\ l - 2w = 1 \end{array}$.

Step 2 Solve the system of equations.

Add the equations.

$$\begin{array}{r} 2l + 2w = 44 \\ + (l - 2w = \ \ 1) \\ \hline 3l \qquad\quad = 45 \end{array}$$

Solve the equation $3l = 45$ for l.

$$\begin{aligned} 3l &= 45 \\ l &= 15 \end{aligned}$$

Substitute 15 for l in the equation $2l + 2w = 44$ and solve for w.

$$\begin{aligned} 2l + 2w &= 44 \\ 2 \bullet 15 + 2w &= 44 \\ 30 + 2w &= 44 \\ 2w &= 14 \\ w &= 7 \end{aligned}$$

The length of the rectangle is 15 ft and the width is 7 ft.

CHECK

Substitute 15 for l and 7 for w in each of the original equations in the system.

$$\begin{aligned} 2l + 2w &= 44 \\ 2 \bullet \mathbf{15} + 2 \bullet \mathbf{7} &\stackrel{?}{=} 44 \\ 30 + 14 &\stackrel{?}{=} 44 \\ 44 &= 44 \checkmark \end{aligned} \qquad \begin{aligned} l - 2w &= 1 \\ \mathbf{15} - 2 \bullet \mathbf{7} &\stackrel{?}{=} 1 \\ 15 - 14 &\stackrel{?}{=} 1 \\ 1 &= 1 \checkmark \end{aligned}$$

Applications: Systems of Linear Equations

Systems of linear equations can model many real-world situations.

Food Service

EXAMPLE 1

At a concession stand at a fair, a small cup of lemonade costs $1.50 and a large cup costs $2. The concession stand workers collected a total of $6600 from the sale of lemonade. They sold twice as many large cups as small cups. How many cups of each size were sold?

A Write a system of equations to model the problem.

SOLUTION

Equation 1 Let s be the number of small cups of lemonade sold and l be the number of large cups of lemonade sold. You are told that twice as many large cups were sold.

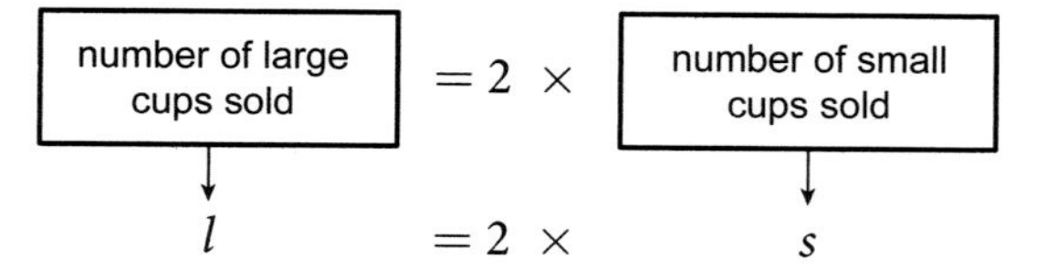

Equation 2 Total sales were \$6600 and you know the price of each type of cup, so you can write an equation to represent the total sales.

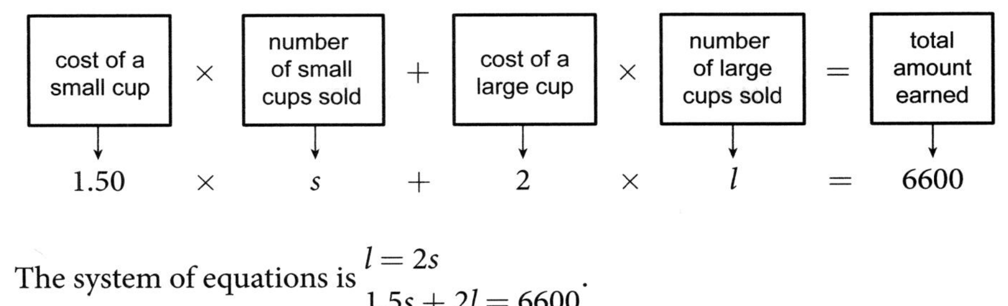

The system of equations is $\begin{matrix} l = 2s \\ 1.5s + 2l = 6600 \end{matrix}$.

B Solve the system of equations.

SOLUTION

Substitute $2s$ for l in the second equation and solve for s.

$1.5s + 2l = 6600$	
$1.5s + 2 \bullet \mathbf{2s} = 6600$	Substitute $2s$ for l.
$1.5s + 4s = 6600$	Simplify.
$5.5s = 6600$	Combine like terms.
$s = 1200$	Divide each side by 5.5.

Substitute 1200 for s in the first equation and solve for l.

$l = 2s$	
$l = 2 \bullet \mathbf{1200}$	Substitute 1200 for s.
$l = 2400$	Multiply.

Altogether, 1200 small and 2400 large cups of lemonade were sold.

CHECK

Substitute 1200 for s and 2400 for l in each equation in the system.

$$\begin{aligned} l &= 2s \\ \mathbf{2400} &\stackrel{?}{=} 2 \cdot \mathbf{1200} \\ 2400 &= 2400 \checkmark \end{aligned} \qquad \begin{aligned} 1.5s + 2l &= 6600 \\ 1.5 \cdot \mathbf{1200} + 2 \cdot \mathbf{2400} &\stackrel{?}{=} 6600 \\ 1800 + 4800 &\stackrel{?}{=} 6600 \\ 6600 &= 6600 \checkmark \end{aligned}$$

The solution is correct. ■

Cellular Phone Service

EXAMPLE 2

A cellular service plan for Company A has unlimited minutes for \$40/month and a text message rate of 10¢/message. A cellular service plan for Company B has unlimited minutes for \$30/month and a text message rate of 10¢/message. When is it cheaper to use Company B's plan?

A Write a system of equations to model the problem.

SOLUTION

Let t be the number of text messages per month and let c be the total monthly cost.

Equation 1 This equation models the total cost per month for Company A.

$$\boxed{\text{total cost}} = \$40 + 10¢ \times \boxed{\text{number of text messages}}$$

$$c = 40 + 0.10 \times t$$

Equation 2 This equation models the total cost per month for Company B.

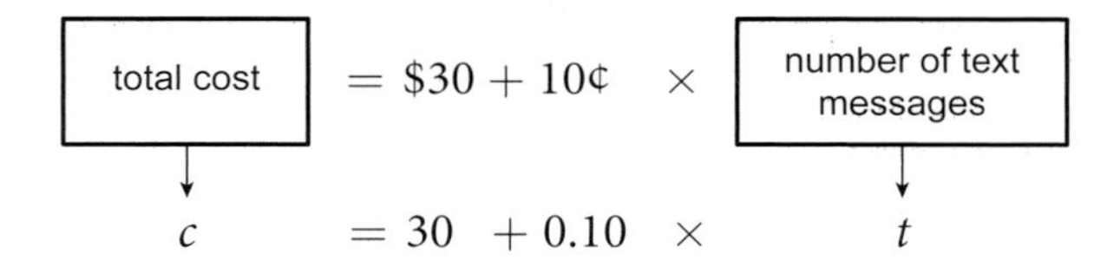

The system of equations is $\begin{matrix} c = 40 + 0.10t \\ c = 30 + 0.10t \end{matrix}$.

B Solve the system of equations.

SOLUTION

Both $40 + 0.10t$ and $30 + 0.10t$ are equal to c, so set them to be equal. Then solve for t.

$$\begin{aligned} 40 + 0.10t &= 30 + 0.10t \\ 40 - 30 + 0.10t &= 30 - 30 + 0.10t \\ 10 + 0.10t &= 0.10t \\ 10 + 0.10t - 0.10t &= 0.10t - 0.10t \\ 10 &= 0 \end{aligned}$$

Since the equation $10 = 0$ is false, there is no solution to the system. The cost is never the same for both services and it is always cheaper to use Company B's plan. ■

Applications of Linear Systems

Find the point where the graphs of two linear equations intersect by solving the system by substitution.

Finding a Break-Even Point

Write a linear equation for the cost of producing an item. Write a second linear equation for the revenue earned from selling the item. The break-even point is the point where the lines representing the two equations intersect.

▶ **Think About It** In business, the break-even point is the point at which the cost of producing and selling a product equals the revenue received for the product.

EXAMPLE 1

Suppose a book publisher is producing and selling a new book about the Amazon River. The publisher has determined that the revenue, in dollars (y), received from sales of the book will be $y = 23.50x$, where x is the number of books sold. The publisher also knows the cost, in dollars (y), to produce x books is $y = 1350 + 10x$.

How many books must the publisher sell to break even? What is the total revenue at the break-even point?

▶ **Think About It** Use substitution if you need to know the exact solution to a system of equations. You can use graphing to solve the system if an estimated solution is good enough. Graphing is also a good way to check your work.

SOLUTION

The two equations above form a system of equations. One way to find the break-even point is to use the substitution method to solve this system of equations. Since $y = 23.50x$, you can substitute $23.50x$ for y in the second equation and solve for x.

$$\begin{aligned} y &= 1350 + 10x \\ 23.50x &= 1350 + 10x \\ 23.50x - 10x &= 1350 + 10x - 10x \\ 13.50x &= 1350 \\ x &= 100 \end{aligned}$$

You can now solve for y by substituting 100 for x in the equation, $y = 23.50x$.

$$\begin{aligned} y &= 23.50x \\ y &= 23.50 \bullet \mathbf{100} \\ y &= 2350 \end{aligned}$$

The break-even point is $(100, 2350)$. The company breaks even after selling 100 books for total revenue of $2350. ■

Finding the Intersection of Price Equations

EXAMPLE 2

Jorge wants to rent office space. Building A charges annual rent of $150 plus $16/ft^2$. Building B charges annual rent of $850 plus $12/ft^2$.

A For each building, write an equation that relates the annual rent, r, to the number of square feet, n.

SOLUTION

For each building, the total annual rent is the sum of the fixed cost and the variable cost.

For Building A, the fixed cost is $150 and the variable cost is $16 times the number of square feet, n.

$$r = 150 + 16n$$

For Building B, the fixed cost is $850 and the variable cost is $12 times the number of square feet, n.

$$r = 850 + 12n$$

B Solve the system of equations by substitution. Interpret the solution and give your answer in a complete sentence.

SOLUTION

The system of equations is

$$r = 150 + 16n$$
$$r = 850 + 12n$$

Since $r = 150 + 16n$, substitute $150 + 16n$ for r into the second equation and solve for n.

$$\begin{aligned} r &= 850 + 12n \\ 150 + 16n &= 850 + 12n \\ 150 - 150 + 16n - 12n &= 850 - 150 + 12n - 12n \\ \frac{4n}{4} &= \frac{700}{4} \\ n &= 175 \end{aligned}$$

Solve for r by substituting $n = 175$ into $r = 150 + 16n$.

$$\begin{aligned} r &= 150 + 16n \\ r &= 150 + 16 \bullet \mathbf{175} \\ r &= 150 + 2800 \\ r &= 2950 \end{aligned}$$

The break-even point is $(175, 2950)$. Annual rent at both buildings is $2950, when the amount of office space rented is 175 ft^2. ■

▶ **Think About It** An office space that is more than 175 ft^2 costs less to rent in Building B, and an office space that is less than 175 ft^2 costs less to rent in Building A.

Mixture Problems

Use system of equations to find the answer to a mixture problem.

Mixing by Volume

EXAMPLE 1

Juan wants to make a juice drink that contains 80% orange juice and 20% grapefruit juice. How many cups of pure orange juice (100% orange juice) should be combined with a mix of 60% orange juice and 40% grapefruit juice to make 3 cups of the 80% orange juice-20% grapefruit juice mixture?

A Write a system of equations to model the problem. Explain what each variable and equation represents.

SOLUTION

The two unknowns in the problem are the number of cups of pure orange juice and the number of cups of the 60% orange juice-40% grapefruit juice mix. Let p represent the number of cups of pure orange juice and m represent the number of cups of the 60% orange juice-40% grapefruit juice mix.

Equation 1 This equation represents the total number of cups of Juan's juice mixture.

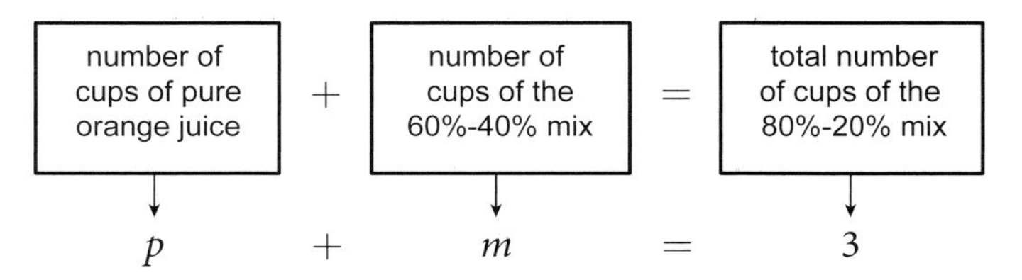

▶ **Think About It** Instead of writing an equation that represents the amount of orange juice in each juice mix, you could write an equation representing the amount of grapefruit juice in each juice mix.

Equation 2 This equation represents the amount of orange juice in each juice.

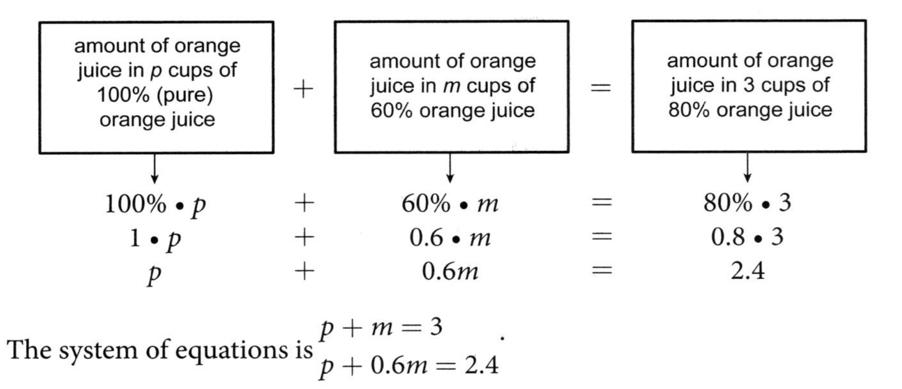

The system of equations is $\begin{matrix} p + m = 3 \\ p + 0.6m = 2.4 \end{matrix}$.

B Solve the system of equations to find the amounts of the two solutions needed to make the mixture.

SOLUTION

Step 1 Solve the first equation for p.

$$\begin{aligned} p + m &= 3 \\ p &= 3 - m \end{aligned}$$

Step 2 Substitute $3 - m$ into the second equation for p.

$$\begin{aligned} p + 0.6m &= 2.4 \\ (3 - m) + 0.6m &= 2.4 \\ -0.4m &= -0.6 \\ m &= 1.5 \end{aligned}$$

Step 3 Substitute 1.5 for m into the equation $p = 3 - m$.

$$\begin{aligned} p &= 3 - m \\ p &= 3 - 1.5 \\ p &= 1.5 \end{aligned}$$

Combine 1.5 cups of pure orange juice and 1.5 cups of 60% orange juice-40% grapefruit juice mix to make 3 cups of the 80% orange juice-20% grapefruit juice mix.

CHECK

Substitute 1.5 for p and 1.5 for m in each equation in the system.

$$\begin{aligned} p + m &= 3 \\ \mathbf{1.5} + \mathbf{1.5} &\stackrel{?}{=} 3 \\ 3 &= 3 \checkmark \end{aligned} \qquad \begin{aligned} p + 0.6m &= 2.4 \\ \mathbf{1.5} + 0.6 \bullet \mathbf{1.5} &\stackrel{?}{=} 2.4 \\ 1.5 + 0.9 &\stackrel{?}{=} 2.4 \\ 2.4 &= 2.4 \checkmark \end{aligned}$$

The solution is correct. ■

EXAMPLE 2

A jeweler has 4 g of a 60% gold alloy and 3 g of pure (100%) gold. He wants to make 6 g of a 75% gold alloy.

▶ **Think About It** An alloy is a mixture of metals.

Does the jeweler have enough of each ingredient to make the 75% gold alloy? Write a system of equations and solve it to answer the question.

SOLUTION

Let s be the amount of 60% gold alloy needed and let p be the amount of pure gold needed.

The equation representing the amount of each substance needed to make a total of 6 g of the 75% gold alloy is

$$a + p = 6.$$

The equation representing the amount of pure gold in each substance is

$$\begin{aligned} 60\% \bullet a + 100\% \bullet p &= 75\% \bullet 6 \\ 0.6 \bullet a + 1 \bullet p &= 0.75 \bullet 6 \\ 0.6a + p &= 4.5. \end{aligned}$$

Solve the first equation for p.

$$\begin{aligned} a + p &= 6 \\ p &= 6 - a \end{aligned}$$

Substitute the value for p into the second equation to solve for a.

$$\begin{aligned} 0.6a + p &= 4.5 \\ 0.6a + 6 - a &= 4.5 \\ 6 - 0.4a &= 4.5 \\ 6 - 6 - 0.4a &= 4.5 - 6 \\ -0.4a &= -1.5 \\ a &= 3.75 \end{aligned}$$

Substitute $a = 3.75$ into the first equation and solve for p.

$$\begin{aligned} 3.75 + p &= 6 \\ 3.75 - 3.75 + p &= 6 - 3.75 \\ p &= 2.25 \end{aligned}$$

The jeweler needs 3.75 g of the 60% alloy and 2.25 g of pure gold to make the 75% alloy. Since there is 4 g of the 60% alloy and 3 g of pure gold, there is enough of each substance to make 6 g of the 75% alloy. ■

Function Basics

Topic List

- Relations
- Functions
- Function Equations
- Linear Function Models
- Interpreting Linear Models
- Applications: Linear Models
- Interpreting Function Graphs
- Function Representations
- Functions in Real-World Situations
- Sketching Function Graphs

A hydroelectric dam is like a machine that turns flowing water into electricity. A mathematical function is a machine that takes a number as an input and produces another number as an output.

Relations

In math, a mapping between two sets is called a relation.

Definition

A **relation** is a mapping from a set of inputs to a set of outputs.

Representing Relations in Different Ways

You can use a set of ordered pairs to represent a relation. The x-coordinates of the ordered pairs are the inputs and the y-coordinates are the outputs. You can also display a relation using an arrow diagram, table, and graph.

EXAMPLE 1

In the relation $\{(8, 3), (8, 4), (10, 5), (12, 8), (13, 9)\}$, each x-coordinate represents a student's age and each y-coordinate represents the student's grade level in school. Display the relation in an arrow diagram, table, and graph.

SOLUTION

Arrow Diagram

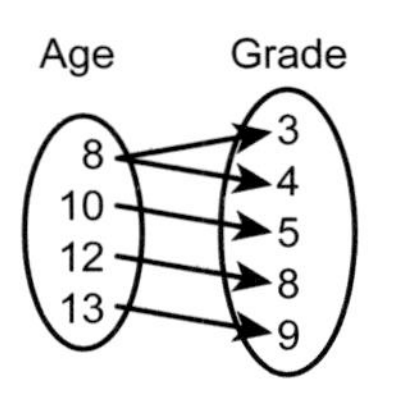

Table

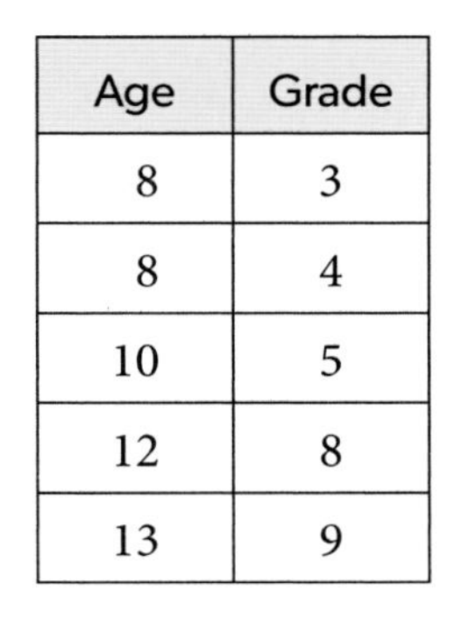

Age	Grade
8	3
8	4
10	5
12	8
13	9

Graph

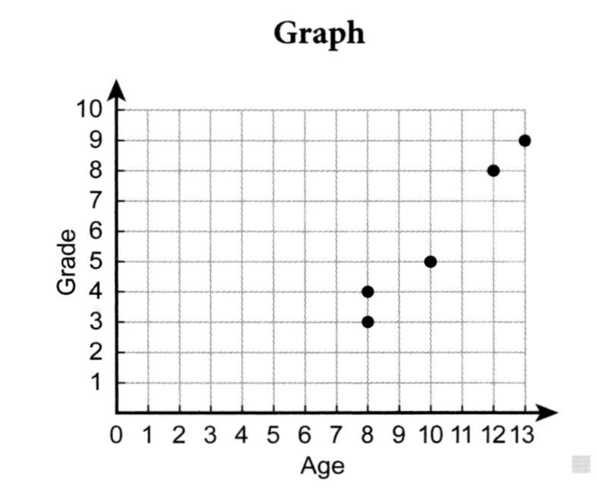

Finding the Domain and Range of a Relation

The **domain** of a relation is the set of allowable inputs and the **range** is the set of possible outputs.

▶ **Think About It** When writing the domain and range, list each number in each set only once.

EXAMPLE 2

Find the domain and range of the relation.

A $\{(-2, -4), (0, 3), (2, -4), (4, 1)\}$

SOLUTION

The domain is the set of x-coordinates: $\{-2, 0, 2, 4\}$. The range is the set of y-coordinates: $\{-4, 1, 3\}$.

B

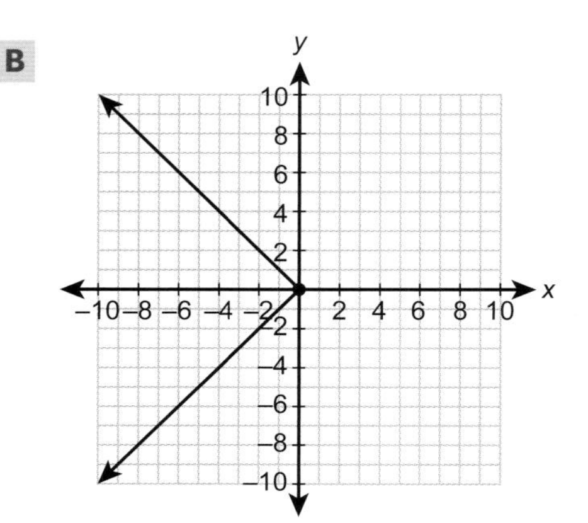

> ▶ **Think About It** On a graph, the horizontal axis represents the values of the domain, which are the values of the independent (input) variable.
>
> The vertical axis represents the values of the range, which are the values of the dependent (output) variable.

SOLUTION

The graph extends horizontally from 0 toward the negative numbers without end, and it extends vertically without beginning or end. The domain is all numbers less than or equal to zero, $\{x \mid x \leq 0\}$, and the range is all real numbers, $\{y \mid y \in \mathbb{R}\}$. ■

> ▶ **Think About It** Inequalities are often used to represent the domain and range of some relations.

Functions

A function is a relation in which each input can have only one output.

Definition

A **function** is a relation in which every element of the domain is assigned to exactly one element of the range.

The relation between people and their heights is a function because no person can have more than one height. For example, George cannot be 58 in. and 60 in. tall at the same time. However, George and Maria can both be the same height.

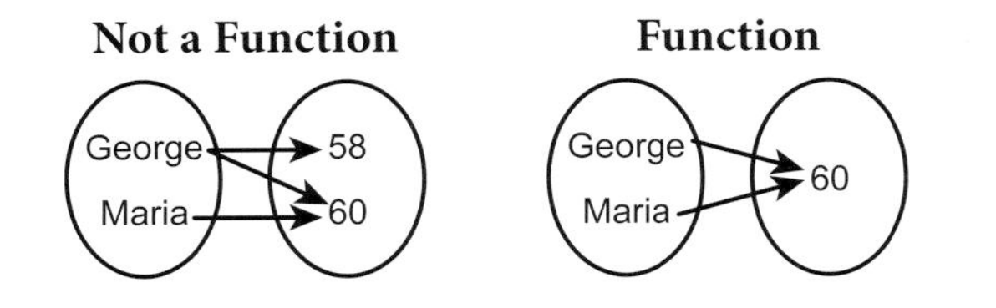

Determining Whether a Relation Is a Function

EXAMPLE 1

Determine whether the relation is a function.

A $\{(-5, 4), (-4, 0), (-2, 4), (-1, 0)\}$

SOLUTION

No element from the domain is paired with more than one element from the range. The relation is a function.

▶ **Think About It** In a table or a set of ordered pairs, if no x-values are repeated, the relation is a function.

B

x	2	2	2	4	5
y	-9	-7	-3	1	8

SOLUTION

The domain value 2 is assigned to -9, -7, and -3. The relation is not a function. ■

Applying the Vertical Line Test

When a function is graphed in the coordinate plane, each x-value is assigned to no more than one y-value. This property makes it impossible for any vertical line to intersect the graph at more than one point.

Vertical Line Test

For any relation, if a vertical line intersects the graph more than once, the relation is not a function.

Also, if you cannot draw a vertical line that intersects a relation more than once, the relation is a function.

▶ **Think About It** Place an uncooked piece of spaghetti over the graph of a relation vertically. Slide it over the graph from left to right. If the spaghetti intersects the graph more than once at any x-value, then the relation is not a function.

EXAMPLE 2

Determine whether the relation is a function.

A

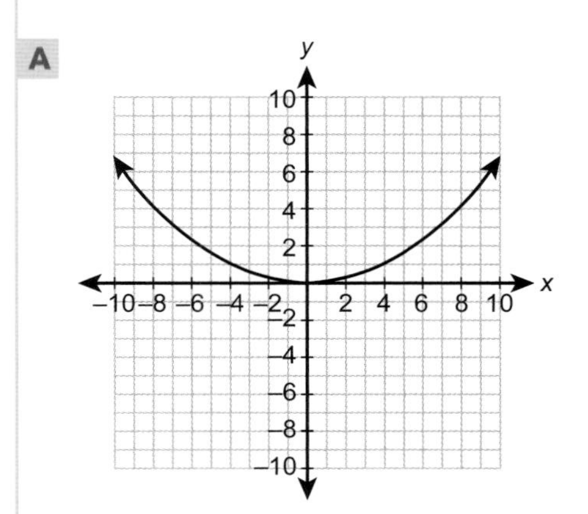

SOLUTION

No vertical line intersects the graph at more than one point. The relation is a function.

B

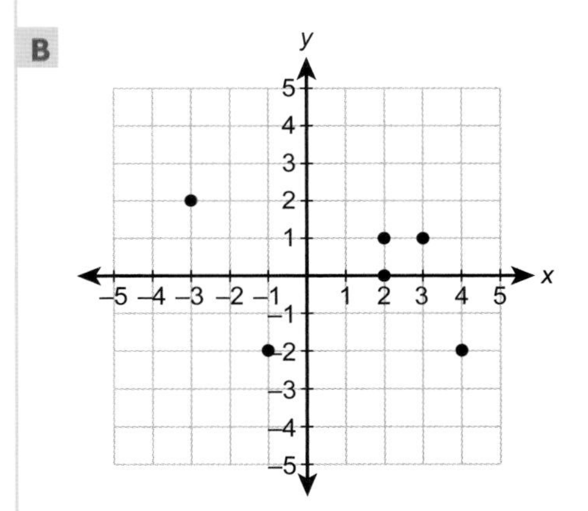

SOLUTION

There is a single vertical line that intersects both $(2, 1)$ and $(2, 0)$. The relation is not a function. ■

Evaluating a Function

To evaluate a function, find the y-value that corresponds to a given x-value.

EXAMPLE 3

Evaluate the function at the given point.

A $x = 3$

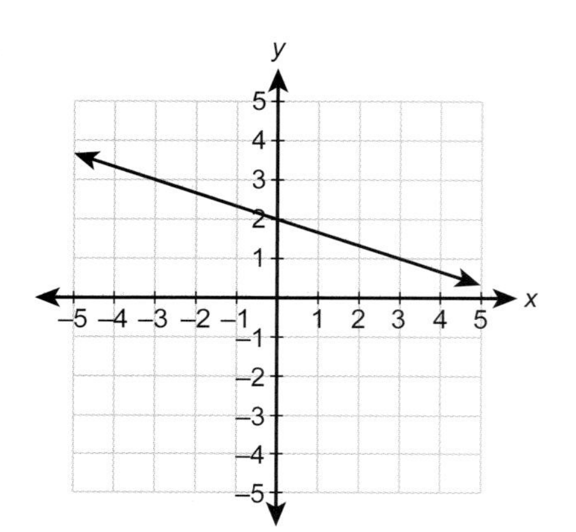

SOLUTION

Place your finger at 3 on the x-axis and slide it vertically until your finger reaches the graph. Then move your finger horizontally to find the corresponding y-value on the y-axis. When $x = 3$, the value of the function is $y = 1$.

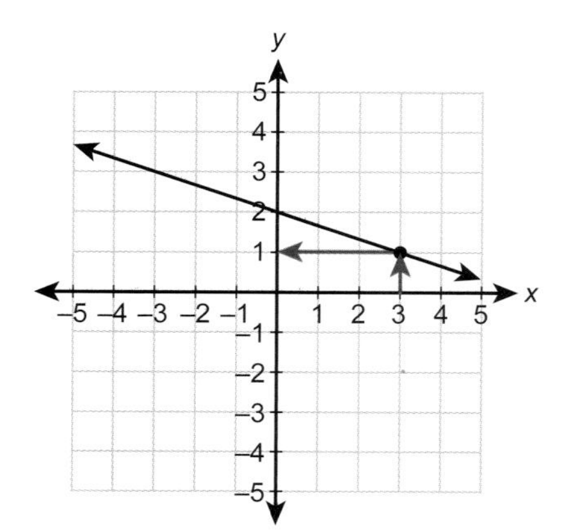

B $x = -1$

x	-3	-2	-1	0	1	2
y	-5	-4	-3	-2	-1	0

SOLUTION

Locate $x = -1$ in the top row of the table and then find the corresponding y-value. The value of the function at $x = -1$ is $y = -3$. ■

Application: Population

EXAMPLE 4

The graph shows the population of North Carolina every decade from 1940 to 2000. Use the graph to estimate the population in 1995.

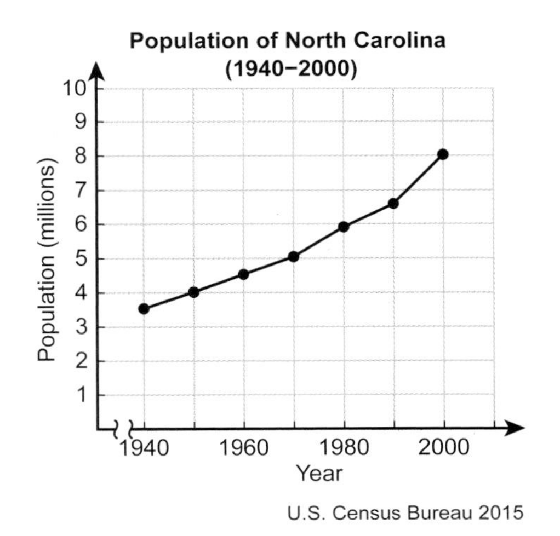

SOLUTION

Locate 1995 on the x-axis by putting your finger halfway between 1990 and 2000. Move your finger vertically until it reaches the graph. Move horizontally to the y-axis to estimate the value: about 7.4 million. ■

Graphing a Function

You can represent a function with a graph on the coordinate plane. Choose several x-values and evaluate the function to determine the corresponding y-values to complete an input/output table. Then graph the ordered pairs from the table and connect them with a line or a smooth curve.

EXAMPLE 5

Graph the function $y = -2x + 5$.

SOLUTION

Set up an input/output table by choosing several input values for x. Then evaluate the function expression for each input value to determine the corresponding output y-value.

Input (x)	Function expression	Output (y)	Ordered pair
x	$-2(\mathbf{x}) + 5$	y	(x, y)
-3	$-2(\mathbf{-3}) + 5$	11	$(-3, 11)$
-2	$-2(\mathbf{-2}) + 5$	9	$(-2, 9)$
-1	$-2(\mathbf{-1}) + 5$	7	$(-1, 7)$
0	$-2(\mathbf{0}) + 5$	5	$(0, 5)$
1	$-2(\mathbf{1}) + 5$	3	$(1, 3)$
2	$-2(\mathbf{2}) + 5$	1	$(2, 1)$
3	$-2(\mathbf{3}) + 5$	-1	$(3, -1)$

Plot the ordered pairs from the table. The pattern that they form is a straight line. Draw a line through the points to represent the function.

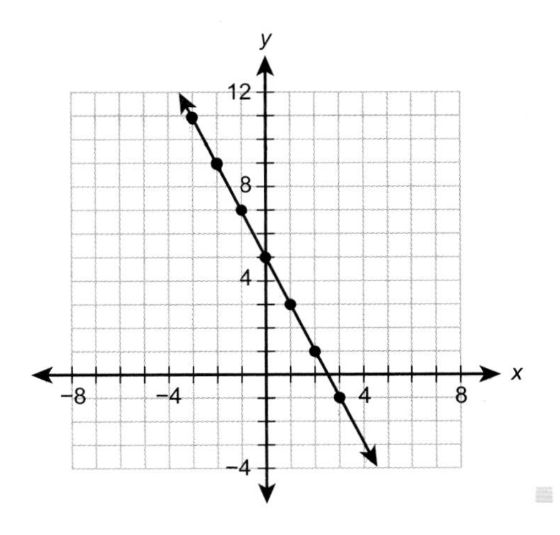

▶ **Think About It** The ordered pairs that you plot determine the shape of the function's graph. Be sure to choose enough input values so that you have a good idea of what the function's graph will look like.

Function Equations

You can use equations to represent many functions.

Suppose every y-value of a function is one greater than 3 times the corresponding x-value. This function can be expressed as the equation $y = 3x + 1$. In this equation, x is the **independent variable** (the input variable), and y is the **dependent variable** (the output variable).

Writing a Function Equation

EXAMPLE 1

Write an equation of the line.

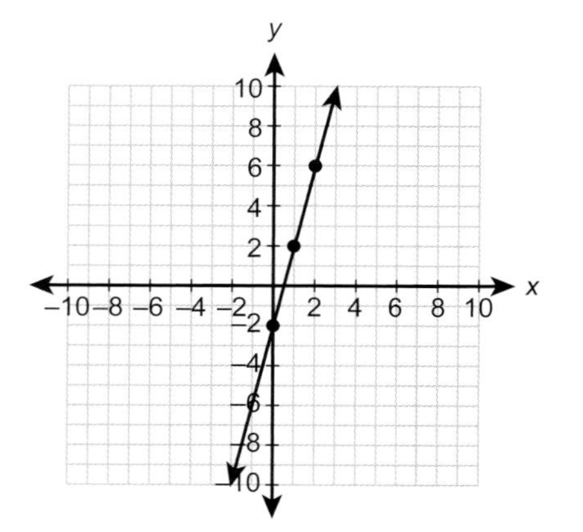

SOLUTION

The line has a slope of 4 and a y-intercept of -2, so write the equation in slope-intercept form.

$$y = 4x - 2$$ ■

▶ **Remember** Slope-intercept form of a line is $y = mx + b$, where m is the slope and b is the y-intercept.

Evaluating Functions

To evaluate a function, substitute the given value of x into the function, and then simplify the expression.

EXAMPLE 2

Evaluate $y = -5x + 4$ for the given value of x.

A $x = -2$

SOLUTION

Substitute -2 for x and simplify.

$y = -5 \cdot (-2) + 4$	Substitute -2 for x.
$= 10 + 4$	Multiply.
$= 14$	Add.

When $x = -2$, $y = 14$.

B $x = 3$

SOLUTION

Substitute 3 for x and simplify.

$y = -5 \cdot 3 + 4$	Substitute 3 for x.
$= -15 + 4$	Multiply.
$= -11$	Add.

When $x = 3$, $y = -11$. ■

EXAMPLE 3

Evaluate $y = 3x^2 - x$ when $x = \frac{1}{3}$.

SOLUTION

Substitute $\frac{1}{3}$ for x, and then simplify.

$y = 3 \cdot \left(\frac{1}{3}\right)^2 - \left(\frac{1}{3}\right)$	Substitute $\frac{1}{3}$ for x.
$= 3 \cdot \frac{1}{9} - \frac{1}{3}$	Evaluate the power.
$= \frac{1}{3} - \frac{1}{3}$	Multiply.
$= 0$	Subtract.

When $x = \frac{1}{3}$, $y = 0$. ■

▶ **Remember** Evaluate powers before multiplying.

Application: Graph of a Real-World Function

EXAMPLE 4

Ronnie went for a 20 min jog. The graph below shows her jogging distance as a function of time.

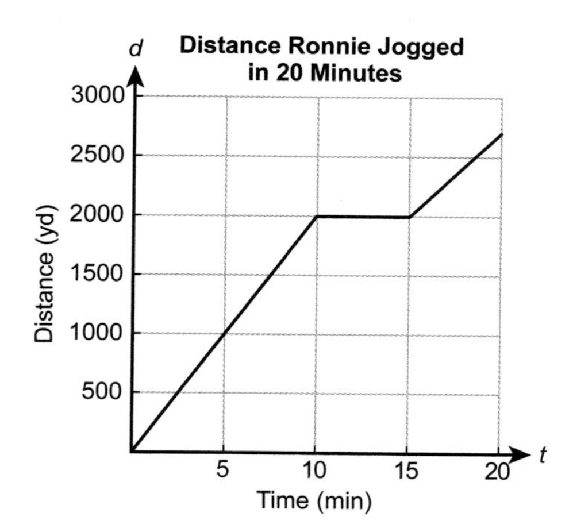

A About how many yards did she jog after 5 min? 12 min?

SOLUTION

The function value at $t = 5$ is 1000, and the function value at $t = 12$ is 2000. After 5 min she jogged 1000 yd, and after 12 min she jogged 2000 yd.

B How would you describe Ronnie's motion in the first 10 min, between 10 and 15 min, and in the last 5 min?

SOLUTION

In the first 10 min the graph goes up at a constant rate, so Ronnie was moving at a constant speed.

The graph is constant from $t = 10$ min to $t = 15$ min, so Ronnie covered no distance and was not moving during this time.

In the last 5 min, she went back to jogging at a slower speed than she moved at during the first 10 min. ■

▶ **Think About It** Many real-world events can be modeled as functions.

Linear Function Models

A linear function equation models a linear relationship between two quantities. You can determine the rate of change and starting value of a function from its equation.

Writing Linear Function Equations

You can write a linear function equation when you know the function's slope and y-intercept.

EXAMPLE 1

Write an equation for the linear function.

A Write an equation for the function described by the table.

x	-2	-1	0	1	2
y	-3	-1	1	3	5

SOLUTION

The y-intercept is the value of y when $x = 0$. From the table, you can see that $y = 1$ when $x = 0$. Therefore, the y-intercept is 1.

Choose any two ordered pairs from the table. Use the slope formula to find the slope.

$$m = \frac{y_2 - y_1}{x_2 - x_1}$$

Let $(x_1, y_1) = (-2, -3)$ and $(x_2, y_2) = (-1, -1)$.

$$\begin{aligned} m &= \frac{-1 - (-3)}{-1 - (-2)} \\ &= \frac{-1 + 3}{-1 + 2} \\ &= \frac{2}{1} \\ &= 2 \end{aligned}$$

Write the function equation in slope-intercept form.

$$y = 2x + 1$$

▶ **Remember** The slope intercept form of an equation is $y = mx + b$, where m is the slope and b is the y-intercept.

B Write an equation for the function whose graph contains the point $(-4, 6)$ and has a slope of $-\frac{3}{4}$.

SOLUTION

Find the y-intercept. Substitute -4 for x, 6 for y, and $-\frac{3}{4}$ for m into the slope-intercept form of the equation of a line $y = mx + b$. Then solve for b.

$$\begin{aligned} 6 &= -\frac{3}{4} \cdot (-4) + b \\ 6 &= 3 + b \\ 3 &= b \end{aligned}$$

Write the function equation in slope-intercept form. Replace m with $-\frac{3}{4}$ and b with 3.

$$y = -\frac{3}{4}x + 3$$

C Write an equation for the linear function that contains the points $(1, -4)$ and $(4, 5)$.

SOLUTION

Find the slope.

$$\begin{aligned} m &= \frac{5 - (-4)}{4 - 1} \\ &= \frac{5 + 4}{3} \\ &= \frac{9}{3} \\ &= 3 \end{aligned}$$

Find the y-intercept. Substitute the x- and y-values of one of the points and substitute 3 for m into the equation $y = mx + b$. Then solve for b.

$$\begin{aligned} 5 &= 3 \bullet 4 + b \\ 5 &= 12 + b \\ -7 &= b \end{aligned}$$

Write the function equation in slope-intercept form. Replace m with 3 and b with -7.

$$y = 3x - 7$$

Interpreting and Writing Functions in a Real-World Context

When a linear function models a real-world situation, the y-intercept, also called the vertical intercept, is often the situation's starting value. The slope is the rate of change.

> **Remember** A rate of change is a ratio of the change in one variable to another variable.

EXAMPLE 2

Snow is falling at a steady rate. The number of inches of snow on the ground is given by the equation $S = 10 + 1.25h$, where S is the number of inches of snow and h is the number of hours the snow falls.

A What is the meaning of the slope of the equation in this problem?

SOLUTION

The slope of the equation is 1.25, which is a rate of change. The amount of snow on the ground, S, increases 1.25 in. each time the number of hours it snows, h, increases by 1. Therefore, the slope tells you that the amount of snow on the ground increases by 1.25 in./h.

▶ **Think About It** The equation $S = 10 + 1.25h$ is written in the slope-form $y = b + mx$. The y-intercept, b, is 10 and the slope, m, is 1.25.

B What is the meaning of the vertical intercept?

SOLUTION

The vertical intercept in this equation is 10, which tells you that S is 10 when h is 0. Since h represents the number of hours it snows, $h = 0$ represents the time before the snow begins to fall. Therefore, the vertical intercept tells you that there are already 10 in. of snow on the ground before it begins to snow. ■

EXAMPLE 3

Alicia is planning to cook salmon and cod for a large dinner party. She has $115 to spend on the fish. Salmon costs $8.25/lb and cod costs $11.80/lb.

A Find a function that relates the number of pounds of salmon and the number of pounds of cod Alicia can buy.

SOLUTION

Let s represent pounds of salmon, and let c represent pounds of cod. The cost of 1 lb of salmon is $8.25, so the cost of s pounds is $8.25s$. The cost of 1 lb of cod is $11.80, so the cost of c pounds is $11.80c$. The total cost of s pounds of salmon and c pounds of cod must equal $115. The equation that models this situation is $8.25s + 11.80c = 115$.

Write a function that relates one variable to the other. To do so, solve for one of the variables.

$$\begin{aligned} 8.25s + 11.80c &= 115 \\ 8.25s - 8.25s + 11.80c &= 115 - 8.25s \\ 11.80c &= 115 - 8.25s \\ \frac{11.80c}{11.80} &= \frac{115}{11.80} - \frac{8.25s}{11.80} \\ c &= 9.75 - 0.7s \end{aligned}$$

In this equation, the number of pounds of cod Alicia buys is a function of the number of pounds of salmon she buys.

B Find the slope, the vertical intercept, and the horizontal intercept of the function $c = 9.75 - 0.7s$.

▶ **Think About It** Just as the *y*-intercept can be referred to as the vertical intercept, the *x*-intercept can be referred to as the horizontal intercept.

SOLUTION

The function equation is almost in slope-intercept form. If you switch the order of the terms on the right side, you can see that the slope is -0.7 and the vertical intercept is 9.75.

To find the horizontal intercept, find the value of s when the function is 0. Replace c with 0 and solve for s.

$$\begin{aligned} 0 &= -0.7s + 9.75 \\ 0 - 9.75 &= -0.7s + 9.75 - 9.75 \\ -9.75 &= -0.7s \\ \frac{-9.75}{-0.7} &= \frac{-0.7s}{-0.7} \\ 13.9 &\approx s \end{aligned}$$

The horizontal intercept is about 13.9.

C Graph the function.

SOLUTION

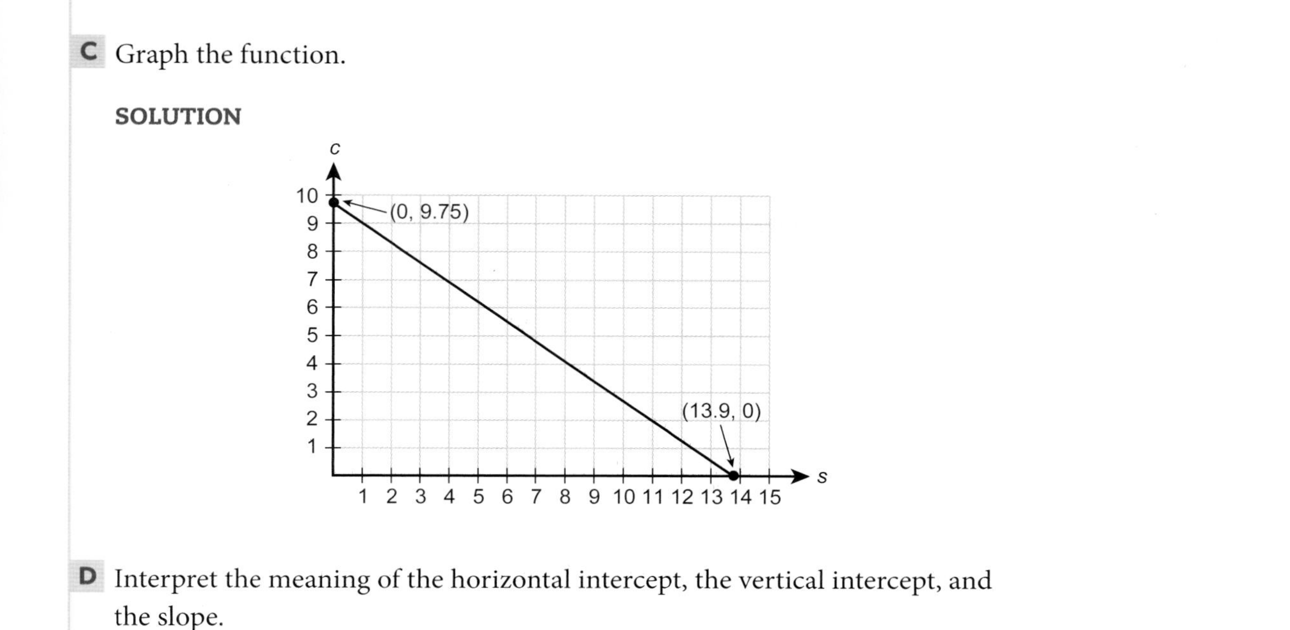

D Interpret the meaning of the horizontal intercept, the vertical intercept, and the slope.

SOLUTION

The horizontal intercept tells you that Alicia can buy about 13.9 lb of salmon if she buys no cod. The vertical intercept tells you that she can buy 9.75 lb of cod if she buys no salmon. The slope tells you that for every 1 lb of salmon Alicia purchases, the amount of cod she can purchase decreases by 0.7 lb. ■

Interpreting Linear Models

In a linear model for which the independent variable is time, the slope of the line passing through the data values is the rate of change of the dependent quantity measured with time. The y-intercept is the initial amount of the dependent quantity.

Rate of Change and Initial Amount

If you are given a graph or a table for a real-world situation, it can help to write a linear equation that models the situation.

Remember The independent variable is represented on the horizontal (usually x) axis, while the dependent variable is represented by the vertical (often y) axis.

EXAMPLE 1

A computer program recorded the altitude of a helicopter. The first recorded altitude, a, was 270 ft, and then the program recorded the helicopter's altitude 10, 20, and 30 s. The graph shows the helicopter's altitude at these times. The computer program drew a straight line through the points.

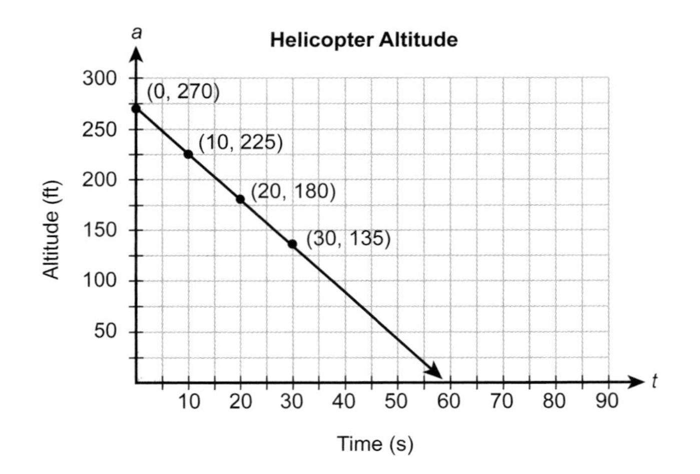

A Find the slope and the y-intercept of the graphed line. Show all work.

▶ **Think About It** If possible, find the y-intercept by looking at the graph instead of calculating it.

SOLUTION

Choose two points on the line to find the slope—for example, $(0, 270)$ and $(30, 135)$.

$$m = \frac{135 - 270}{30 - 0} = \frac{-135}{30} = -4.5$$

Look at the point where the line crosses the y-axis to find the y-intercept. The slope of the line is -4.5 and the y-intercept is 270.

B How do the slope and the y-intercept of the line relate to the helicopter's motion?

SOLUTION

The graphed line represents the motion of the helicopter. Since the helicopter's motion is a linear model, the slope of the line represents the rate of change in the altitude of the helicopter with time. Since the slope is negative, the helicopter is descending at a rate of -4.5 ft/s.

The y-intercept of the line corresponds to the time when the altitude was first measured, at time $t = 0$ s. ■

EXAMPLE 2

The water level l, in meters, in a tank is modeled by the linear equation $l = 35 + 1.2t$, where t is elapsed time in hours.

A Explain what the numbers 35 and 1.2 in the equation represent in this situation.

SOLUTION

The equation is linear, so the equation represents a line with a slope of 1.2 and a y-intercept of 35.

The slope of the line represents the rate of change in the water level with time, so the water level is rising at a rate of 1.2 m/h.

The y-intercept represents the initial value of l at $t = 0$, so the initial level of water in the tank is 35 m.

B Each equation represents the water level in other, similar tanks. Describe the situation each equation represents.

$$l = 35 + 0.7t$$
$$l = 35 - 1.4t$$
$$l = 42 - 1.1t$$

▸ **Q&A**

Q What situation would an equation with zero slope represent?

A a tank with a constant (unchanging) water level

SOLUTION

The equation $l = 35 + 0.7t$ represents an initial level of 35 m and a rise in the water level at a rate of 0.7 m/h.

The equation $l = 35 - 1.4t$ represents an initial level of 35 m and a decline in the water level at a rate of 1.4 m/h.

The equation $l = 42 - 1.1t$ represents an initial level of 42 m and a decline in the water level at a rate of 1.1 m/h.

C How could you represent the water level in a tank that is empty at first but rises at a rate of 2.1 m/s?

SOLUTION

The water level can be modeled by a linear equation. The slope is the rate of change of the water level, so it is equal to 2.1. The y-intercept is equal to the initial amount of water in the tank, so it is equal to 0.

The equation $l = 2.1t$ models the water level in the tank. ■

Applications: Linear Models

Use a table of values to help you understand and solve application problems involving constant rates.

Distance

EXAMPLE 1

The distance, d, that Cosimo can walk is given by the linear equation $d = 3.5t$, where t is the time in hours and d is the distance in miles. Make a table showing the values for d when $t = 1, 2, 3$, and 4. Then graph the linear equation.

SOLUTION

Step 1 Make a table. Substitute each value of t into the equation and solve for d.

t	1	2	3	4
d	$d = 3.5t$ $= 3.5 \cdot 1$ $= 3.5$	$d = 3.5t$ $= 3.5 \cdot 2$ $= 7$	$d = 3.5t$ $= 3.5 \cdot 3$ $= 10.5$	$d = 3.5t$ $= 3.5 \cdot 4$ $= 14$

Step 2 Plot the ordered pairs $(1, 3.5)$, $(2, 7)$, $(3, 10.5)$, and $(4, 14)$. Then draw the line. Since distance and time cannot be negative, the graph of the line is restricted to Quadrant I.

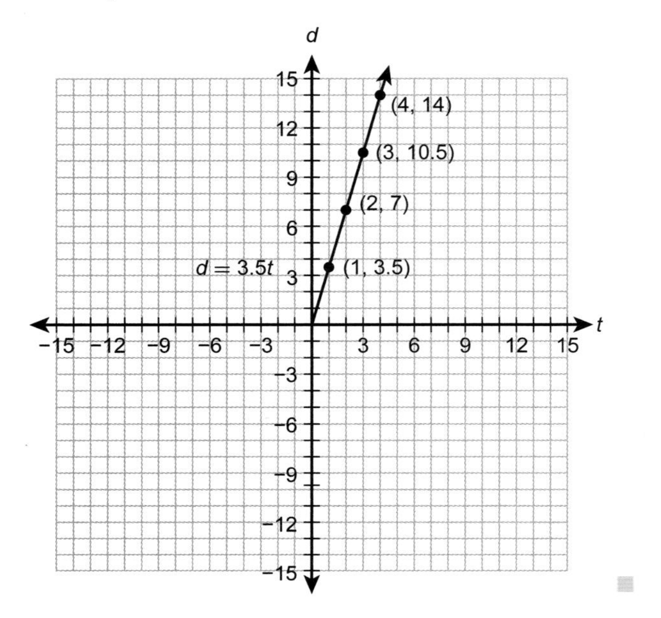

Cost

EXAMPLE 2

An online movie rental company charges customers \$5 to sign up and a monthly fee of \$10. The total cost, C, for n months can be modeled by the equation $C = 10n + 5$.

A Complete a table of values. What is the total cost for 1 month? 5 months? 7 months? 1 year?

SOLUTION

Substitute each value of n into the equation and solve for C. The variable n is time in months, so change 1 year to 12 months.

n	1	5	7	12
C	$C = 10n + 5$ $= 10 \bullet \mathbf{1} + 5$ $= 10 + 5$ $= 15$	$C = 10n + 5$ $= 10 \bullet \mathbf{5} + 5$ $= 50 + 5$ $= 55$	$C = 10n + 5$ $= 10 \bullet \mathbf{7} + 5$ $= 70 + 5$ $= 75$	$C = 10n + 5$ $= 10 \bullet \mathbf{12} + 5$ $= 120 + 5$ $= 125$

When n is 1, C is 15, so the total cost for 1 month is \$15. When n is 5, C is 55, so the total cost for 5 months is \$55. When n is 7, C is 75, so the total cost for 7 months is \$75. When n is 12, C is 125, so the total cost for 12 months is \$125.

B Is this a linear model? Explain.

SOLUTION

Examine the rate of change between values.

$(1, 15)$ and $(5, 55)$ rate of change $= \frac{y_2 - y_1}{x_2 - x_1} = \frac{55 - 15}{5 - 1} = \frac{40}{4} = \mathbf{10}$

$(5, 55)$ and $(7, 75)$ rate of change $= \frac{y_2 - y_1}{x_2 - x_1} = \frac{75 - 55}{7 - 5} = \frac{20}{2} = \mathbf{10}$

$(7, 75)$ and $(12, 125)$ rate of change $= \frac{y_2 - y_1}{x_2 - x_1} = \frac{125 - 75}{12 - 7} = \frac{50}{5} = \mathbf{10}$

The rates of change are equal. Therefore, the model is linear. Another way to determine whether the model is linear is to look at the equation $C = 10n + 5$. Notice the equation is in slope-intercept form where the slope of the line is 10 and the vertical intercept is 5. Only linear equations are written in slope-intercept form. ■

Interpreting Function Graphs

The shape and behavior of a function graph describe the relationship between the independent and dependent variables of the function.

Linear and Nonlinear Functions

Definitions

A **linear function** is a function whose graph is a straight line.

A **nonlinear function** is a function whose graph is not a straight line.

EXAMPLE 1

Determine whether the function is linear or nonlinear.

A $y = 2x - 1$

SOLUTION

Create a table of ordered pairs, and then plot the points.

x	$y = 2x - 1$
−2	−5
−1	−3
0	−1
1	1
2	3

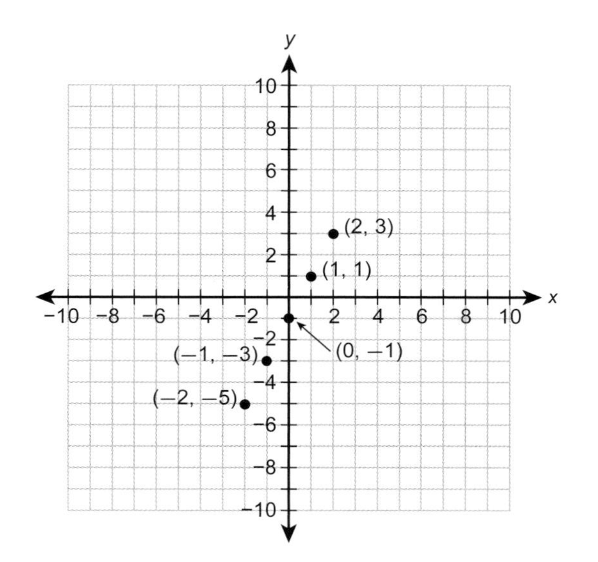

The points lie in a straight line. The function is linear.

B

x	−2	−1	0	1	2
y	4	1	0	1	4

SOLUTION

Plot the points.

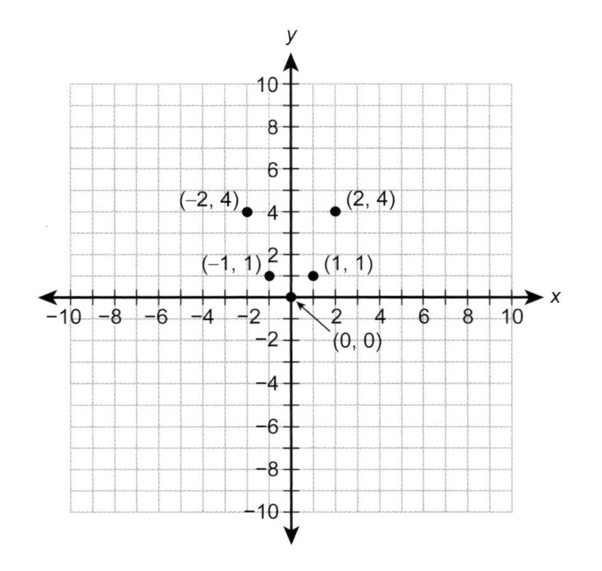

The points do not lie in a straight line. The function is nonlinear.

Increasing and Decreasing Functions

A function is **increasing** if the function value increases as x increases. Similarly, a function is **decreasing** if the function value decreases as x increases.

▶ **Think About It** The graphs in Examples 2A and 2B are linear functions. Linear functions that have a positive slope are increasing. Linear functions that have a negative slope are decreasing.

EXAMPLE 2

Determine whether the graph is increasing or decreasing.

A

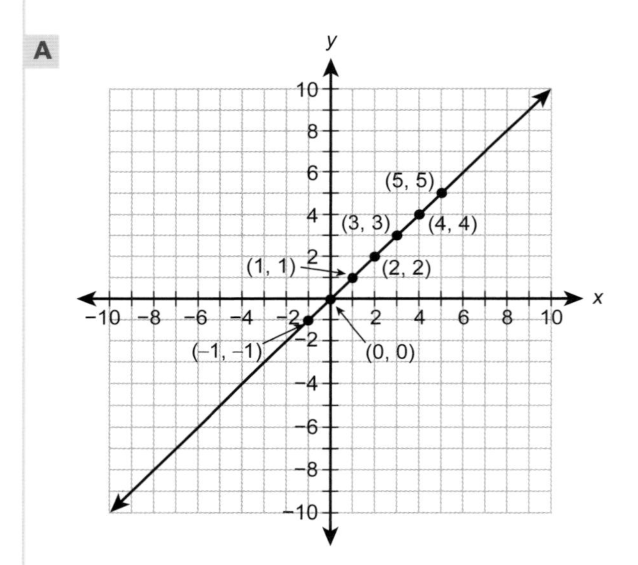

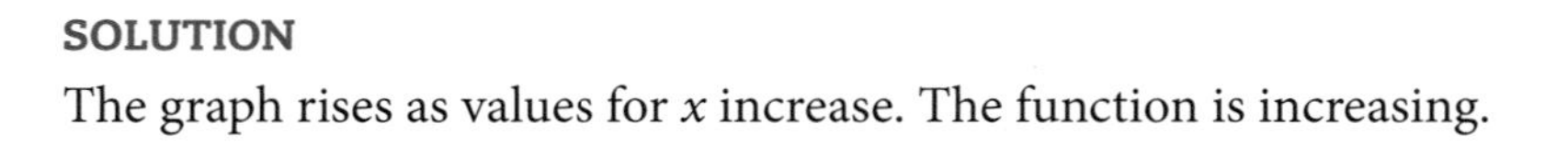

SOLUTION

The graph rises as values for x increase. The function is increasing.

B

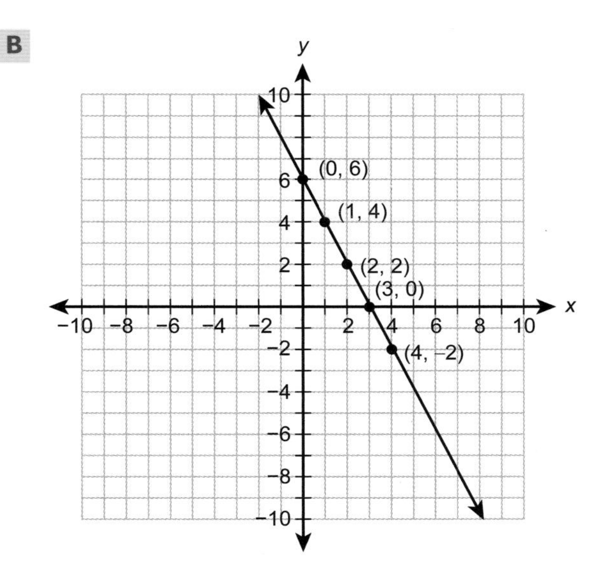

SOLUTION

The graph falls as values for x increase. The function is decreasing.

C

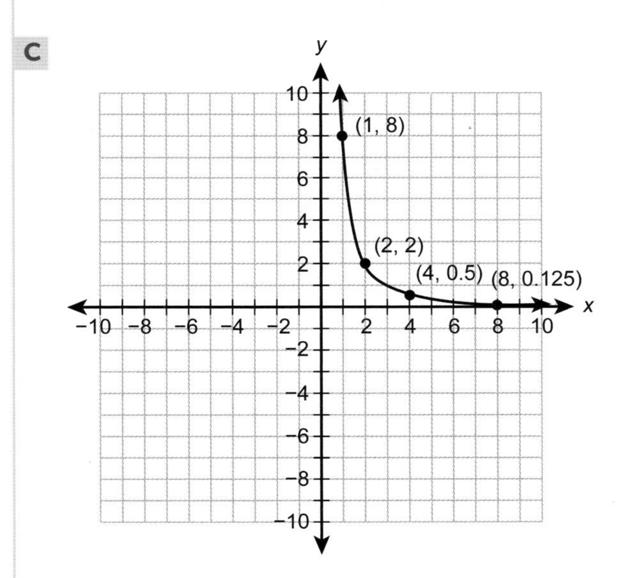

SOLUTION

The graph falls as values for x increase. The function is decreasing.

D

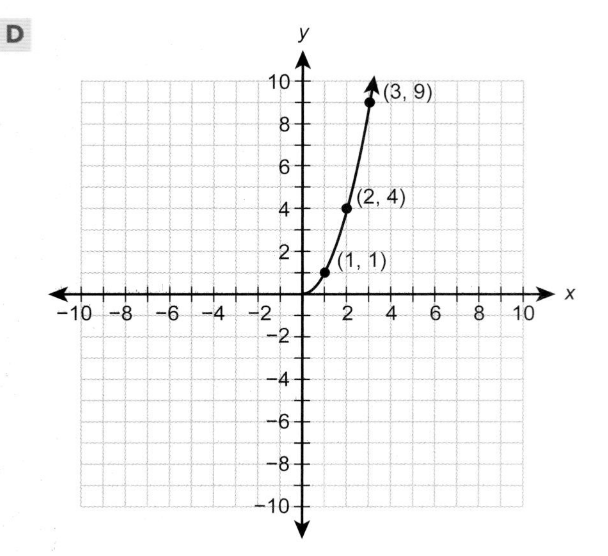

SOLUTION

The graph rises as values for x increase. The function is increasing.

When a function neither rises nor falls as x increases, the function is said to be **constant**.

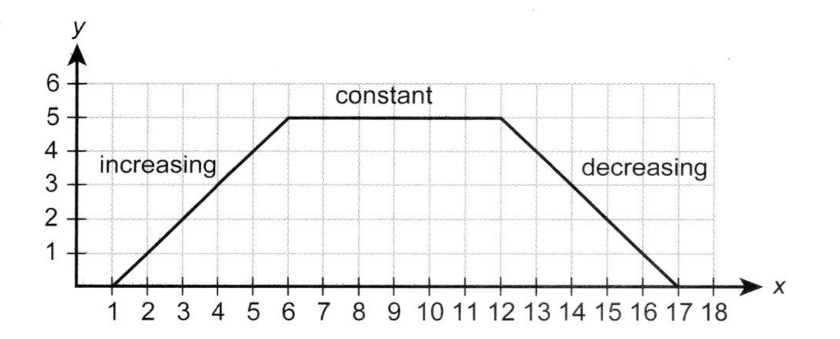

The graph of the function can be described in these terms:

- The function is increasing from $x = 1$ to $x = 6$.
- The function is constant from $x = 6$ to $x = 12$.
- The function is decreasing from $x = 12$ to $x = 17$.

EXAMPLE 3

Refer to the graph to answer the questions.

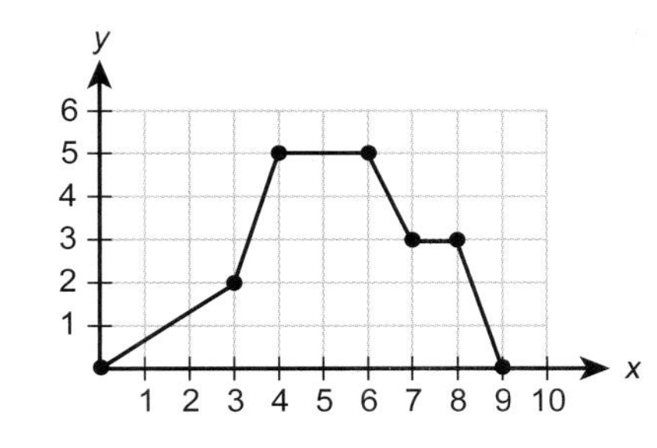

A When is the function increasing?

SOLUTION

The function is increasing from $x = 0$ to $x = 3$ and from $x = 3$ to $x = 4$.

> **Q&A**
>
> **Q** When is the function increasing more rapidly, from $x = 0$ to $x = 3$ or from $x = 3$ to $x = 4$?
>
> **A** The slope from $x = 3$ to $x = 4$ is steeper than the slope from $x = 0$ to $x = 3$. Therefore, the function is increasing more rapidly from $x = 3$ to $x = 4$.

B When is the function decreasing?

SOLUTION

The function is decreasing from $x = 6$ to $x = 7$ and from $x = 8$ to $x = 9$.

C When is the function constant?

SOLUTION

The function is constant from $x = 4$ to $x = 6$ and from $x = 7$ to $x = 8$. ■

Function Representations

Functions can be compared by examining their rates of change and intercepts.

Comparing Functions

Functions can be presented in different forms. They can appear as equations, graphs, tables, and even verbal sentences. To make meaningful comparisons between functions, compare their rates of change and intercepts.

EXAMPLE 1

Determine which function has a negative rate of change.

Function 1

x	y
−1	3
2	−6
3	−9

Function 2

$6x + -3y = 9$

SOLUTION

The slope of a linear function is its rate of change. Find the slope of both functions.

Function 1 To find the slope, choose two sets of ordered pairs from the table and substitute their coordinates into the slope formula.

$$m_1 = \frac{y_2 - y_1}{x_2 - x_1}$$

Let $(x_1, y_1) = (-1, 3)$ and $x_2, y_2 = (2, -6)$.

$$\begin{aligned} m_1 &= \frac{-6 - 3}{2 - (-1)} \\ &= \frac{-9}{3} \\ &= -3 \end{aligned}$$

Function 2 The function is written in standard form $Ax + Bx = C$, where $A = 6$, $B = -3$, and $C = 9$. The slope is $-\frac{A}{B}$.

Therefore, $m_2 = -\frac{6}{-3} = -(-2) = 2$.

Function 1 has a negative rate of change.

EXAMPLE 2

Determine which function has the greater rate of change.

A **Function 1**

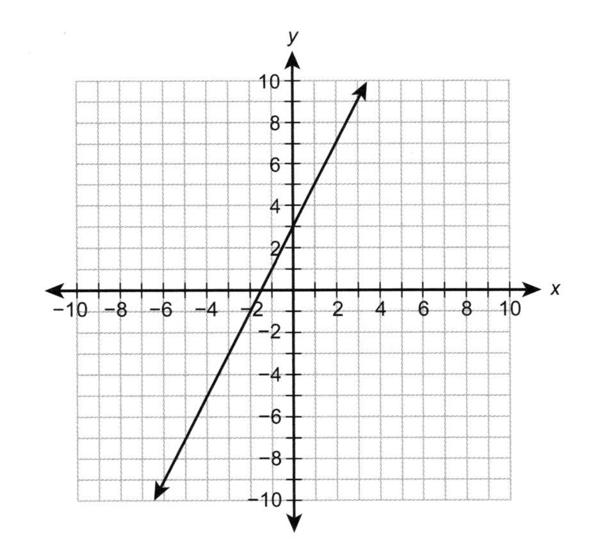

Function 2 $y = \frac{1}{3}x - 2$

SOLUTION

Begin by finding the slopes of both functions.

Function 1 Choose two points on the graph and substitute their coordinates into the slope formula.

$$m_1 = \frac{y_2 - y_1}{x_2 - x_1}$$

Let $(x_1, y_1) = (0, 3)$ and $(x_2, y_2) = (1, 5)$.

$$\begin{aligned} m_1 &= \frac{5 - 3}{1 - 0} \\ &= \frac{2}{1} \\ &= 2 \end{aligned}$$

Function 2 The function is written in slope-intercept form. From the equation, you can see that the slope, m_2, is $\frac{1}{3}$.

Since both functions have positive slopes, both functions are increasing. Now compare the absolute values of the slopes.

$$|m_1| = |2| = 2$$

$$|m_2| = \left|\frac{1}{3}\right| = \frac{1}{3}$$

Since $2 > \frac{1}{3}$, Function 1 is increasing at a faster rate than Function 2.

Therefore, Function 1 has the greater rate of change.

B **Function 1**

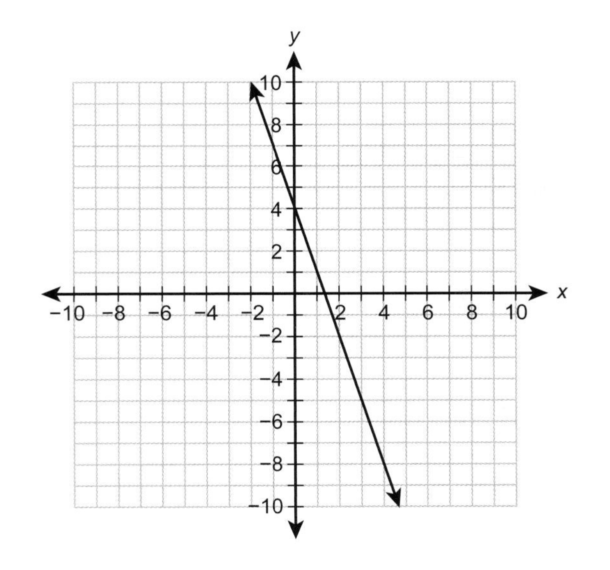

Function 2 $y = -x + 1$

SOLUTION

Begin by finding the slopes of both functions.

Function 1 Choose two points on the graph and substitute their coordinates into the slope formula.

$$m_1 = \frac{y_2 - y_1}{x_2 - x_1}$$

Let $(x_1, y_1) = (0, 4)$ and $(x_2, y_2) = (1, 1)$.

$$m_1 = \frac{1 - 4}{1 - 0}$$

$$= \frac{-3}{1}$$

$$= -3$$

Function 2 The function is written in slope-intercept form. From the equation, you can see that the slope, m_2, is -1.

Since both functions have negative slopes, both functions are decreasing. Compare the absolute values of the slopes.

$$|m_1| = |-3| = 3$$

$$|m_2| = |-1| = 1$$

Since $3 > 1$, Function 1 is decreasing at a faster rate than Function 2. Therefore, Function 1 has the greater rate of change. ■

▶ **Think About It** The line with the steeper slope has the greater rate of change. If you were to graph the line for Function 2 on the same coordinate plane as Function 1, you would see that Function 1 has a steeper slope than Function 2.

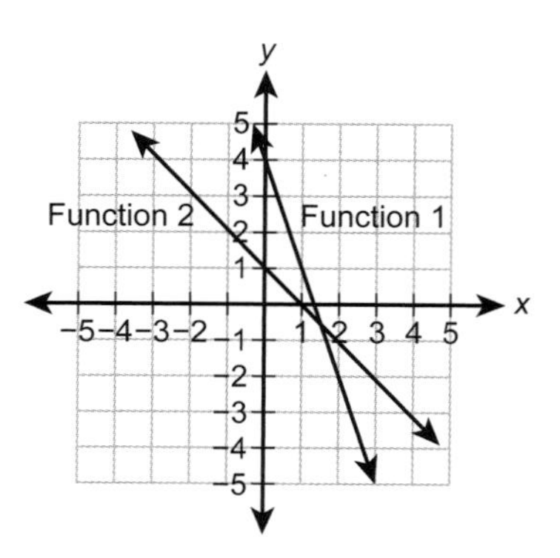

Comparing Functions in Real-World Situations

EXAMPLE 3

Tameka and Fontana are neighbors. Each summer they fill their swimming pools with water. Tameka thinks her pool fills at a faster rate than Fontana's. To make her point, Tameka kept a table showing the amount of water in her pool at the end of each of the first 4 h.

Hours	0	1	2	3	4
Gallons	500	570	640	710	780

Fontana also kept track of the amount of water in her pool at the end of each hour, but she chose to keep track of this information using an equation. She let g stand for the number of gallons in the pool and h stand for the number of hours.

$$g(h) = 60h + 420$$

A Whose pool filled at a faster rate?

SOLUTION

This question asks you to compare the rates of change of the functions. Therefore, compare their slopes. To find the rate of change for Tameka's pool, choose two ordered pairs (h, g) from the table and substitute their coordinates into the slope formula.

$$m_T = \frac{g_2 - g_1}{h_2 - h_1}$$

Let $(g_1, h_1) = (0, 500)$ and $(g_2, h_2) = (1, 570)$.

$$\begin{aligned} m_T &= \frac{570 - 500}{1 - 0} \\ &= \frac{70}{1} \\ &= 70 \end{aligned}$$

Tameka's pool fills at a rate of 70 gal/h.

To find the rate of change for Fontana's pool, look at the function equation. The equation is written in slope-intercept form. The slope, m_F, is 60. Therefore, Fontana's pool fills at a rate of 60 gal/h.

Since $|70| > |60|$, Tameka's pool fills at a faster rate.

B Both pools had some water in them before Fontana and Tameka began filling them. Whose pool had more water in it before it was filled?

SOLUTION

To answer this question, you must find the value of the functions when h is 0. From the table, you can see that there were 500 gal of water in Tameka's pool when h was 0. Therefore, Tameka's pool had 500 gal of water in it before she began filling it.

Now look at the function equation for Fontana's pool.

$$g(h) = 60h + 420$$

The value of $g(h)$ when h is 0 is the vertical intercept of the function. The vertical intercept is 420. Therefore, Fontana's pool had 420 gal of water in it before she began filling it. Since $500 > 420$, you can conclude that Tameka's pool had more water in it than Fontana's pool. ■

Functions in Real-World Situations

The behavior of a function graph can provide you with information about the real-world situation that the graph represents.

Interpreting the Behavior of Functions in Real-World Situations

The graph of a function can tell a story. When you interpret a function graph, look for some key features:

- axis labels
- intervals where the graph increases, decreases, or is constant
- horizontal and vertical intercepts

Then use these features to draw conclusions about the situation the graph models.

EXAMPLE 1

The graph shows the distance Ms. Wong traveled when she walked to the bus stop. Explain what Ms. Wong might be doing at each part of the graph.

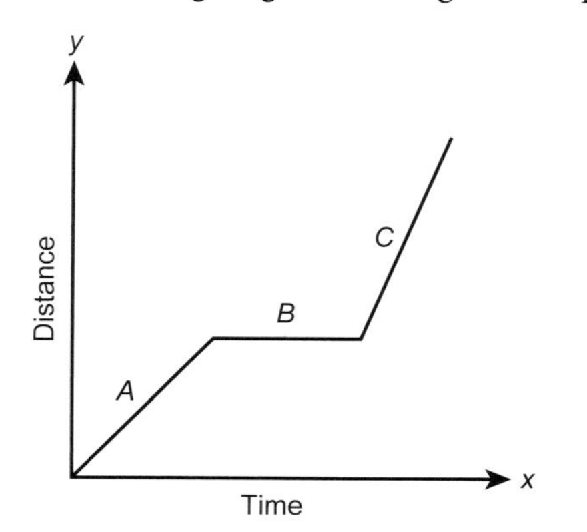

▶ **Think About It** You can draw conclusions about an object's speed by examining the slope of its distance-time graph. The steeper the slope of a distance/time graph, the faster the object is moving.

SOLUTION

In segment A, you can see that the graph is increasing, which means that the distance Ms. Wong walked is increasing. The fact that the line is straight and increasing tells you that she's walking at a constant rate.

In segment B, however, the graph is constant, which means that the distance Ms. Wong walked is neither increasing nor decreasing. Therefore, you can conclude that she stopped walking for a period of time.

In segment C, the graph is increasing again, which means Ms. Wong resumes walking at a constant rate to the bus stop. Notice that the graph in segment C is steeper than it is in segment A. This steeper slope tells you that Ms. Wong walked at a faster rate in segment C than she did in segment A. ■

It is very important to look at the labels of the axes when interpreting functions. Different labels can result in very different interpretations.

EXAMPLE 2

Graph A and Graph B look the same but represent different information. Graph A shows Matthew's distance from his starting position as a function of time. Graph B shows Carl's running speed as a function of time. Refer to the graphs to answer the question.

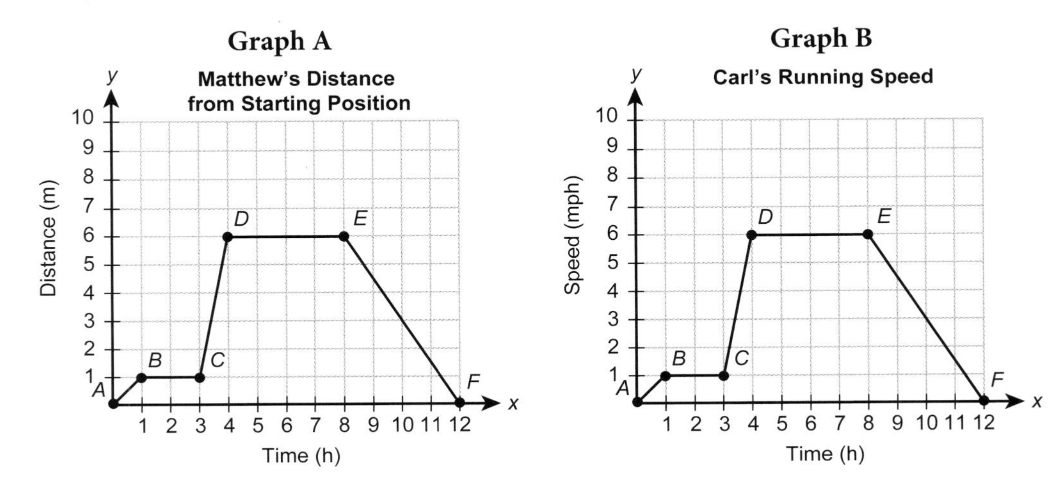

What is happening from point A to point C in the two graphs?

▸ Q&A

Q Since Matthew's graph is a distance-time graph, the slope tells you how fast Matthew is moving away from or toward his starting position. Carl's graph is a speed-time graph. What does the steepness of this graph tell you?

A The steepness of the graph tells you how quickly Carl is speeding up or slowing down.

SOLUTION

Matthew's graph displays his distance from his starting position over time. Point A is his starting position. From point A to point B, the function is increasing, so his distance is increasing. Therefore, he is moving away from his starting position at a constant rate. From point B to point C, the function is constant, so his distance is neither increasing nor decreasing. Therefore, he isn't moving any farther from or any closer to his starting position, which means he has stopped.

Carl's graph displays his speed over time. At point A, Carl's speed is 0 mph, so he is stopped. From point A to point B, the function is increasing, so his speed is increasing. From point B to point C, the function is constant, so his speed is neither increasing nor decreasing. Therefore, he's running at a constant speed. ■

Sketching Function Graphs

You can sketch a function graph to model a real-world situation. Verbal descriptions can tell you where the function increases or decreases and changes rate.

Sketching Graphs from Words

EXAMPLE 1

Avani drove her car at a constant rate to the train station. At the train station, she waited for the train to arrive. After she boarded the train, she traveled at a constant rate, faster than she drove her car. At the next stop, she got off the train and waited for a taxi. She entered the taxi and traveled at a constant speed. This speed was equal to the speed at which she had driven her car earlier. After some time, she arrived at her destination. Sketch a graph that models the distance Avani traveled.

SOLUTION

Break the story down into segments, and graph each segment.

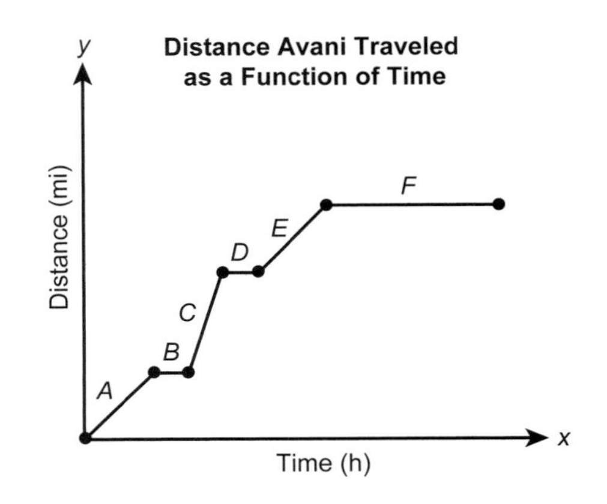

A *Avani drove her car at a constant rate to the train station.*
Avani's distance traveled increased at a constant rate, so draw a straight line with a positive slope.

B *At the train station, she waited for the train to arrive.*
Avani stopped traveling, so draw a horizontal line segment to show that her distance traveled remained constant.

C *After she boarded the train, she traveled at a constant rate, faster than she drove her car.*
Avani's distance traveled increased at a constant rate. This rate was faster than the rate in segment A, so draw a line segment with a steeper slope than the line in segment A.

***D** At the next stop, she got off the train and waited for a taxi.*
Avani stopped traveling, so draw a horizontal line segment.

***E** She entered the taxi and traveled at a constant speed. This speed was equal to the speed at which she had driven her car earlier.*
Avani's distance traveled increased at a constant rate equal to her rate in segment A, so draw a line segment with the same slope as the segment you drew for segment A.

***F** After some time, she arrived at her destination.*
Avani stopped traveling, so draw a horizontal line. ■

EXAMPLE 2

Emilio rides his bike at a constant rate from his house to the baseball field. On his way, he passes the bagel shop and the post office.

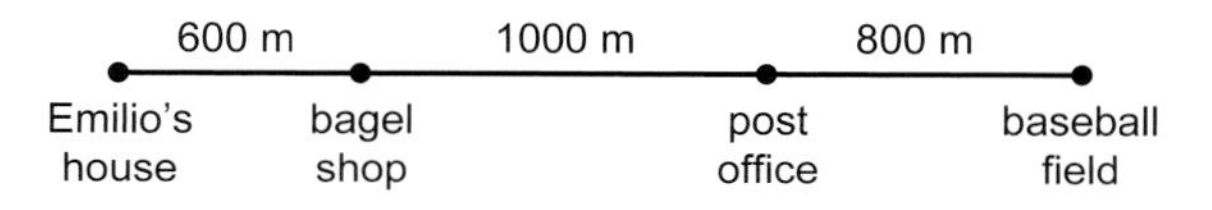

A Sketch a graph of the distance between Emilio and his house as a function of time.

SOLUTION
For this situation, the vertical axis represents the distance Emilio travels away from his house, and the horizontal axis represents time. Emilio's starting location is his house, which you model with the point $(0, 0)$.

Emilio moves away from his house at a constant speed. The total distance he travels is $600 + 1000 + 800 = 2400$ m. Draw a straight line with a positive slope until you reach 2400 along the vertical axis.

At the baseball field, Emilio's distance from home becomes constant. Draw a horizontal line segment to show that his distance from home is constant.

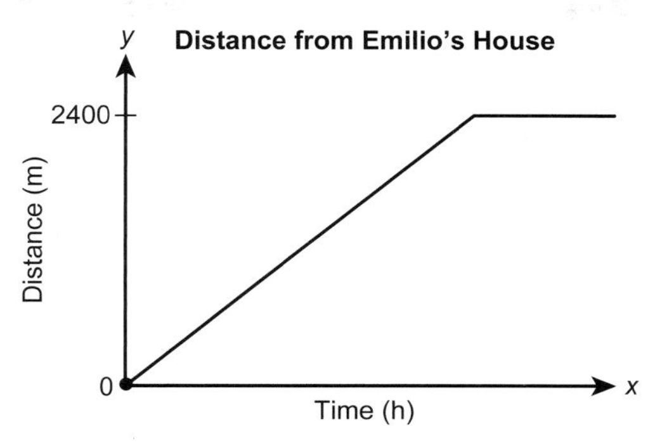

B Sketch a graph of the distance between Emilio and the baseball field as a function of time.

SOLUTION

For this situation, the vertical axis represents Emilio's distance from the baseball field. Emilio begins his trip from home, which is 2400 m away from the baseball field. Therefore, your graph should begin at the point $(0, 2400)$.

Emilio moves toward the baseball field at a constant speed. Therefore, his distance from the baseball field decreases at a constant rate until he reaches the field. When he reaches the field, his distance from the field is 0 m. Draw a line with negative slope until it intersects the horizontal axis.

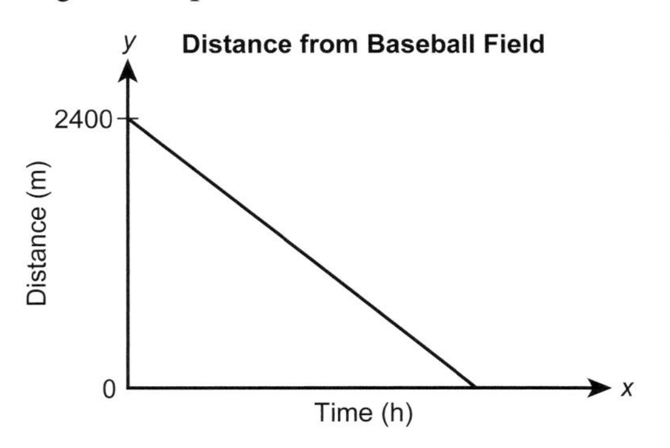

C Sketch a graph of the distance between Emilio and the bagel shop as a function of time.

SOLUTION

For this situation, the vertical axis represents Emilio's distance from the bagel shop. Emilio's house is 600 m from the bagel shop, so his starting position is $(0, 600)$.

Once he leaves his house, his distance from the bagel shop decreases at a constant rate until he reaches the shop. At the moment he passes the shop, his distance from the shop is 0 m. Draw a line with a negative slope until it intersects the horizontal axis.

Once Emilio passes the bagel shop, his distance from the shop increases at a constant rate. To show that his distance is increasing, draw a line with a positive slope. The distance from the bagel shop to the baseball field is $1000 + 800$, or 1800 m. Therefore, this line should extend until it reaches 1800 along the vertical axis.

Emilio stops riding his bike when he reaches the baseball field. Draw a horizontal line to show that his distance from the bagel shop becomes constant.

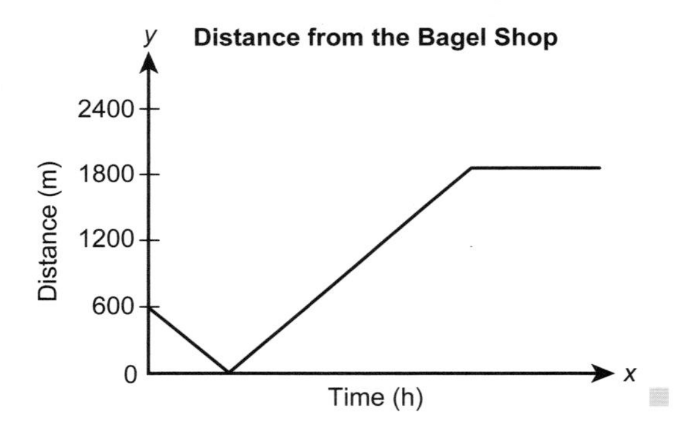

Linear Data Models

Topic List

- Patterns in Two-Way Tables
- Scatter Plots
- Clusters and Outliers
- Associations in Scatter Plots
- Fitting a Line to Data
- Interpreting Slopes and Intercepts

The distance a plane can travel relates to the amount of fuel it has. Travel time relates to distance. A pilot's years of experience relates to salary. A linear model can help you see relationships between pairs of data sets and enable you to make predictions and decisions.

Patterns in Two-Way Tables

Two-way tables can be used to summarize categorical data.

Creating a Two-Way Table

Definitions

A **categorical variable** is a variable that has two or more categories.

A **two-way table** is a frequency table for two categorical variables.

Each entry in a two-way table is a frequency. To create a two-way table, count the number of times the variable categories pair.

▸ **Think About It** Categorical data are data that can be broken down into separate categories.

EXAMPLE 1

A poll asked 20 sixth and seventh grade students whether they play on a sports team. The results of the poll are shown in the table. Create a two-way table of the data.

▸ **Remember** A frequency table is used to keep track of data counts.

Person	Grade	Plays on a team?
1	6	Yes
2	7	Yes
3	6	Yes
4	7	Yes
5	7	No
6	6	No
7	6	Yes
8	7	Yes
9	7	Yes
10	7	Yes
11	6	No
12	6	No
13	6	Yes
14	6	Yes
15	7	Yes
16	6	No
17	7	No
18	6	Yes
19	6	No
20	7	Yes

SOLUTION

Two variables are represented in this table. One represents grade level and the other represents team membership. Each variable is broken into two categories. The grade-level categories are grade 6 and grade 7. The categories for team membership are Yes (the student plays on a team) or No (the student does not play on a team).

To set up a two-way table, list the categories of one variable horizontally across the top of the table, and list the categories of the other variable vertically along the left side of the table. Then count the number of times categories pair and record the totals in the table.

There are 6 students who are in grade 6 and play on a team, and there are 7 students who are in grade 7 and play on a team. There are 5 students in grade 6 who do not play on a sports team, and there are 2 students in grade 7 who do not play on a sports team.

	On a team	Not on a team
Grade 6	6	5
Grade 7	7	2

Think About It To confirm that you counted every data item, add the values from all the cells. In this case, the sum of the values is

$$6 + 5 + 7 + 2 = 20,$$

which equals the number of students surveyed.

Interpreting Two-Way Tables

Definition

A **two-way relative frequency table** is a table that shows the relative frequencies of each data value in a two-way table.

You can create a two-way relative frequency table from any two-way table. Two-way relative frequency tables allow you to study the relationships between categorical variables.

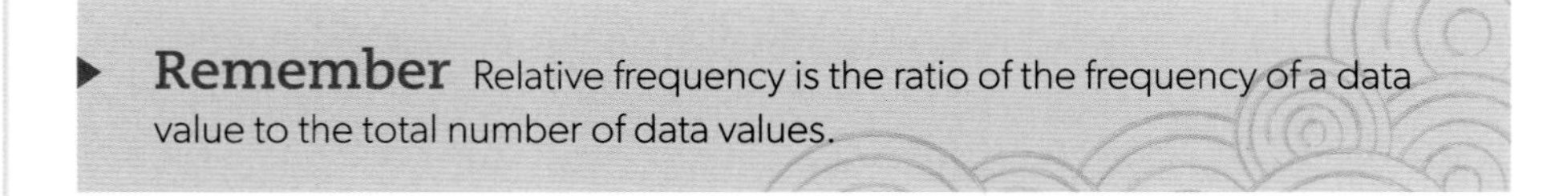

Remember Relative frequency is the ratio of the frequency of a data value to the total number of data values.

EXAMPLE 2

Twenty people who own either a cat or a dog (but not both) were asked whether they live in an apartment or in a townhouse. The responses are listed in the table.

	Cat	Dog
Apartment	5	3
Townhouse	6	6

A Of the people polled, how many live in an apartment and how many live in a townhouse?

SOLUTION

Add across the row labeled Apartment.

$$5 + 3 = 8$$

Eight people who live in an apartment were polled.

Add across the row labeled Townhouse.

$$6 + 6 = 12$$

Twelve people who live in a townhouse were polled.

B Create a two-way relative frequency table that displays the proportion of people living in an apartment or a townhouse who own a cat or a dog.

SOLUTION

For this problem, find the relative frequencies for each row of the two-way table. Divide each entry in the table by the total of its row.

	Cat	Dog
Apartment	$\frac{5}{8} = 0.625$	$\frac{3}{8} = 0.375$
Townhouse	$\frac{6}{12} = 0.5$	$\frac{6}{12} = 0.5$

▶ **Think About It** You can find relative frequencies for the columns, as well as the rows, of a two-way table. The relative frequencies for the columns of the two-way table in Example 2 are found by dividing each table entry by its corresponding column total.

C What proportion of people living in an apartment own only a cat, and what proportion of people living in a townhouse own only a cat?

SOLUTION

Express the relative frequencies as percentages.

Of people who live in an apartment, 62.5% own a cat.

Of people who live in a townhouse, 50% own a cat.

D Based on the data, do you think there's an association between type of housing and choice of pet?

SOLUTION

There appears to be some association between type of housing and choice of pet. A higher percentage of people living in an apartment own a cat than of people living in a townhouse. Also, a higher percentage of people living in a townhouse own a dog than of people living in an apartment.

EXAMPLE 3

Fifty people were asked where they prefer to swim as well as whether they prefer to travel by car or by plane. The results of the survey are summarized in the two-way table.

	Ocean	Pool	Lake
Car	9	12	6
Plane	8	13	2

A How many people prefer to swim in the ocean? In a pool? In a lake?

SOLUTION

Add down each column.

$$9 + 8 = 17$$

Seventeen people prefer to swim in the ocean.

$$12 + 13 = 25$$

Twenty-five people prefer to swim in a pool.

$$6 + 2 = 8$$

Eight people prefer to swim in a lake.

B Create a two-way table that displays the proportion of people preferring to swim in the ocean, a pool, or a lake who would rather travel by car or by plane.

SOLUTION

For this problem, find the relative frequencies of the columns of the two-way table. Divide each entry in the table by its column's total.

	Ocean	Pool	Lake
Car	$\frac{9}{17} \approx 0.53$	$\frac{12}{25} = 0.48$	$\frac{6}{8} = 0.75$
Plane	$\frac{8}{17} = 0.47$	$\frac{13}{25} = 0.52$	$\frac{2}{8} = 0.25$

C Based on the data, do you think there is an association between preferred swimming location and preferred mode of transportation?

SOLUTION

There appears to be some association between preferred swimming location and preferred mode of transportation. A higher percentage of people who prefer to swim in a lake prefer to travel by car than of those who prefer to swim in the ocean or a pool. Also, a higher percentage of people who prefer to swim in a pool prefer to travel by plane than of those who prefer to swim in the ocean or a lake. ■

Scatter Plots

Scatter plots are used to display two-dimensional data.

Definition

A **scatter plot** is a graph that displays data as points.

Creating Scatter Plots

To create a scatter plot, graph points as you would on the coordinate plane. Label the horizontal axis with one variable and the vertical axis with the other variable. Be sure to consider appropriate scales for both axes.

How do sales and income tax rates compare to each other across several states? How do populous states compare to lower population states in terms of sales and income tax rates? A scatter plot is a good way to compare.

The table shows sales tax rates and highest income tax rates (in 2010) for a sample of low-population states (fewer than 1 million residents).

2010 Tax Rates for Low-Population States

State	SD	VT	ND	AK	WY	DE	MT	RI	NH	ME
Highest income tax rate (%)	0	9	4.9	7	0	7	6.9	9.9	5	6.9
Sales tax rate (%)	4	6	5	6	4	0	0	7	0	5

Tax Foundation 2015a, b

Sales tax rates range from 0% to 9.9%, while highest income tax rates range from 0% to 7%. Therefore, it makes sense to have a range of 0 to 8 for the vertical axis, and 0 to 11 for the horizontal axis.

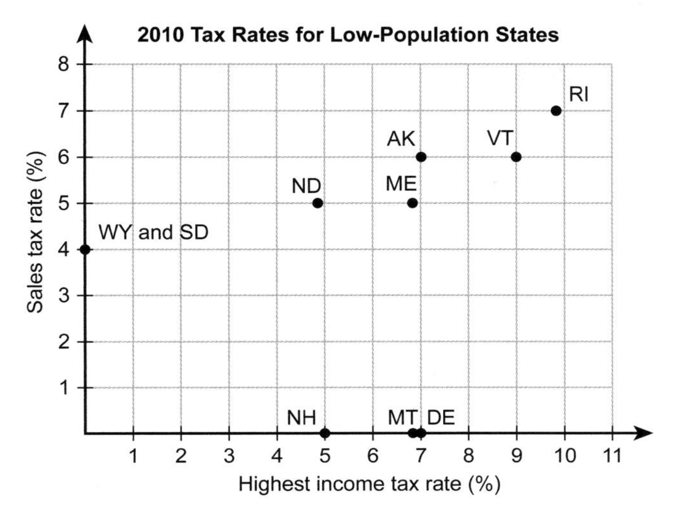

EXAMPLE 1

Use the data table relating the hours Travis worked to the tips he earned to create a scatter plot.

Hours Travis worked in the summer	30	13	5	35	25	38	17	20	22	8
Money earned as tips ($)	248	135	30	280	175	342	136	198	132	64

SOLUTION

Identify the variables. Label the axes and choose appropriate scales. Then graph the points.

The money Travis earned as tips depends on the hours he worked. Therefore, label the x-axis "Time worked (h)," and label the y-axis "Tips earned ($)."

The number of hours Travis worked ranges from 5 to 38, so it's appropriate to make the range of the x-axis 0 to 40 with a scale of 5. The amount of money Travis earned as tips ranges from \$30 to \$342, so it makes sense to set the range of the y-axis from 0 to 400 with a scale of 50.

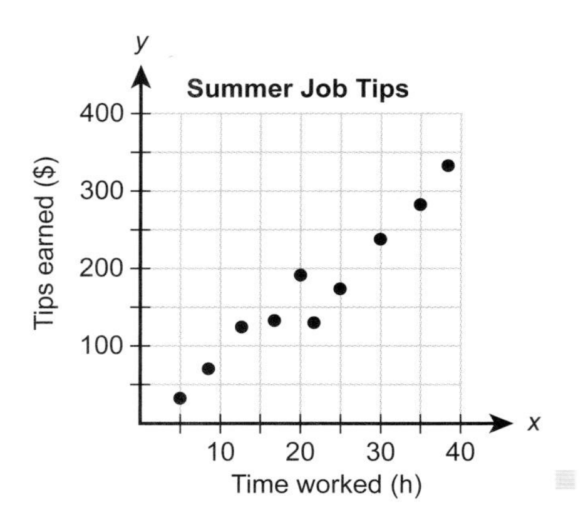

Finding Patterns in the Points

Scatter plots can show patterns in data. In some scatter plots, the points appear to follow a line upward or downward. In other scatter plots, the points seem to follow a curve. Sometimes the points seem to follow no pattern at all.

EXAMPLE 2

Do the points in the scatter plots appear to follow a pattern? If so, what kind of pattern?

A

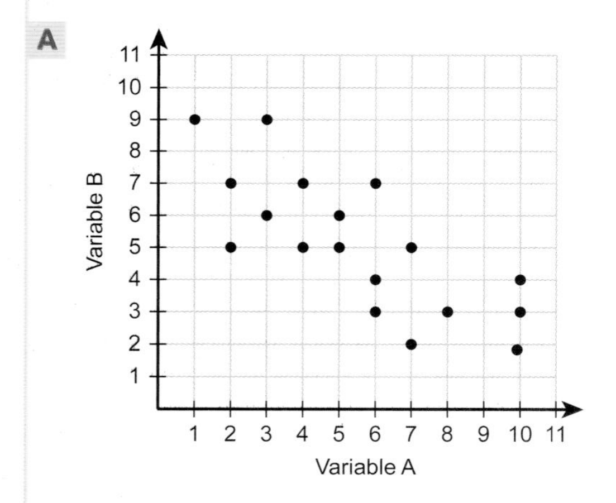

SOLUTION

The points appear to follow a line with a negative slope.

B

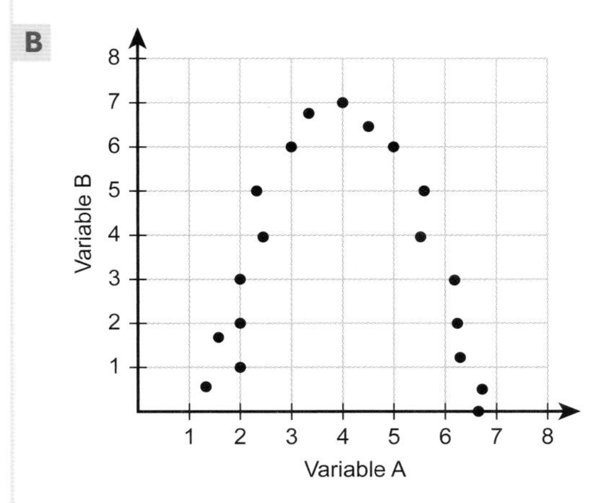

SOLUTION

The points appear to follow an upside-down U-shaped curve.

C

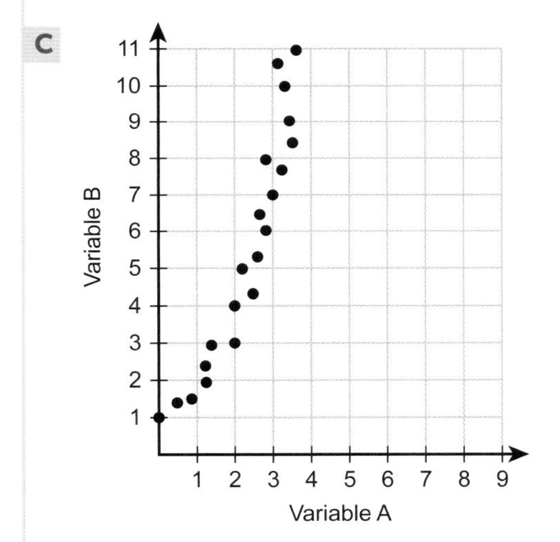

SOLUTION

The points appear to follow an upward curve.

D

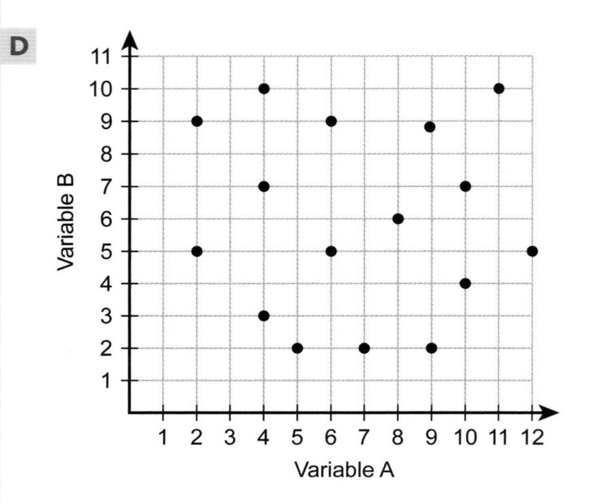

SOLUTION

The points appear to follow no pattern at all.

Interpreting Scatter Plots

You can use scatter plots to gather information about data.

EXAMPLE 3

Refer to the scatter plot.

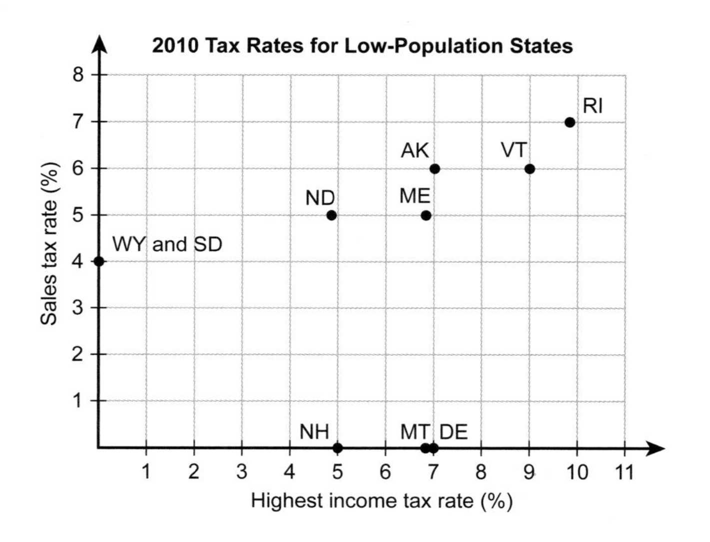

A What was the median of the sales tax rates for low-population states in 2010?

SOLUTION

The y-coordinates of the points are the sales tax rates for the states. List the tax rates from least to greatest. Then find the middle rate.

$$0, 0, 0, 4, 4, 5, 5, 6, 6, 7$$

The middle rate is 4. Therefore, the median of the sales tax rates for low-population states in 2010 was 4%.

B What was the mean highest income tax rate for low-population states in 2010?

SOLUTION

There are 10 data points. The x-coordinates of the points are the highest income tax rates for the states. Add the sales tax rates, and divide the sum by 10.

$$\frac{0 + 0 + 4.9 + 5 + 6.9 + 6.9 + 7 + 7 + 9 + 9.9}{10} \approx 5.7$$

The mean sales tax rate was about 5.7%. ■

Clusters and Outliers

Scatter plots help you identify data clusters and outliers.

Identifying Clusters and Outliers

Definitions

An **outlier** is a point that is far from other data points.

A **cluster** is a group of points that are close together in comparison to other points.

A scatter plot makes it easier to identify patterns that a table alone can't reveal. For example, the scatter plot shows that Texas and Florida have close to the same sales tax rate and no income tax (as of the tax year 2010). It also shows that California is an outlier, with greater sales tax and higher income tax rates than any other state in the sample for 2010.

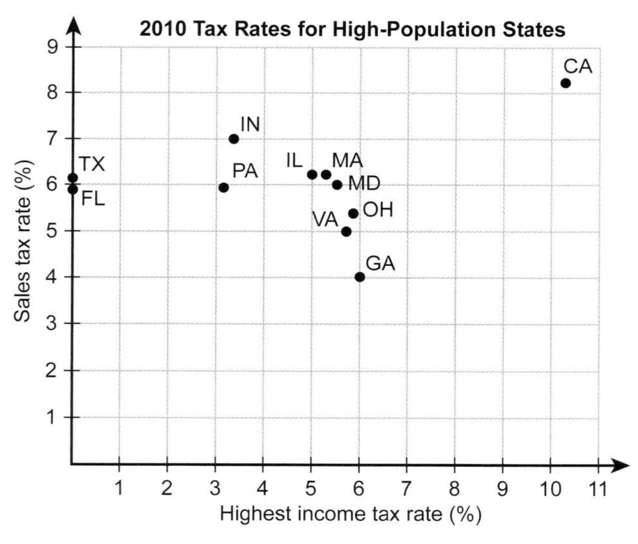

Tax Foundation 2015a, b

▶ **Think About It** In clusters, data points have many neighbors. In contrast, outliers are data points that have few or no neighbors.

In the scatter plot, there is a grouping of six states (Illinois, Massachusetts, Maryland, Ohio, Virginia, and Georgia) where sales tax rates and highest income tax rates are similar. This grouping, which is revealed clearly in the scatter plot, is an example of a cluster.

EXAMPLE 1

The scatter plot shows blood pressure vs. the height of an animal's head above its heart.

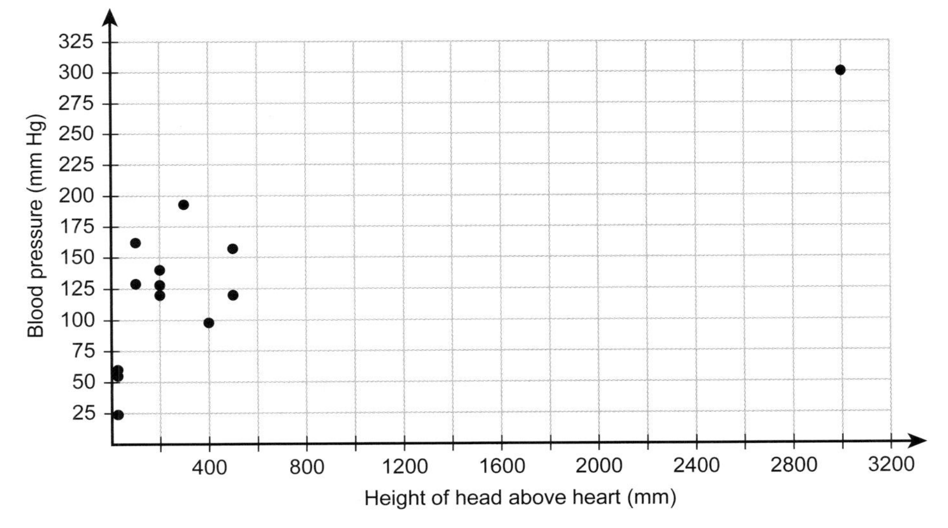

Watkins 2014

▶ **Think About It** The abbreviation mm Hg stands for millimeters of mercury.

A What head height above heart is a possible outlier? How can you tell? What is the blood pressure of the animal with this head height?

SOLUTION

The head height of 3000 mm above the heart is a possible outlier. You can tell that this point is an outlier because it is not near any other point in the graph. The blood pressure for the animal with this head height is 300 mm Hg.

B For what range of head heights do you find a cluster? What is the approximate range in blood pressure for these head heights?

SOLUTION

There is a cluster for head heights ranging from 0 to about 500 mm above the heart. Blood pressure for these head heights ranges from about 24 to 198 mm Hg. ■

Identifying Outliers in a Table

An outlier is a data point that doesn't appear to follow the same pattern as the rest of the data. Its value is either much larger or much smaller than the other values. Sometimes you can identify an outlier from a table of data.

EXAMPLE 2

Consider the data in the table. Which data point is the outlier?

x	−5	−4	−3	−2	−1	0	1	2	3	4	5
y	−9.1	−7.4	−4.9	8	−0.9	0.8	3.2	6	7.4	8.6	11.2

SOLUTION

As the x-coordinates increase by 1, the y-coordinates increase by a value of about 1 to 3. However, from $x = -3$ to $x = -2$, the y-coordinate increases by 12.9, from -4.9 to 8. Therefore, the point $(-2, 8)$ is an outlier. You can verify this by creating a scatter plot.

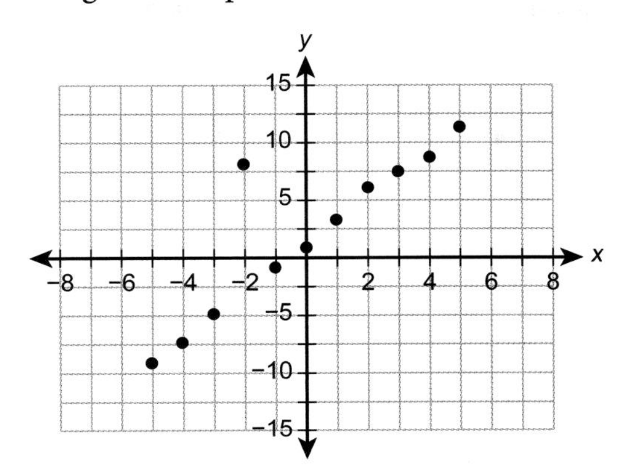

Notice that the point $(-2, 8)$ is not near the rest of the data points and does not follow the same pattern.

Associations in Scatter Plots

The points on scatter plots often display noticeable patterns.

Definitions

A scatter plot shows a **positive association** when the points increase from left to right.

A scatter plot shows a **negative association** when the points decrease from left to right.

Determining Direction of Association

The scatter plot shows the average price for a gallon of gasoline in nine different states in mid-May 2010 and mid-May 2011. Looking at the scatter plot, you can see a trend in the relationship between these two variables: The greater the average price of gas in mid-May 2010, the greater the average price of gas in mid-May 2011.

This scatter plot shows a positive association, where the points in a scatter plot increase from left to right.

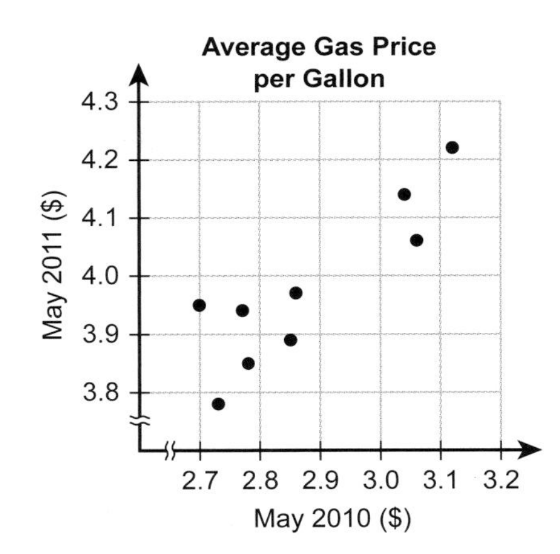

This scatter plot shows average gas price per gallon and average number of miles driven per day. It also shows another trend: As average gas prices increase, the average number of miles driven per day decreases. This scatter plot shows a negative association, where points in a scatter plot decrease from left to right.

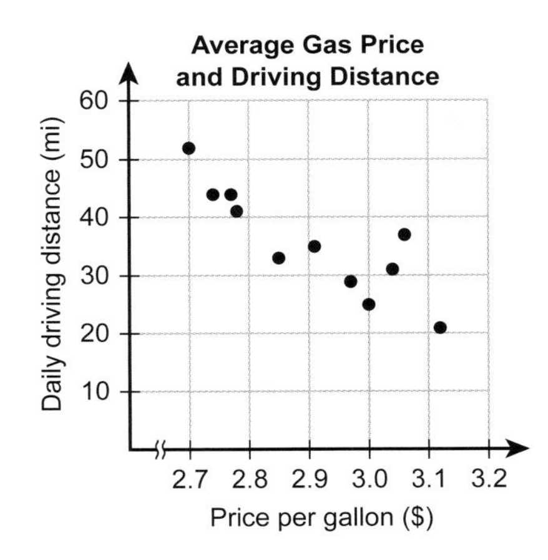

Definition

A scatter plot shows **no association** when the points show no pattern of increase or decrease from left to right.

This scatter plot shows student shoe sizes and test scores. Notice that the points do not demonstrate any recognizable pattern. Test scores do not appear to go up or down as shoe size increases. This scatter plot shows no association.

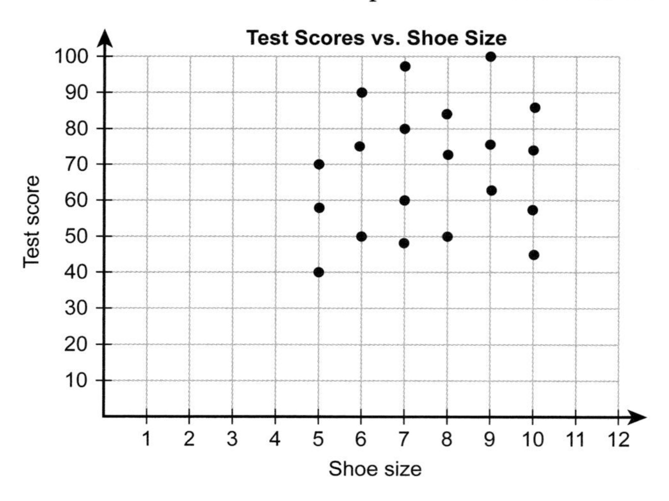

> ▶ **Think About It** Consider the variable *amount of time studying*. Can you think of a variable that would be positively associated with this variable?

Identifying Linear or Nonlinear Association

Definitions

A scatter plot shows a **linear association** when the points follow a pattern that resembles a line.

A scatter plot shows a **nonlinear association** when the points follow a pattern that does not resemble a line.

The pattern of the points in a scatter plot can take on different shapes. Patterns that resemble a line show a linear association. Patterns that resemble a curve show a nonlinear association.

EXAMPLE 1

State whether the scatter plot shows a positive linear association, a positive nonlinear association, a negative linear association, or a negative nonlinear association.

A

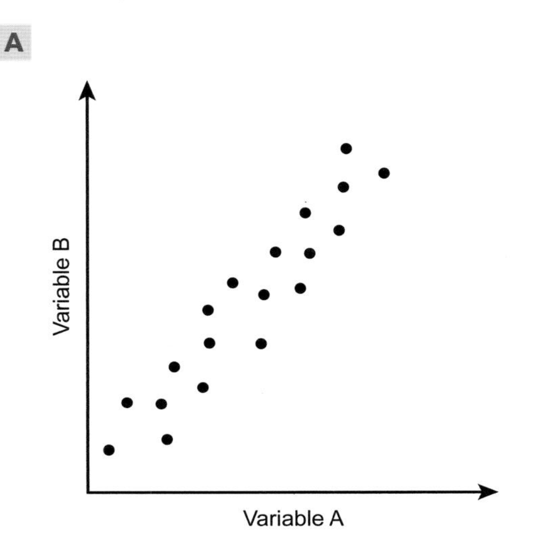

SOLUTION

The scatter plot shows a positive linear association.

B

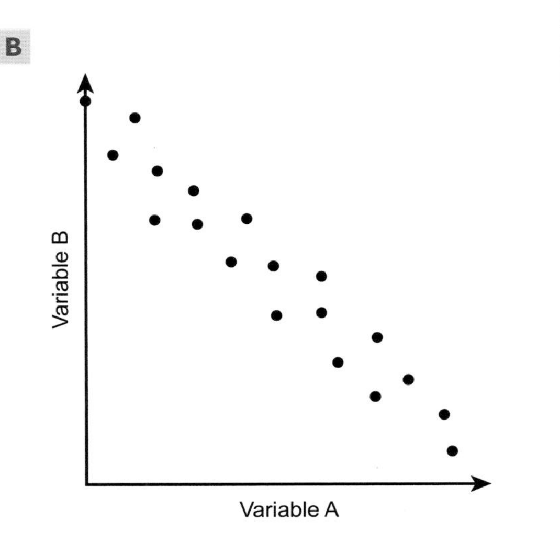

SOLUTION

The scatter plot shows a negative linear association.

C

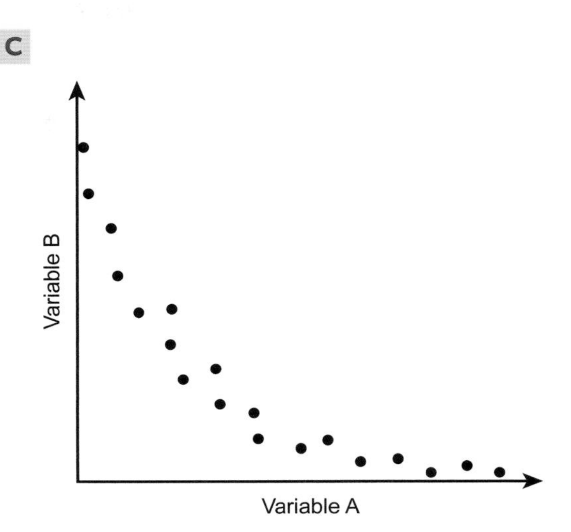

SOLUTION

The scatter plot shows a negative nonlinear association.

D

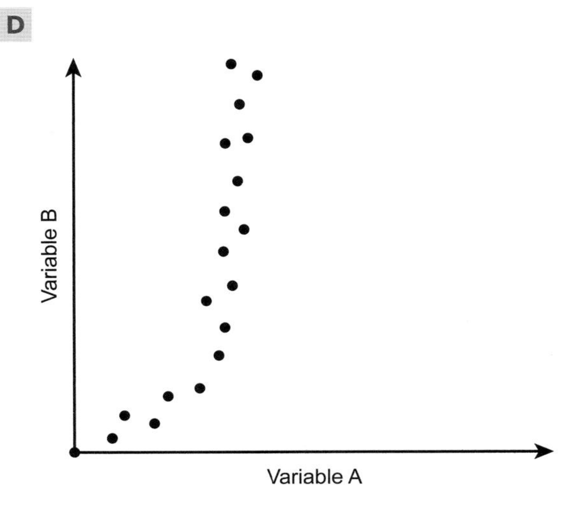

SOLUTION

The scatter plot shows a positive nonlinear association.

Determining Association from Data

When given a set of data presented in a table or as a set of ordered pairs, you can use a scatter plot to determine whether the data show a positive or a negative linear or nonlinear association.

EXAMPLE 2

Determine whether the set of data shows a positive linear association, a positive nonlinear association, a negative linear association, or a negative nonlinear association.

A

Years since 1790	0	10	20	30	40	50	60	70
New Jersey population (in ten thousands)	1.84	2.11	2.46	2.78	3.21	3.73	4.90	6.72

Wu 2010

SOLUTION

Create a scatter plot of the data. Let the horizontal axis represent the number of years since 1790, and let the vertical axis represent the state's population in ten thousands.

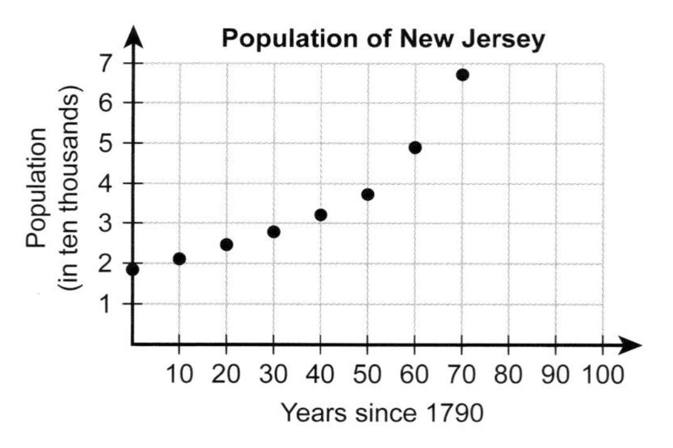

The points increase from left to right in a curved pattern. Therefore, the data show a positive nonlinear association between state population and number of years since 1790.

B The ordered pairs list the average weight and life spans of different breeds of dogs. The x-coordinate is average weight, in pounds, and the y-coordinate is average life span, in years.

$\{(50, 11), (24, 12), (85, 10), (70, 12), (155, 7), (55, 12), (31, 12), (14, 14), (20, 13), (110, 9)\}$

SOLUTION

Create a scatter plot of the data. Let the horizontal axis represent weight in pounds, and let the vertical axis represent life span in years.

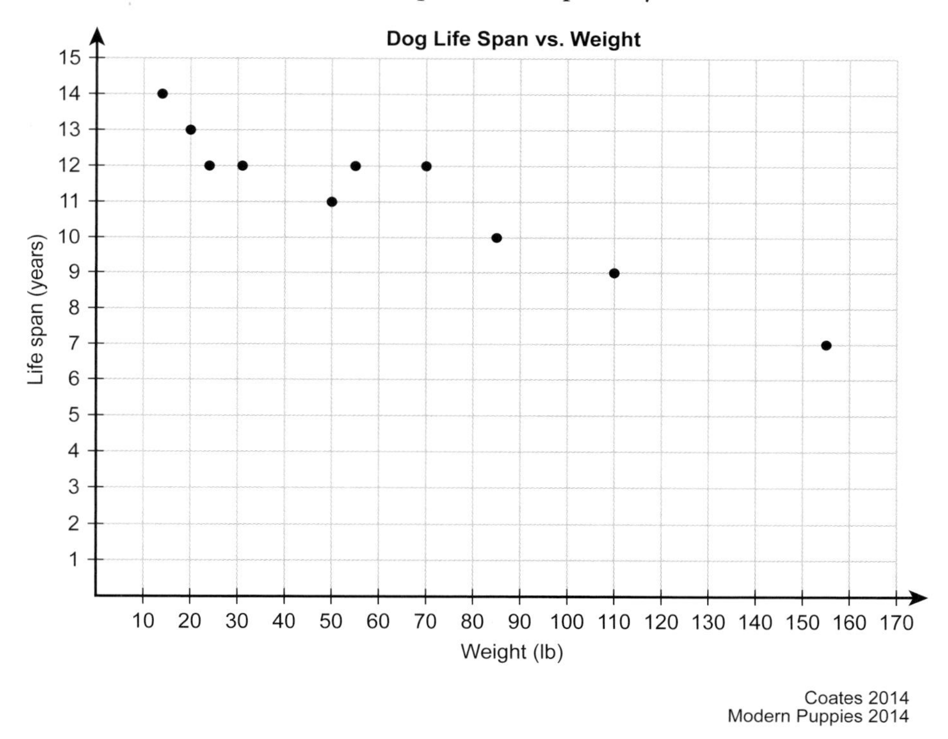

As the weight of a dog increases, its life span appears to decrease in a linear pattern. Therefore, the data show a negative linear association between a dog's life span and its weight.

Fitting a Line to Data

A line can be used to summarize a linear trend in a scatter plot.

Drawing a Line to Model a Set of Data

When a scatter plot shows a linear association, the data points can be modeled with a line. If the scatter plot shows a positive association, the line will have a positive slope. If the scatter plot shows a negative association, the line will have a negative slope.

EXAMPLE 1

The table gives the maximum amount of time allotted for boys to complete the shuttle run to qualify for the Presidential Physical Fitness Award. Create a scatter plot of the data. Then draw a line that does a good job of modeling the data.

Age (years)	6	7	8	9	10	11	12
Time (s)	12.1	11.5	11.1	10.9	10.3	10.0	9.8

The President's Challenge 2014

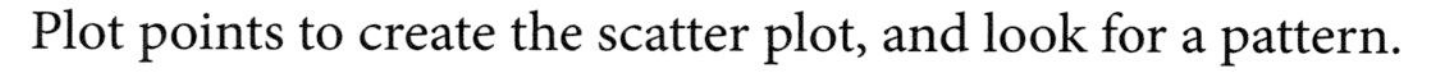

SOLUTION

Plot points to create the scatter plot, and look for a pattern.

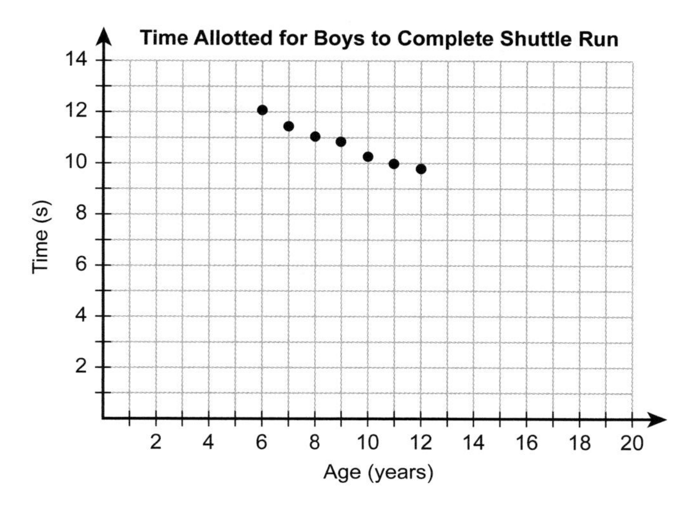

The points show a negative correlation. Therefore, you can use a line with a negative slope to model the data.

To draw a line that fits the data well, sketch the line so that about half of the points lie above the line and half lie below the line.

▶ **Think About It** It's good if two or more of the data points are on the line, but this is not absolutely necessary.

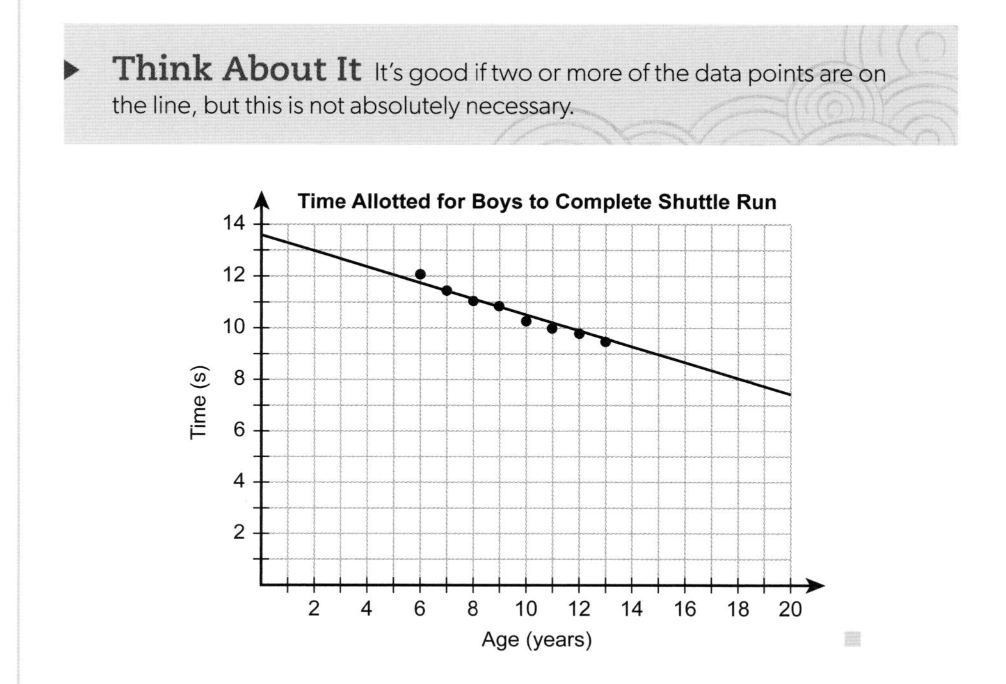

▶ **Think About It** There may be more than one line that appears to model the data. Choose the line that seems to fit the data most closely.

Assessing the Fit and Finding the Equation of a Line

The closer the points are to the linear model, the better the line models the data. When the data are close to a model, the model has good fit. A model with good fit does a good job of representing the relationship between the two sets of data. For example, the line in Graph A is a better fit for the data than the line in Graph B because the points in Graph A lie closer to the line than do the points in Graph B.

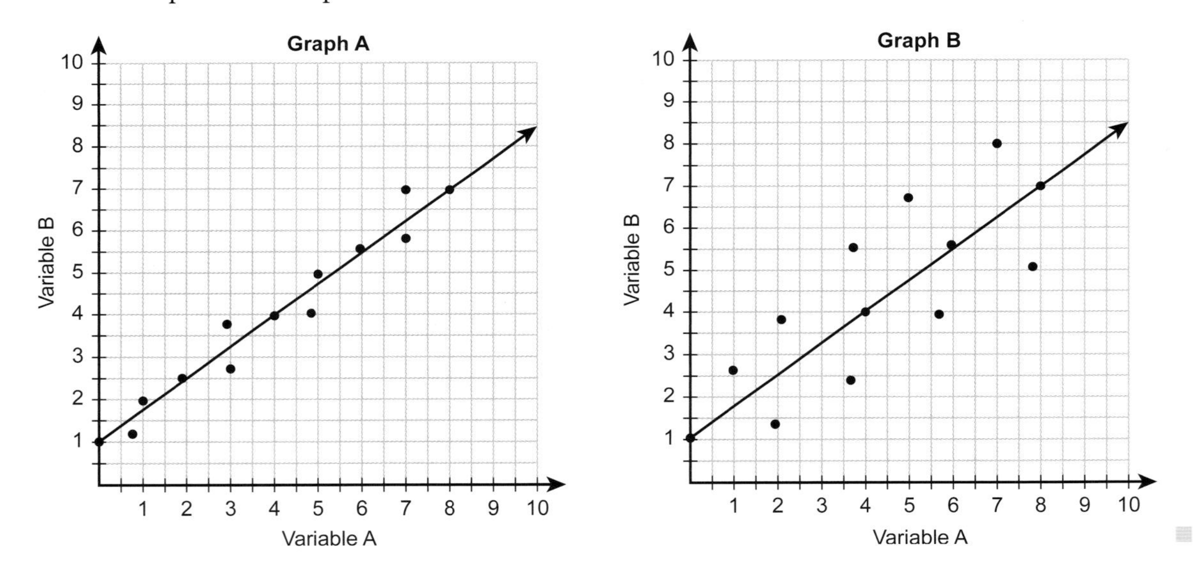

EXAMPLE 2

The scatter plot shows the minimum number of curl-ups that girls must complete to qualify for the Presidential Physical Fitness Award.

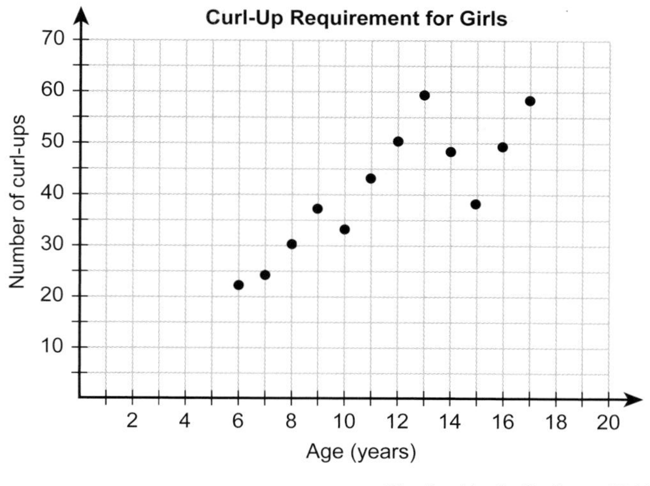

The President's Challenge 2014

A Draw a line that fits the data well.

SOLUTION

Sketch a line so that about half of the points lie above and about half of the points lie below the line.

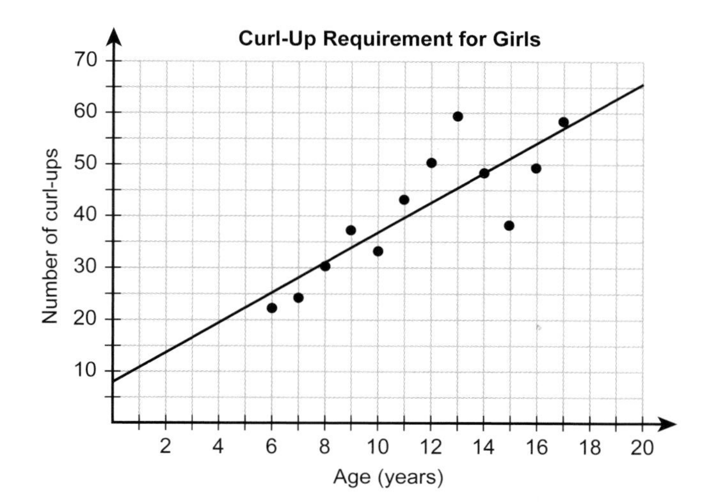

B How well does the line fit the data?

SOLUTION

From age 6 to 11, the points lie very close to the line. From age 12 to 16, some of the points are more spread out from the line. In general, the line describes the trend of the data points, so the line is a fairly good fit for the data. ■

When a scatter plot can be modeled by a line, you can write a linear function model of the data.

EXAMPLE 3

The table shows the number of automobiles sold in selected years at Harold's Car Emporium.

Years since opening business	2	5	7	8	11	12	15	20
Auto sales per year (units of 10)	14	22	21	24	35	34	38	55

A Create a scatter plot of the data.

SOLUTION

Plot points to create the scatter plot.

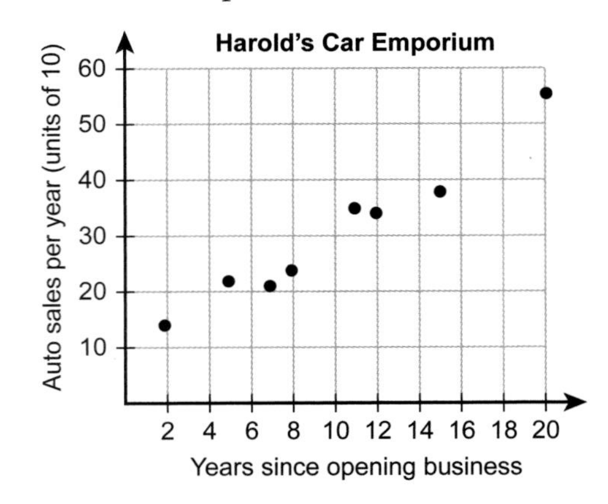

B Draw a line that models the relationship.

SOLUTION

Sketch a line so that about half of the points lie above and about half of the points lie below the line. If possible, let the line pass through at least two data points.

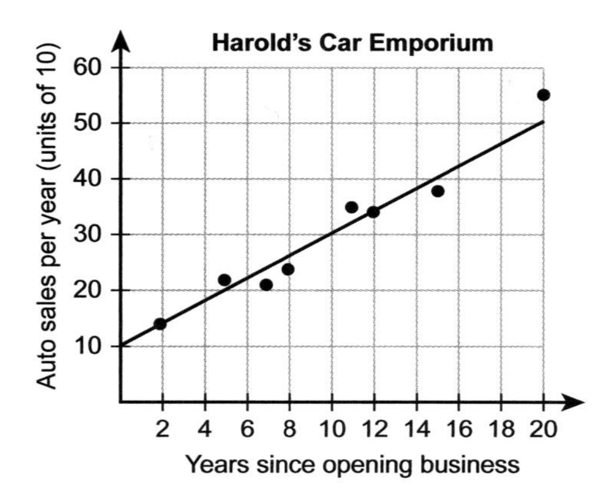

C Find the equation of the linear model.

SOLUTION

The linear model passes through two data points, $(2, 14)$ and $(12, 34)$. Use these points to find the slope of the line.

$$m = \frac{y_2 - y_1}{x_2 - x_1}$$

$$= \frac{34 - 14}{12 - 2} \qquad \text{Let } (x_1, y_1) = (2, 14) \text{ and } (x_2, y_2) = (12, 34).$$

$$= \frac{20}{10}$$

$$= 2$$

Substitute the slope and one of the points into the point-slope form of the equation of a line. Then solve for y to write the equation in $y = mx + b$ form.

$$y - y_1 = m(x - x_1)$$

$$y - 14 = 2(x - 2) \qquad \text{Let } m = 2 \text{ and } (x_1, y_1) = (2, 14).$$

$$y - 14 = 2x - 4$$

$$y - 14 + 14 = 2x - 4 + 14$$

$$y = 2x + 10$$

D Using the equation of the linear model, about how many auto sales did Harold's Car Emporium have in its tenth year of business?

SOLUTION

Let $x = 10$, and solve for y.

$$\begin{aligned} y &= 2x + 10 \\ &= 2 \bullet 10 + 10 \\ &= 20 + 10 \\ &= 30 \end{aligned}$$

The y-coordinates are in units of 10, so Harold's probably had about $30 \bullet 10$, or 300 auto sales in its tenth year of business. ■

Interpreting Slopes and Intercepts

Some data can be modeled with a linear function. The slope and y-intercept of the line provide information about the rate and initial value of the model.

Drawing Conclusions from Linear Models

In general, when you write the equation for a linear model, you write the equation in slope-intercept form. In any linear model, the slope is a rate and the y-intercept is the initial value of the function. You can interpret the slope and the y-intercept within the context of the situation that the equation represents.

EXAMPLE

Emily researched the average prices of desktop computers worldwide since 2000. She could only find data from 2005 to 2010. She created a scatter plot of the data and drew a linear model. The equation for the line is $y = -39x + 988$.

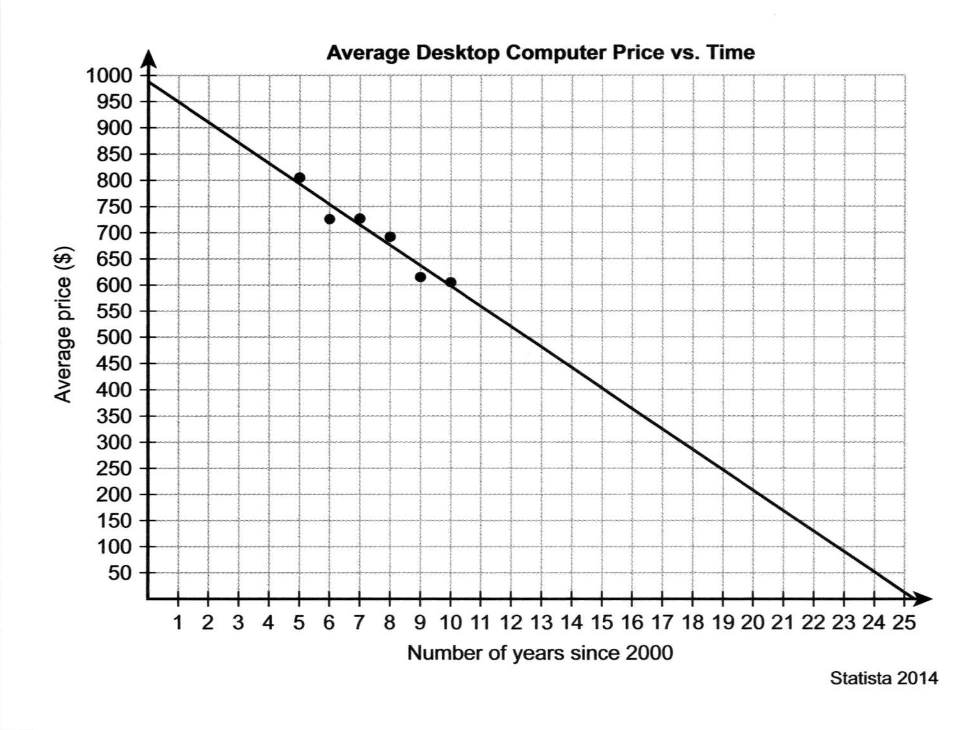

A What is the relationship between the average price of desktop computers and the number of years that have passed since 2000?

SOLUTION

The slope is negative, so the variables are negatively associated. The price of desktop computers decreases as the number of years since 2000 increases.

B What does Emily's model predict the average price of desktop computers to be in 2017?

SOLUTION

The year 2017 is 17 years beyond 2000. Replace x with 17 in the equation and solve for y.

$$
\begin{aligned}
y &= -39x + 988 \\
y &= -39 \cdot 17 + 988 \\
&= -663 + 988 \\
&= 325
\end{aligned}
$$

The model predicts that the average price of a desktop computer in 2017 will be \$325.

C What does the number -39 mean in the context of average price of a desktop computer vs. years since 2000?

SOLUTION

The number -39 is the slope. Within the context of this problem, -39 is the rate at which the price of a desktop computer changes per year. Therefore, according to the model, the average price of a desktop computer has been decreasing \$39/year since the year 2000.

▶ **Remember** The initial value of a function is y-value when $x = 0$.

D What does the number 988 mean in the context of the average price of a desktop computer as a function of years since 2000?

SOLUTION

The number 988 is the y-intercept, which is the initial value of the model. The initial value of the model is the price of a desktop computer in 2000. Therefore, according to the model, the price of a desktop computer in 2000 was \$988. ■

Basic Geometric Shapes

Topic List

- Pairs of Angles
- Parallel Lines and Transversals
- Triangles
- Angles of a Triangle
- Exterior Angles
- Polygons

The architect I.M. Pei is known for his striking use of geometric shapes in his designs. In many of his buildings, you can see parallel lines, triangles, and intersecting shapes that come together to create a place of beauty and functionality.

Pairs of Angles

Some angle pairs are special because of their orientation or the sum of their measures.

In relation to an angle, a point can be in one of three places. Here, point *B* is on the angle, point *D* is in the interior of the angle, and point E is in the exterior of the angle.

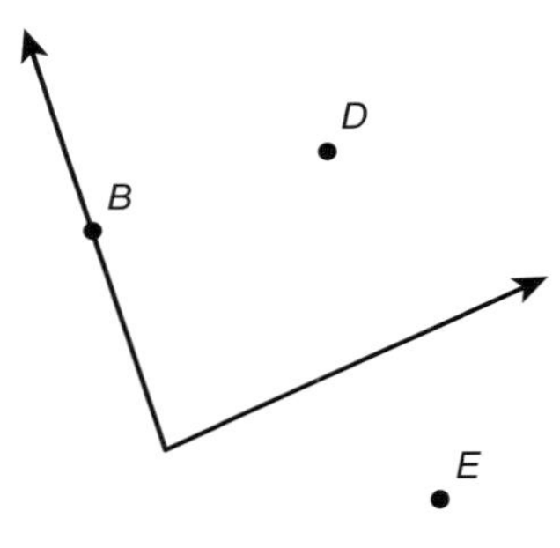

If angles in the same plane share a vertex and a side, but do not share any interior points, they are **adjacent angles**. Angles 1 and 2 are adjacent.

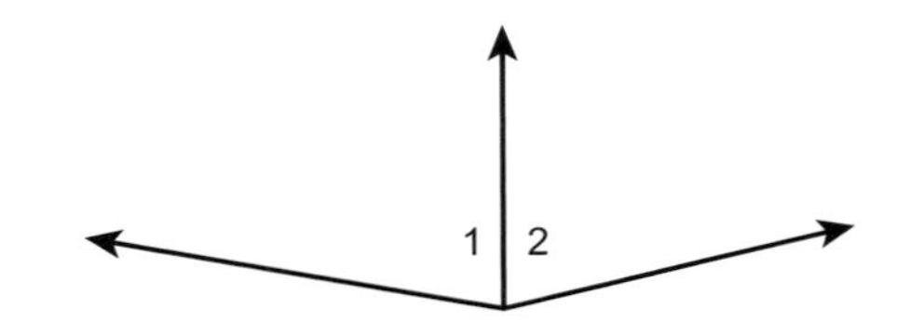

▶ **Think About It** If a point is in the interior of an angle, then it lies on a segment that has one endpoint on one of the angle's rays and the other endpoint on the other ray.

Identifying Linear Pairs and Vertical Angles

Definitions

A **linear pair** is made up of two angles that have a common side and whose other sides point in opposite directions.

Vertical angles are a pair of nonadjacent angles formed by two intersecting lines.

▶ **Think About It** A linear pair is always an adjacent pair of angles.

EXAMPLE 1

Given that $\overleftrightarrow{RQ}$ and $\overleftrightarrow{NT}$ intersect at point E, identify the pair of angles as a linear pair, vertical angles, adjacent angles that are not a linear pair, or none of these.

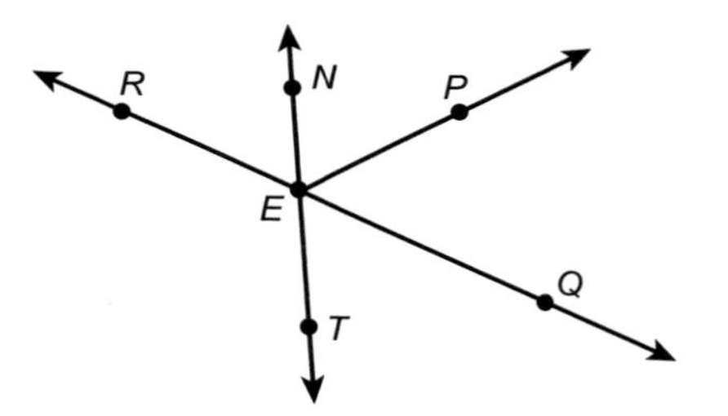

A $\angle REN$ and $\angle TEQ$

SOLUTION
They are nonadjacent angles formed by $\overleftrightarrow{RQ}$ and $\overleftrightarrow{NT}$. They are vertical angles.

B $\angle RET$ and $\angle NEP$

SOLUTION

They are nonadjacent angles, but they are not formed from two intersecting lines. The answer is none of these.

C $\angle NER$ and $\angle RET$

SOLUTION

They are adjacent angles with common side $\overrightarrow{ER}$. The other sides, $\overrightarrow{EN}$ and $\overrightarrow{ET}$, point in opposite directions, forming a line. The angles form a linear pair.

D $\angle NEP$ and $\angle PEQ$

SOLUTION

They are adjacent angles with common side $\overrightarrow{EP}$. The other sides, $\overrightarrow{EN}$ and $\overrightarrow{EQ}$, do not form a line. They are adjacent angles that do not form a linear pair. ■

Using Properties of Angle Pairs

Properties of Angle Pairs

The sum of the angle measures in a linear pair is 180°. Vertical angles have equal measures.

EXAMPLE 2

Find the angle measure.

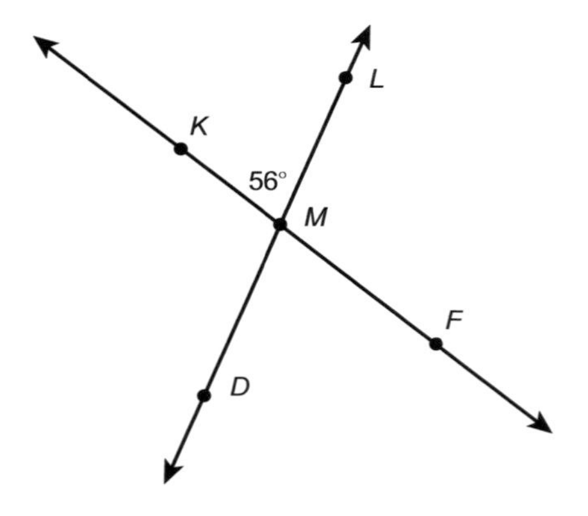

A Find $m\angle KMD$.

▶ **Think About It** A lowercase *m* before an angle means "the measure of," so $m\angle KMD$ means the measure of angle *KMD*.

SOLUTION

$\angle KMD$ and $\angle KML$ form a linear pair.

Write and solve an equation.

$m\angle KMD + m\angle KML = 180°$

$x + 56° = 180°$	Substitute.
$x = 180° - 56°$	Subtract 56° from both sides.
$x = 124°$	Simplify.

The measure of $\angle KMD$ is 124°.

B Find $m\angle LMF$.

SOLUTION

$\angle LMF$ and $\angle KMD$ are vertical angles, so their measures are equal.

$$m\angle LMF = m\angle KMD = 124°$$ ■

EXAMPLE 3

Find the angle measure.

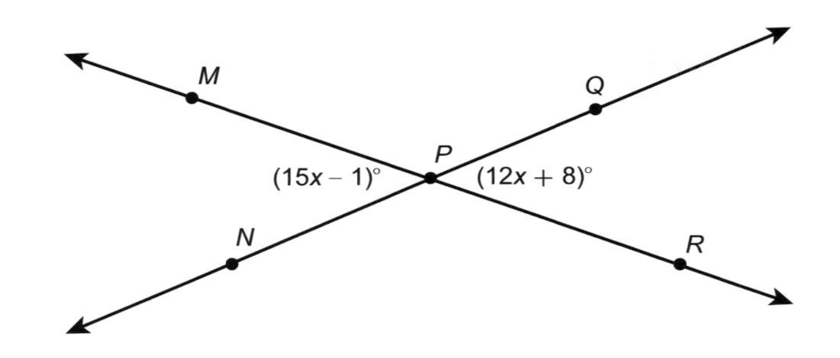

A Find $m\angle QPR$.

SOLUTION

$\angle MPN$ and $\angle QPR$ are vertical angles.

Step 1 Write an equation and solve for x.

$m\angle MPN = m\angle QPR$

$15x - 1 = 12x + 8$	Substitute.
$3x - 1 = 8$	Subtract $12x$ from both sides.
$3x = 9$	Add 1 to both sides.
$x = 3$	Divide each side by 3.

Step 2 Substitute 3 for x in the expression for $m\angle QPR$.

$$\begin{aligned} m\angle QPR &= (12x + 8)^\circ \\ &= (12(3) + 8)^\circ \\ &= 44^\circ \end{aligned}$$

B Find $m\angle RPN$.

SOLUTION

$\angle RPN$ and $\angle QPR$ are a linear pair, so their angle measures have a sum of 180°.

$$\begin{aligned} m\angle RPN + m\angle QPR &= 180^\circ \\ m\angle RPN + 44^\circ &= 180^\circ \\ m\angle RPN &= 180^\circ - 44^\circ = 136^\circ \end{aligned}$$

Identifying Complementary and Supplementary Angles

Definitions

A pair of angles is **complementary** if the sum of their measures is 90°.

A pair of angles is **supplementary** if the sum of their measures is 180°.

Complementary and supplementary angle pairs may or may not be adjacent. Points H, M, and L are collinear.

Remember Remember that points are collinear if they all fall along the same line.

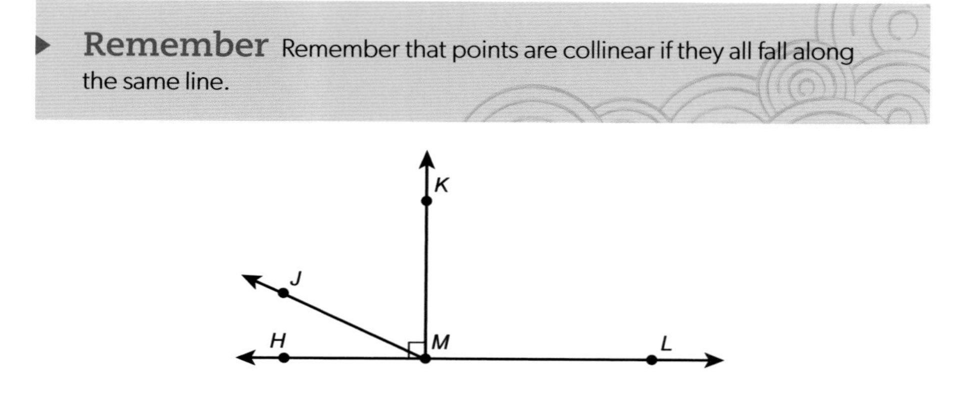

$\angle HMJ$ and $\angle JMK$ are complementary.

$\angle HMK$ and $\angle KML$ are supplementary.

$\angle HMJ$ and $\angle JML$ are supplementary.

Think About It The square symbol drawn in $\angle HMK$ indicates that it is a right angle.

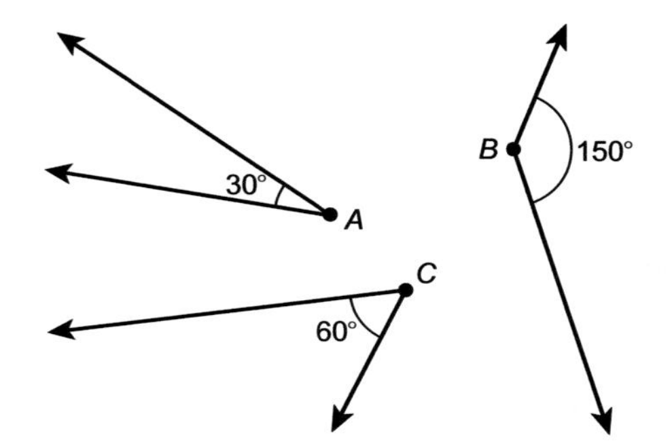

$\angle A$ and $\angle C$ are complementary.

$\angle A$ and $\angle B$ are supplementary.

Finding Measures of Complements and Supplements

EXAMPLE 4

Find the measure of the complement and the supplement of an angle with the measure.

A 82°

SOLUTION

The complement has a measure of $90° - 82° = 8°$.
The supplement has a measure of $180° - 82° = 98°$.

> ▶ **Think About It** If two angles are supplementary, you can write their measures as x and $180° - x$.

B 105°

SOLUTION

The angle does not have a complement. The supplement has a measure of $180° - 105° = 75°$. ■

EXAMPLE 5

$\angle A$ and $\angle B$ are complementary angles. The measure of $\angle B$ is twice the measure of $\angle A$. Find the measure of each angle.

SOLUTION

Let $m\angle A = x$. Then $m\angle B = 90° - x$.

Step 1 Write an equation. The measure of $\angle B$ is twice the measure of $\angle A$.

$m\angle B = 2 \bullet m\angle A$

$90° - x = 2x$	Substitute.
$90° = 3x$	Add x to both sides.
$30° = x$	Divide each side by 3.

Step 2 Substitute 30° for x in each expression.

$$m\angle A = x \qquad m\angle B = 90° - x$$
$$= 30° \qquad = 90° - 30°$$
$$= 60°$$

$m\angle A = 30°$ and $m\angle B = 60°$ ■

Application: Hobbies

EXAMPLE 6

An antique bicycle wheel has only a few spokes remaining.

Use the diagram to answer the questions. $\overline{CF}$ and $\overline{AE}$ intersect at center K.

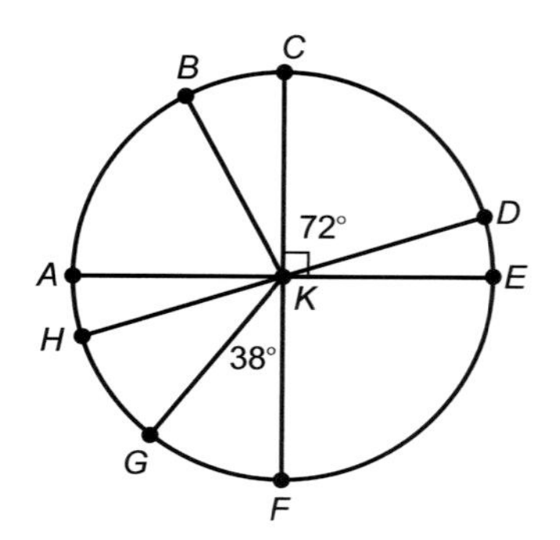

A What is $m\angle HKG$?

SOLUTION

$m\angle HKF = 72°$ because $\angle HKF$ and $\angle CKD$ are vertical angles.

$$m\angle HKG = m\angle HKF - m\angle GKF = 72° - 38° = 34°$$

B What is $m\angle DKF$?

SOLUTION

$\angle CKD$ and $\angle DKF$ are a linear pair.

$$m\angle DKF = 180° - 72° = 108°$$

C Name a pair of supplementary angles that are congruent.

SOLUTION

Angles that are supplementary and congruent each measure 90°.

One pair of supplementary congruent angles is $\angle AKC$ and $\angle CKE$. ■

Parallel Lines and Transversals

Two lines either intersect or do not intersect each other.

▶ **Think About It** Like roads at an intersection, lines can intersect or cross one another.

Parallel lines are lines on the same plane that never intersect. The symbol for parallel is $\parallel$. $a \parallel b$ is read "line *a* is parallel to line *b*."

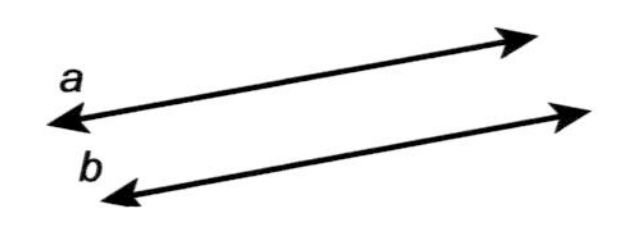

In the figure, line $f \parallel$ line g. Line $e \nparallel$ line f and line $e \nparallel g$ because line *e* and the other lines are not on the same plane.

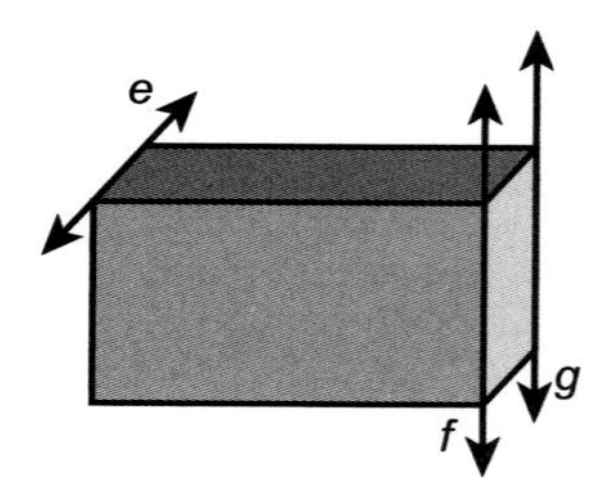

▶ **Think About It** The symbol $\nparallel$ is read "is not parallel to."

A **transversal** is a line that intersects two or more lines in a plane. Line *t* is a transversal to lines *m* and *n*.

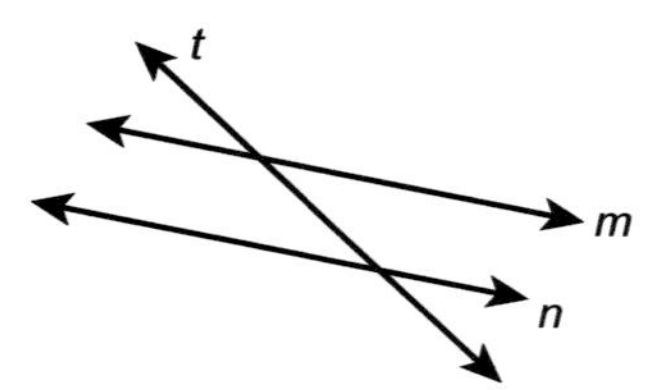

Pairs of Angles

Notice that eight angles are formed when a transversal crosses two lines.

Corresponding angles are angles that lie in the same position or match up with respect to the transversal when the transversal crosses two lines. Pairs of corresponding angles in this figure are $\angle 1$ and $\angle 5$, $\angle 2$ and $\angle 6$, $\angle 3$ and $\angle 7$, and $\angle 4$ and $\angle 8$.

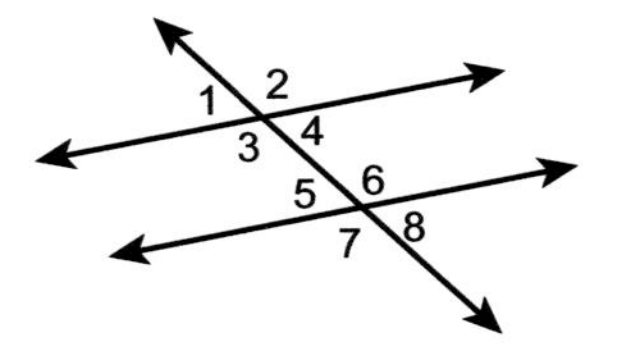

Alternate interior angles are the inside angles that do not share the same vertex and are on opposite sides of a transversal crossing two lines. Pairs of alternate interior angles in this figure are $\angle 3$ and $\angle 6$, as well as $\angle 4$ and $\angle 5$.

Alternate exterior angles are the outside angles that do not share the same vertex and are on opposite sides of a transversal crossing two lines. In the figure, the alternate exterior angles are the angle pair $\angle 1$ and $\angle 8$ and the angle pair $\angle 2$ and $\angle 7$.

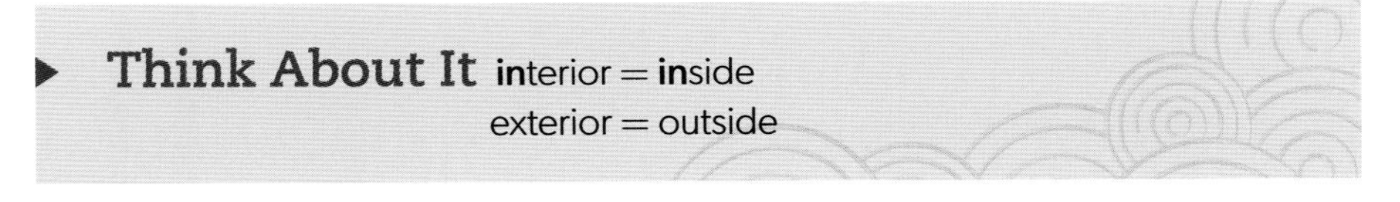

▶ **Think About It** **in**terior = **in**side
exterior = outside

Adjacent angles are angle pairs with a common side and a common vertex that do not overlap. There are several adjacent angles in the figure, including $\angle 1$ and $\angle 2$, $\angle 1$ and $\angle 3$, $\angle 3$ and $\angle 4$, $\angle 5$ and $\angle 7$, $\angle 5$ and $\angle 6$, and $\angle 7$ and $\angle 8$.

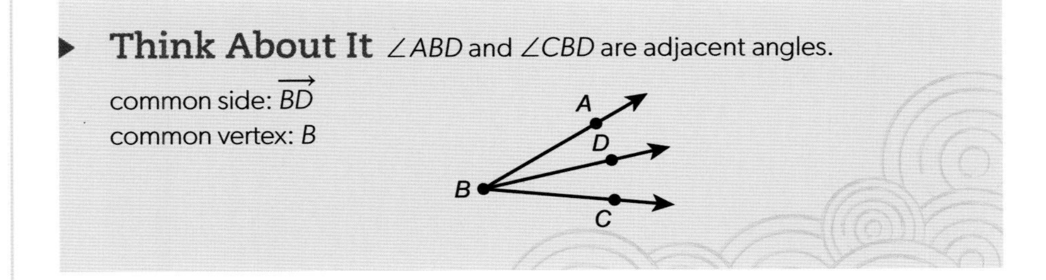

▶ **Think About It** $\angle ABD$ and $\angle CBD$ are adjacent angles.

common side: $\overrightarrow{BD}$
common vertex: B

EXAMPLE 1

Identify the pair of angles as corresponding, alternate interior, alternate exterior, adjacent, or none of these.

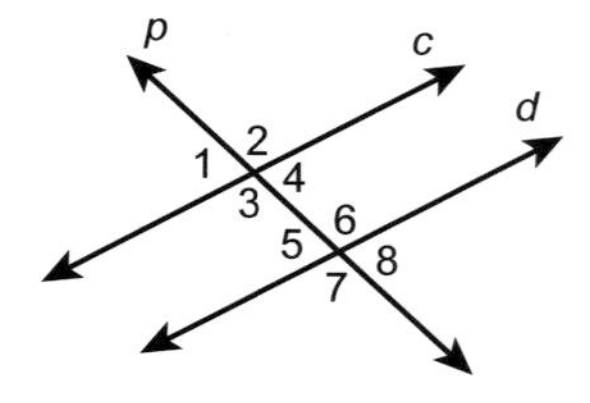

A $\angle 3$ and $\angle 6$

SOLUTION

$\angle 3$ and $\angle 6$ are on opposite sides of the transversal, line p, and they do not share a vertex. They are in between lines c and d, so they are alternate interior angles.

B $\angle 2$ and $\angle 7$

SOLUTION

$\angle 2$ and $\angle 7$ are on opposite sides of the transversal, line p, and they do not share the same vertex. They are outside of lines c and d, so they are alternate exterior angles.

C $\angle 5$ and $\angle 6$

SOLUTION

$\angle 5$ and $\angle 6$ share a common side and a common vertex. They are adjacent angles.

D $\angle 4$ and $\angle 8$

SOLUTION

$\angle 4$ and $\angle 8$ are in the same position within their group of four angles. They are corresponding angles. ■

Finding Angle Measures

▶ **Remember** The letter m is used to represent the word *measure*. So $m\angle 1$ is read as "the measure of angle 1."

The sum of the measures of two adjacent angles equals the measure of the angle formed by the sides that are not common.

In the figure, $m\angle ABD + m\angle DBC = m\angle ABC$.

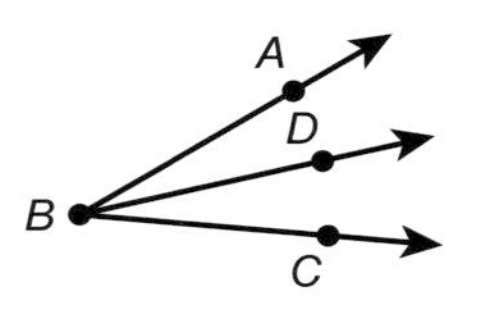

If $m\angle ABD = 20°$ and $m\angle DBC = 17°$, then $m\angle ABC = 37°$.

Properties of Special Angle Pairs

When two lines are crossed by a transversal, the sum of the measures of any two adjacent angles is 180°.

When the two lines crossed by the transversal are parallel, the following statements are also true:

- The measures of any pair of corresponding angles are equal.
- The measures of any pair of alternate interior angles are equal.
- The measures of any pair of alternate exterior angles are equal.

EXAMPLE 2

Find the measure of the angle if $j \parallel k$.

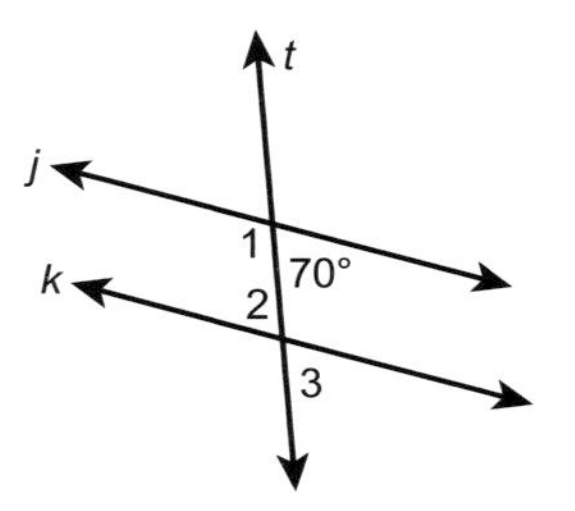

A $m\angle 1$

SOLUTION

$\angle 1$ is adjacent to the 70° angle. Because the sum of these angles is 180°, $m\angle 1 = 180° - 70° = 110°$.

B $m\angle 2$

SOLUTION

$\angle 2$ and the 70° angle are alternate interior angles, so they have the same measure: $m\angle 2 = 70°$.

C $m\angle 3$

SOLUTION

$\angle 3$ and the 70° angle are corresponding angles, so they have the same measure: $m\angle 3 = 70°$.

EXAMPLE 3

Find the measure of the angle if $m\angle 1 = 45°$ and $m \parallel n$.

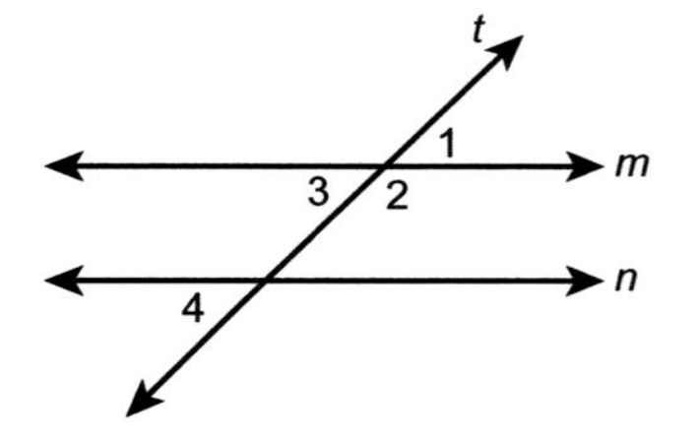

A $m\angle 2$

SOLUTION

$\angle 2$ is adjacent to $\angle 1$, so $m\angle 2 = 180° - 45° = 135°$.

B $m\angle 3$

SOLUTION

$\angle 3$ is adjacent to $\angle 2$, so $m\angle 3 = 180° - 135° = 45°$.

C $m\angle 4$

SOLUTION

$\angle 4$ and $\angle 1$ are alternate exterior angles, so they have the same measure: $m\angle 4 = 45°$.

Triangles

Many figures can be formed when parts of lines, rather than lines, are used.

Definition

A **line segment** is part of a line. It includes any two points on the line and all the points between those points.

A line segment is named by its endpoints. The points can be written in any order: segment ST, segment TS, $\overline{ST}$, or $\overline{TS}$.

T
S

Think About It A line segment is often more simply called a segment.

Definition

A **triangle** is a figure made up of three segments joined at their endpoints. Each endpoint is a vertex.

To name a triangle, use all three vertices. They can be listed in any order. Two possible names for this triangle are $\triangle FGH$ or $\triangle GHF$.

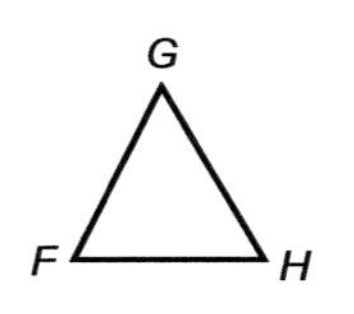

▸ **Think About It** The plural of *vertex* is *vertices*.

Classifying Triangles by Angle Measures

Every triangle can be classified according to its angle measures.

Definitions

An **acute triangle** is a triangle with three acute angles.

A **right triangle** is a triangle with a right angle.

An **obtuse triangle** is a triangle with an obtuse angle.

EXAMPLE 1

Classify the triangle as acute, right, or obtuse.

A

B
30°
A 28° 122° C

SOLUTION

Because $m\angle C > 90°$, $\angle C$ is an obtuse angle, so the triangle is an obtuse triangle.

B

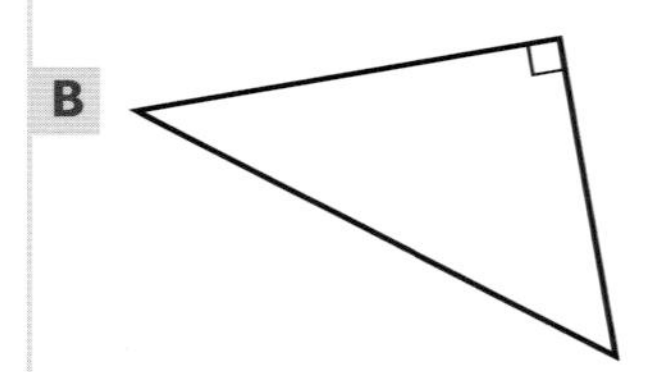

SOLUTION

Because one of the angles is a right angle, the triangle is a right triangle. ■

Using the Triangle Angle Sum Property

▶ **Think About It** It is not possible for a triangle to have more than one right angle or more than one obtuse angle.

Triangle Angle Sum Property

The sum of the measures of the angles of any triangle is 180°.

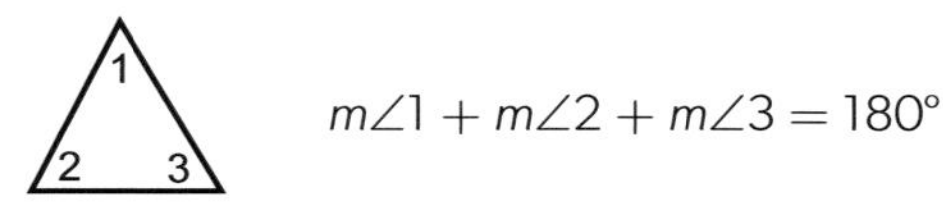

$m\angle 1 + m\angle 2 + m\angle 3 = 180°$

EXAMPLE 2

Find the value of x in the triangle.

A

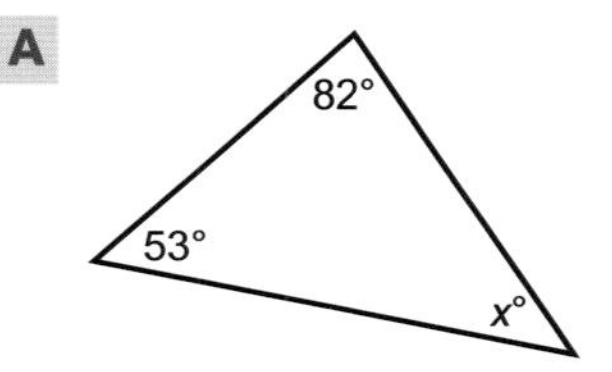

SOLUTION

Find the sum of the measures of the two known angles: $82° + 53° = 135°$.
Subtract this sum from 180°: $180° - 135° = 45°$.

$$x = 45$$

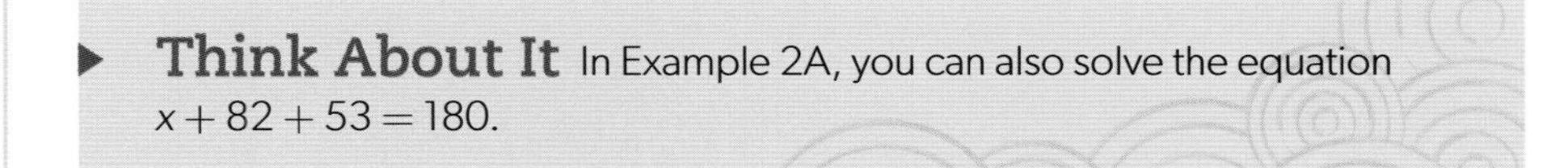

▶ **Think About It** In Example 2A, you can also solve the equation $x + 82 + 53 = 180$.

B

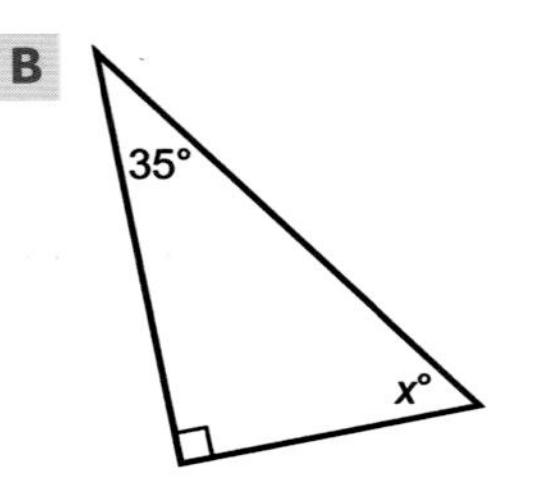

SOLUTION

Because the triangle is a right triangle, the sum of the measures of the two acute angles must be 90°.

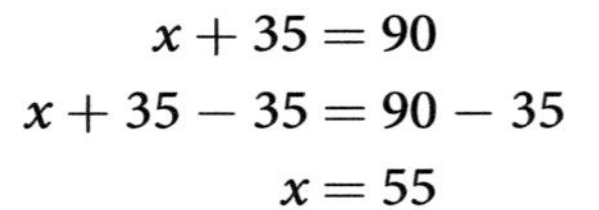

$$x + 35 = 90$$
$$x + 35 - 35 = 90 - 35$$
$$x = 55$$

C

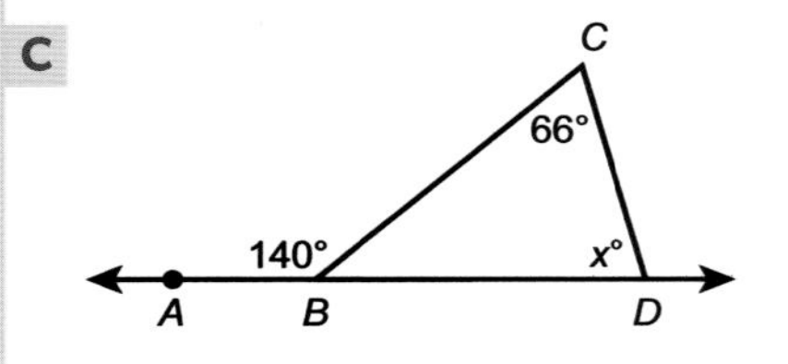

SOLUTION

$\angle ABC$ and $\angle CBD$ are adjacent angles and form a straight line, so $m\angle CBD = 180° - 140° = 40°$. Since the sum of the angles in a triangle equals 180°, $40 + 66 + x = 180$.

$$40 + 66 + x = 180$$
$$106 + x = 180$$
$$x = 180 - 106$$
$$x = 74$$

Application: Home Improvement

EXAMPLE 3

A homeowner leans a ladder against her house so that the bottom of the ladder makes a 62° angle with the ground. What angle does the top of the ladder make with the building?

SOLUTION

Draw a model. Assume that the ground is perpendicular to the building. The ladder, ground, and building form a right triangle.

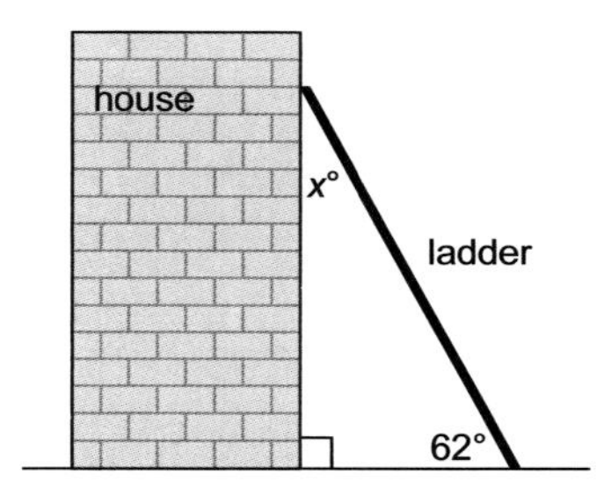

$$x + 62 = 90$$
$$x = 90 - 62$$
$$x = 28$$

▶ **Think About It** Two lines, or segments, that form right angles are perpendicular to each other.

CHECK

$$28 + 62 + 90 = 180 \checkmark$$

The top of the ladder makes a 28° angle with the building.

Angles of a Triangle

You can use parallel lines or three copies of a triangle to prove that the sum of the angles of the triangle is 180°.

Using Parallel Lines to Prove the Triangle Sum Theorem

You can use what you know about the angles formed by parallel lines and a transversal to prove that the sum of the angles of a triangle is 180°.

EXAMPLE 1

Given that $m \parallel \overleftrightarrow{AB}$, prove that the sum of the interior angles of $\triangle ABC$ is 180°.

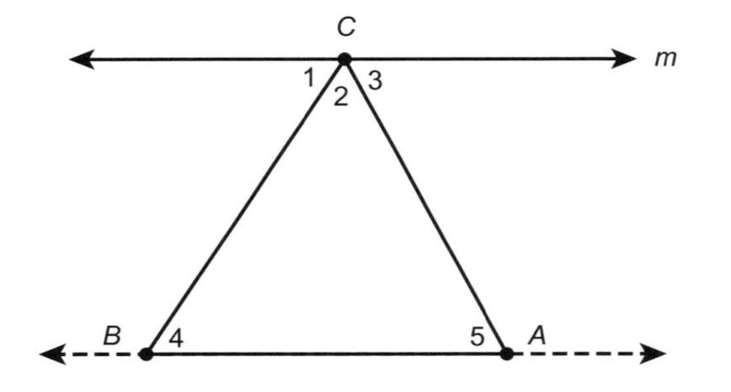

SOLUTION

$\angle 1$, $\angle 2$, and $\angle 3$ form a straight angle. Therefore, you can write the equation $m\angle 1 + m\angle 2 + m\angle 3 = 180°$.

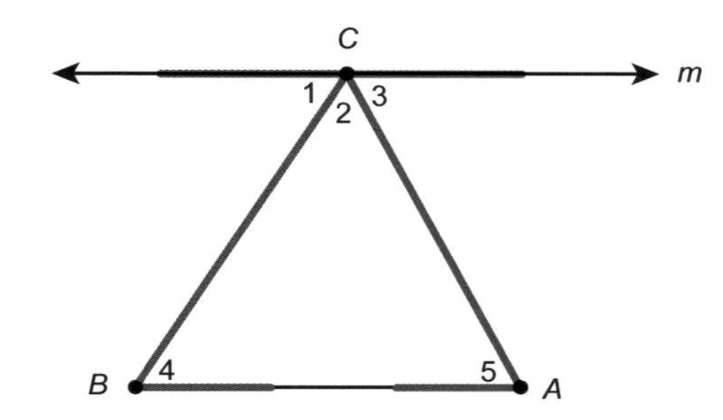

$\angle 1$ and $\angle 4$ are alternate interior angles. Therefore, $m\angle 4 = m\angle 1$.

$\angle 5$ and $\angle 3$ are alternate interior angles. Therefore, $m\angle 5 = m\angle 3$.

▶ **Remember** The measures of alternate interior angles are equal.

In the equation $m\angle 1 + m\angle 2 + m\angle 3 = 180°$, replace $m\angle 1$ with $m\angle 4$, and replace $m\angle 3$ with $m\angle 5$.

$$m\angle 4 + m\angle 2 + m\angle 5 = 180°$$

The sum of the angles of the triangle is 180°. ■

Using Copies of a Triangle to Prove the Triangle Sum Theorem

Another way to prove the triangle sum theorem is by rotating three copies of the same triangle.

EXAMPLE 2

Prove that the sum of the angles of the triangle is 180°.

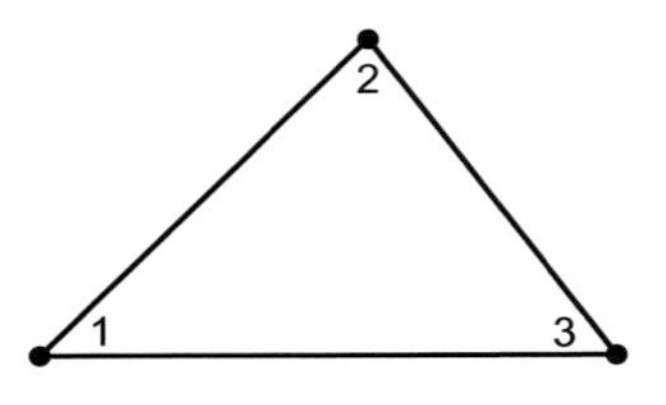

SOLUTION

Make a copy of the triangle. Rotate and position the copy so that $\angle 2$ is adjacent to $\angle 3$.

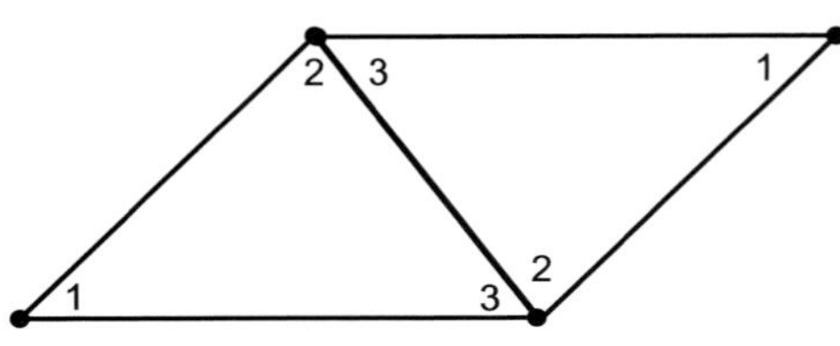

Then make another copy of the triangle. Rotate and position this copy so that $\angle 1$ of the second copy is adjacent to $\angle 2$ of the first copy.

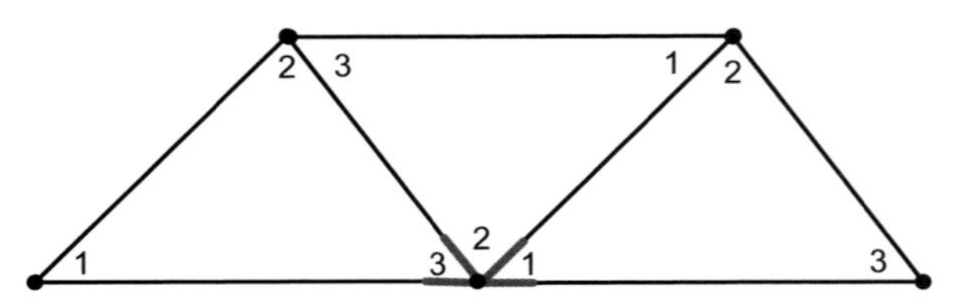

Notice that $\angle 1$, $\angle 2$, and $\angle 3$ form a straight angle. Therefore, $m\angle 1 + m\angle 2 + m\angle 3 = 180°$. Since these angles also make up the triangle, you can conclude that the measures of the angles of the triangle total 180°. ■

▶ **Remember** A straight angle is an angle whose measure is 180°.

Exterior Angles

You can use the properties of the interior angles of a triangle to learn about the properties of the exterior angles of a triangle.

Identifying the Exterior Angles of a Triangle

Exterior Angle Theorem

The measure of an exterior angle of a triangle is equal to the sum of the measures of the two nonadjacent interior angles.

▶ **Think About It** A theorem is a statement that can be proved to be true.

An **exterior angle** is formed when you extend a side of a triangle.

$\angle 4$ is an exterior angle to $\triangle ABC$. $\angle 1$, $\angle 2$, and $\angle 3$ are interior angles. $\angle 3$ is adjacent to $\angle 4$. $\angle 1$ and $\angle 2$ are not adjacent to $\angle 4$. The exterior angle theorem states that the measure of an exterior angle is equal to the sum of the measures of the two nonadjacent interior angles. Therefore, the measure of $\angle 4$ is equal to the sum of the measures of $\angle 1$ and $\angle 2$. You can use what you know about linear pairs and the sum of the measures of the interior angles of a triangle to show why this is true.

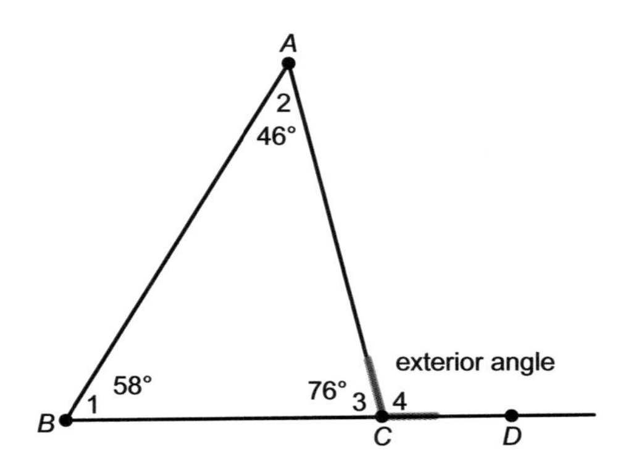

$\angle 3$ and $\angle 4$ form a linear pair. Therefore, $m\angle 3 + m\angle 4 = 180°$.

$\angle 1$, $\angle 2$, and $\angle 3$ are the interior angles of the triangle, so $m\angle 1 + m\angle 2 + m\angle 3 = 180°$.

> **Remember** The sum of the measures of the interior angles of a triangle is 180°.

Since $m\angle 3 + m\angle 4 = 180°$ and $m\angle 1 + m\angle 2 + m\angle 3 = 180°$, you can say that $m\angle 3 + m\angle 4 = m\angle 1 + m\angle 2 + m\angle 3$.

Subtract $m\angle 3$ from both sides.

$$m\angle 3 - m\angle 3 + m\angle 4 = m\angle 1 + m\angle 2 + m\angle 3 - m\angle 3$$
$$m\angle 4 = m\angle 1 + m\angle 2$$

EXAMPLE 1

Find $m\angle EFG$.

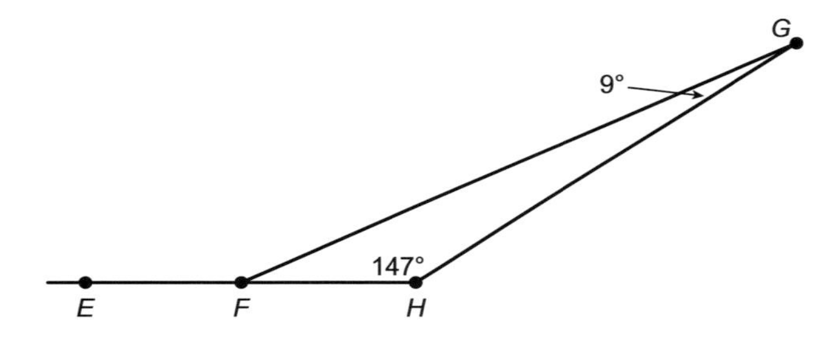

SOLUTION

$\angle EFG$ is an exterior angle to $\triangle FGH$. $\angle FGH$ and $\angle FHG$ are the two interior angles that are not adjacent to $\angle EFG$.

$$\begin{aligned} m\angle EFG &= m\angle FGH + m\angle FHG \\ &= 9° + 147° \\ &= 156° \end{aligned}$$

The measure of $\angle EFG$ is 156°. ■

EXAMPLE 2

Find $m\angle STU$.

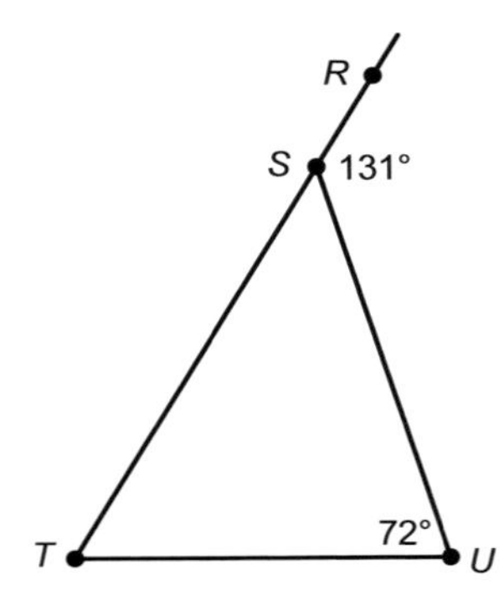

SOLUTION

$\angle RSU$ is an exterior angle to $\triangle STU$. $\angle STU$ and $\angle SUT$ are the two interior angles that are not adjacent to $\angle RSU$.

$$\begin{aligned} m\angle RSU &= m\angle STU + m\angle SUT \\ 131^\circ &= m\angle STU + 72^\circ \\ 131^\circ - 72^\circ &= m\angle STU + 72^\circ - 72^\circ \\ 59^\circ &= m\angle STU \end{aligned}$$

The measure of $\angle STU$ is 59°. ■

Polygons

Geometric figures can include segments or curves and can be open or closed.

Identifying Polygons

Definitions

A **polygon** is a closed figure formed by three or more line segments in a plane, such that each line segment intersects two other line segments at their endpoints only. The segments are called **sides** and the endpoints are called **vertices**.

EXAMPLE 1

Classify the figure as a polygon or as not a polygon.

A

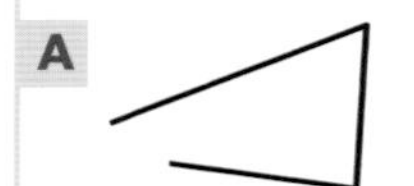

SOLUTION
The figure is not a polygon because it is not closed.

B

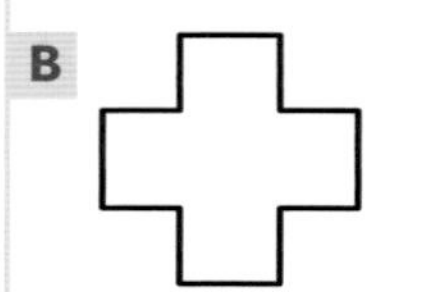

SOLUTION
The figure is closed and made up of segments that meet at their endpoints. It is a polygon.

C

SOLUTION
The figure is closed and made up of segments that meet at their endpoints. It is a polygon.

D

SOLUTION
The figure is made up of two segments and a curve. It is not a polygon.

E

SOLUTION
The four segments do not intersect at their endpoints only. The figure is not a polygon.

F

SOLUTION
A polygon must contain at least three line segments. The figure is not a polygon. ■

Identifying Regular Polygons

Definitions

An **equiangular polygon** is a polygon whose angle measures are all equal.

An **equilateral polygon** is a polygon whose side lengths are all equal.

A **regular polygon** is both equiangular and equilateral.

EXAMPLE 2

Which polygons appear to be regular polygons?

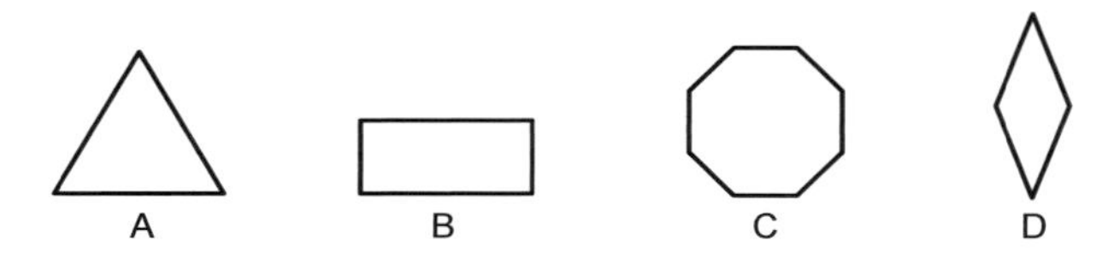

SOLUTION

Polygons A and C appear to be regular polygons because in both figures, the sides appear to be the same length and the angles appear to be the same measure. However, polygons B and D do not appear to be regular polygons. Polygon B has equal angle measures (all 90°), but the side lengths are not all the same. Polygon D has equal side lengths, but not all the angle measures are the same. ■

▶ **Think About It** Polygon B is equiangular but not equilateral. Polygon D is equilateral but not equiangular.

EXAMPLE 3

The interior angles formed by the sides of a regular hexagon (a polygon with six sides) have measures that sum to 720°. What is the degree measure of each angle?

SOLUTION

Let d represent the measure of an angle in the regular hexagon.

$6d = 720$	A regular hexagon has six congruent angles.
$\frac{6d}{6} = \frac{720}{6}$	Divide both sides by 6.
$d = 120$	Simplify.

Each interior angle of a regular hexagon measures 120°. ■

Classifying a Polygon by Its Number of Sides

Polygons can also be classified according to the number of sides that form the figure.

Number of sides	Polygon name
3	triangle
4	quadrilateral
5	pentagon
6	hexagon
7	heptagon
8	octagon
10	decagon
n	n-gon

▸ **Think About It** A triangle is the polygon with the fewest possible sides.

EXAMPLE 4

Classify the polygon by its number of sides. Determine whether the polygon appears to be regular or not regular.

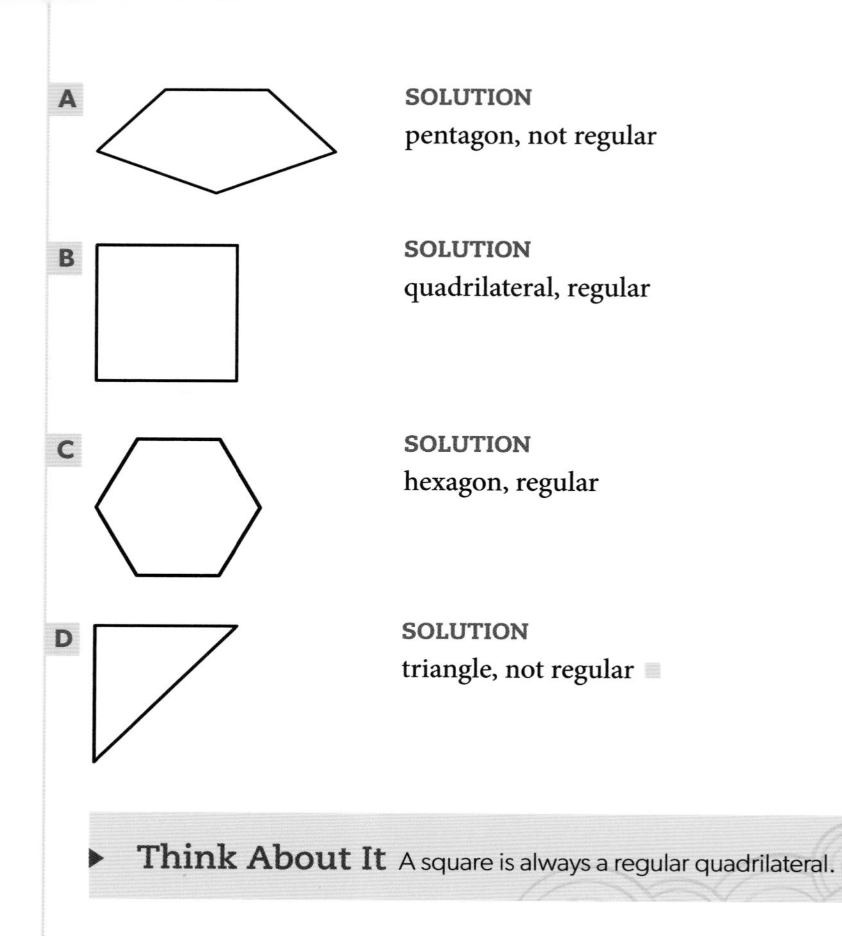

A

SOLUTION

pentagon, not regular

B

SOLUTION

quadrilateral, regular

C

SOLUTION

hexagon, regular

D

SOLUTION

triangle, not regular

▶ **Think About It** A square is always a regular quadrilateral.

Application: Perimeter

EXAMPLE 5

A A regular 15-gon has a perimeter of 450 cm. What is the length of each side of the polygon?

SOLUTION

A 15-gon is a polygon with 15 sides. Because the polygon is regular, all the sides are equal in length. You can use division to find the length of each side.

$$450 \div 15 = 30$$

The length of each side is 30 cm.

B Six sides of a decagon each measure 7 in. The perimeter of the decagon is 78 in. What is the length of each remaining side if each remaining side has the same length?

SOLUTION

A decagon has 10 sides. The lengths of six of the sides are known, so there are $10 - 6 = 4$ remaining sides of unknown length.

total length of six known sides: $6 \cdot 7 = 42$

total length of remaining sides: $78 - 42 = 36$

length of each remaining side: $36 \div 4 = 9$

CHECK

$$6 \cdot 7 + 4 \cdot 9 = 42 + 36 = 78 \checkmark$$

Each of the four remaining sides has a length of 9 in. ■

Volume

Topic List

- Volumes of Cylinders
- Applications of Cylinders
- Volumes of Cones
- Applications of Cones
- Volumes of Spheres
- Applications of Spheres

An empty ice-cream cone has volume. A scoop of ice cream, in the shape of a ball (the math term is sphere), has volume as well. Could the cone hold the entire scoop of ice cream if it melted? To find out, you could wait—until the ice cream melted—or you could use some handy formulas and enjoy a treat.

Volumes of Cylinders

Many food and drink containers have the shape of a cylinder.

Finding the Volume of a Cylinder

The bases of a **cylinder** are circles. A cylinder has one curved lateral surface.

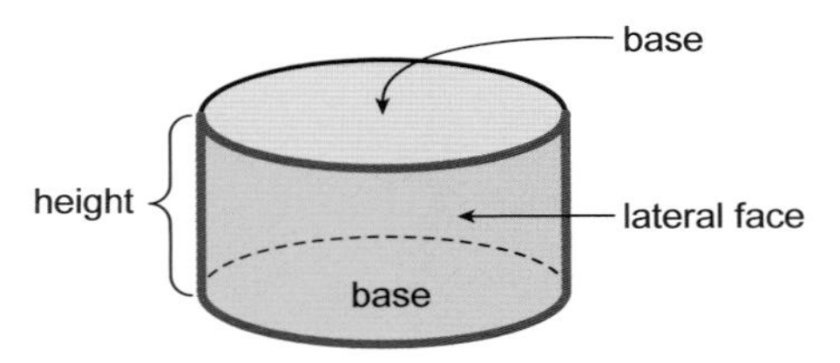

The volume of a cylinder can be found by multiplying the base area, B, by the height, h, of the cylinder. Since the base of a cylinder is a circle, you can use the formula $B = \pi r^2$ to determine the base area. The volume of an object is defined in cubic units—for example, cubic feet, cubic meters, or cubic inches.

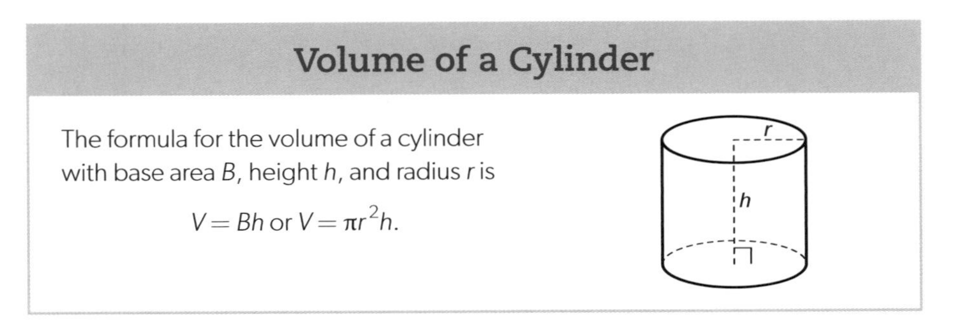

You can use 3.14 to approximate π or you can use the symbol π to show an exact answer.

EXAMPLE 1

A Find the exact volume of the cylinder.

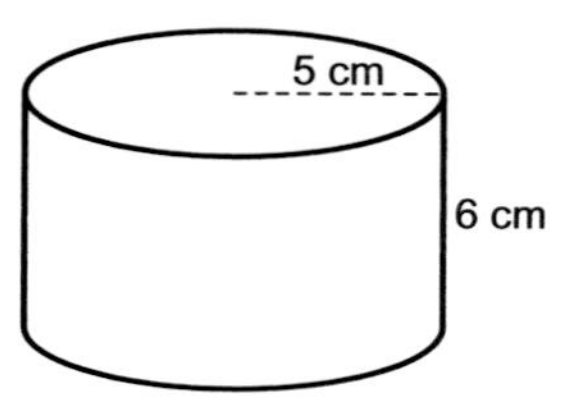

SOLUTION

Leave your answer in terms of π.

$V = \pi r^2 h$	Write the volume formula.
$= \pi \cdot 5^2 \cdot 6$	Substitute for r and h.
$= 150\pi$	Simplify.

The volume of the cylinder is exactly 150π cm^3.

B Find the approximate volume of the cylinder.

SOLUTION

Use 3.14 to approximate π.

$V = 150\pi$	Start with the exact volume.
$\approx 150 \cdot 3.14$	Use 3.14 for π.
≈ 471	Simplify.

The volume of the cylinder is approximately 471 cm^3. ■

Application: Problems Involving Cylinders

EXAMPLE 2

A cylindrical vase has a diameter of 10 cm and a height of 9 cm. What is the volume of the vase?

SOLUTION

Since the vase has a diameter of 10 cm, its radius is 5 cm. Apply the volume formula. Let $r = 5$ and $h = 9$.

$$\begin{aligned} V &= \pi r^2 h \\ &= \pi \bullet 5^2 \bullet 9 \\ &= \pi \bullet 25 \bullet 9 \\ &= \pi \bullet 225 \\ &\approx 3.14 \bullet 225 \\ &\approx 706.5 \end{aligned}$$

The volume of the vase is about 706.5 cm^3. ■

EXAMPLE 3

A cylindrical barrel has a diameter of 2 ft and a volume of 14.13 ft^3. What is the height of the barrel?

SOLUTION

Since the barrel has a diameter of 2 ft, its radius is 1 ft. Substitute 1 for r and 14.13 for V in the volume formula, and solve for h.

$$\begin{aligned} V &= \pi r^2 h \\ 14.13 &= \pi \bullet 1^2 \bullet h \\ 14.13 &= \pi \bullet h \\ 14.13 &\approx 3.14 \bullet h \\ \frac{14.13}{3.14} &\approx \frac{3.14h}{3.14} \\ 4.5 &\approx h \end{aligned}$$

The height of the barrel is about 4.5 ft. ■

Applications of Cylinders

Many real-world problems involve finding the volumes of cylinders.

Solving Problems Involving Volumes of Cylinders

▶ **Remember** The formula for finding the volume of a cylinder with base area B, height h, and radius r is

$$V = Bh \text{ or } V = \pi r^2 h.$$

EXAMPLE 1

A cylindrical jar has a height of 6 in. and a diameter of 4 in. The jar is three-quarters full of coffee grinds. To remove coffee from the jar, Andrea uses a cylindrical scoop that has a height of 1 in. and a diameter of 2 in. One scoop holds 0.6 oz of coffee grinds and makes 1 cup of coffee.

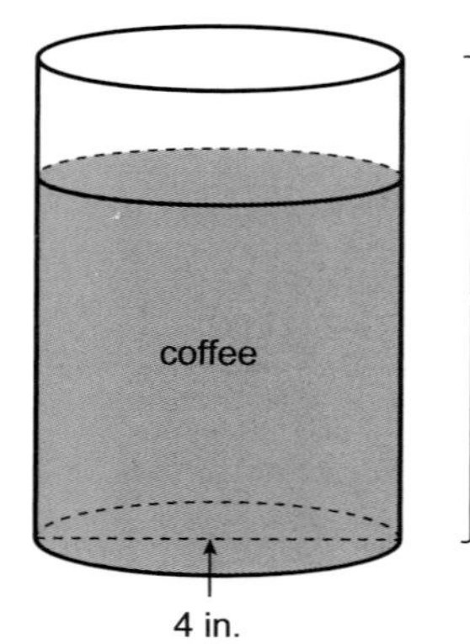

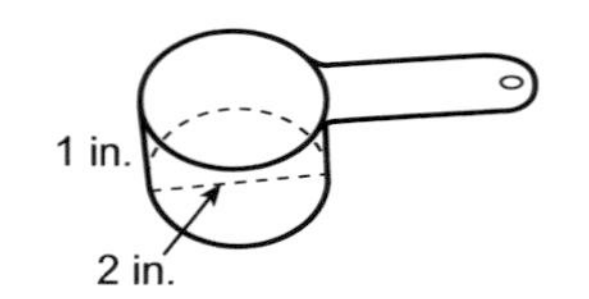

A How many cups of coffee can Andrea make from the coffee grinds that are currently in the jar?

SOLUTION

Step 1 Find the exact total capacity of the coffee jar in cubic inches. Apply the volume formula. Since the diameter is 4 in., the radius is 2 in. Let $r = 2$ and $h = 6$.

$$\begin{aligned} V &= \pi r^2 h \\ &= \pi \cdot 2^2 \cdot 6 \\ &= \pi \cdot 4 \cdot 6 \\ &= 24\pi \end{aligned}$$

The jar has a capacity of 24π in^3 of coffee grinds.

Step 2 Find the number of cubic inches of coffee grinds currently in the jar.

The jar is three-quarters full, so it's holding $\frac{3}{4} \cdot 24\pi$, or 18π in^3, of coffee grinds.

Step 3 Find the exact number of cubic inches of coffee grinds that the cylindrical scoop can hold. Apply the volume formula. Since the scoop's diameter is 2 in., its radius is 1 in. Let $r = 1$ and $h = 1$.

$$\begin{aligned} V &= \pi r^2 h \\ &= \pi \cdot 1^2 \cdot 1 \\ &= \pi \cdot 1 \cdot 1 \\ &= \pi \end{aligned}$$

The scoop can hold about π in^3.

Step 4 Find the number of scoops of coffee grinds that are in the jar. Divide the volume of the coffee grinds in the jar by the volume of coffee grinds in a single scoop.

$$\frac{\text{volume of coffee in the jar}}{\text{volume of 1 scoop}} = \frac{18\pi}{\pi} = 18$$

There are 18 scoops of coffee grinds in the jar. Since 1 scoop of grinds makes 1 cup of coffee, Andrea can make about 18 cups of coffee from the container.

B How many ounces of coffee grinds are in the jar?

SOLUTION

Each scoop of coffee grinds is 0.6 oz, and there are 18 scoops in the jar. Multiply 0.6 by 18.

$$0.6 \bullet 18 = 10.8$$

There are 10.8 oz of coffee grinds in the jar. ■

EXAMPLE 2

A case of juice contains 24 cans. The cans are packed in a box for shipping as shown in the diagram. Each can is a cylinder with a radius of 3 cm. If there are 9072 mL of juice in the entire case, what is the height of each can? Assume each can is completely full.

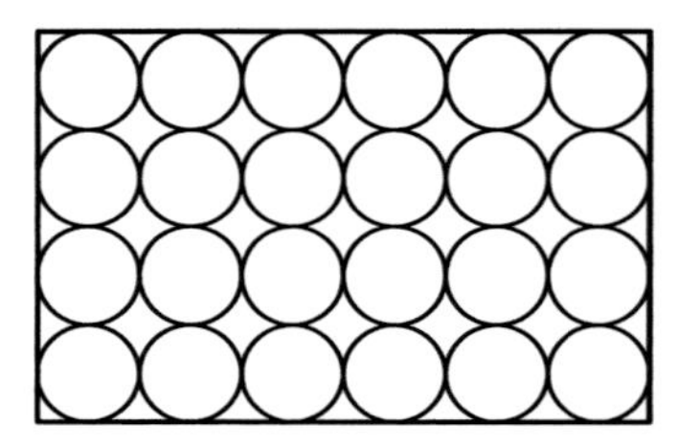

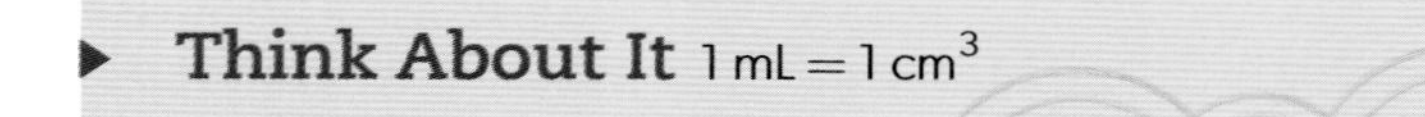

▶ **Think About It** $1 \text{ mL} = 1 \text{ cm}^3$

SOLUTION

Use the total capacity to find the capacity of 1 can. Then convert capacity to volume and use the volume formula to find the height of a can.

$9072 \text{ mL} \div 24 = 378 \text{ mL}$ Find the capacity of each can.

Each can contains 378 mL of juice. The volume of each can is 378 cm^3.

$V = \pi r^2 h$ Write the volume formula.

$378 = \pi \cdot 3^2 h$ Substitute for V and r.

$378 = 9\pi h$ Simplify.

$\frac{378}{9\pi} = h$ Divide both sides by 9π.

$\frac{42}{\pi} = h$ Simplify.

$\frac{42}{3.14} \approx h$ Use 3.14 for π.

$13.4 \approx h$ Simplify.

The height of each can is about 13.4 cm. ■

Volumes of Cones

The volume of a cone is one-third the volume of a cylinder whose radius and height are equal to the radius and height of the cone.

Finding the Volume of a Cone

The base of a **cone** is a circle. A cone has one curved lateral surface and a single vertex. Its height is measured from the base to the vertex along a line perpendicular to the base.

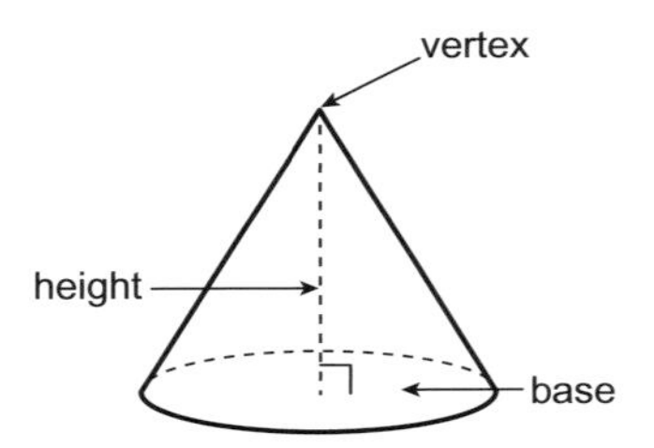

The volume of a cone is one-third the product of the base area, B, and the height, h, of the cone. Since the base of a cone is a circle, you can use the formula $B = \pi r^2$ to determine the base area.

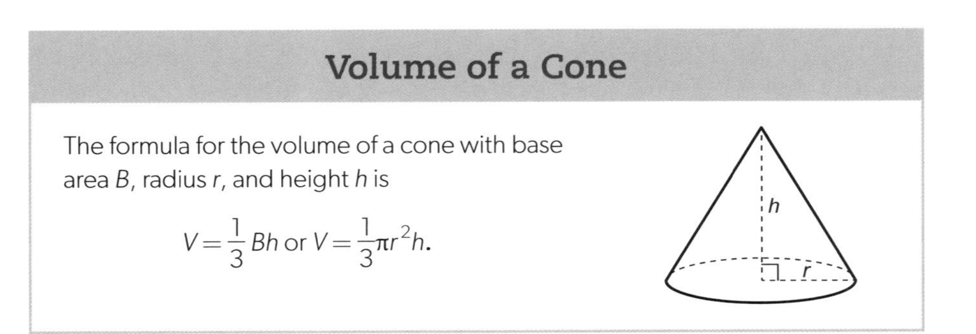

Volume of a Cone

The formula for the volume of a cone with base area B, radius r, and height h is

$$V = \frac{1}{3}Bh \text{ or } V = \frac{1}{3}\pi r^2 h.$$

EXAMPLE 1

Use the formula for the volume of a cone.

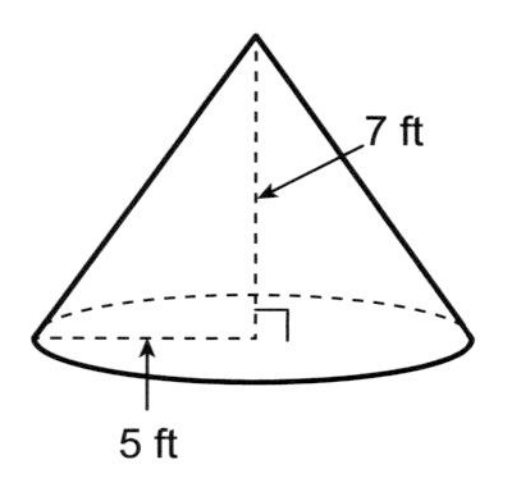

A Find the exact volume of the cone.

SOLUTION

Leave your answer in terms of π.

$V = \frac{1}{3}\pi r^2 h$	Write the volume formula.
$= \frac{1}{3}\pi \cdot 5^2 \cdot 7$	Substitute 5 for r and 7 for h.
$= \frac{1}{3} \cdot \pi \cdot 25 \cdot 7$	Evaluate the power.
$= \frac{175\pi}{3}$	Simplify.

The volume of the cone is exactly $\frac{175\pi}{3}$ ft^3.

▶ **Remember** You can use 3.14 to approximate π or you can treat π as a numeral in your calculations.

B Find the approximate volume of the cone. Round to the nearest whole number.

SOLUTION

Use 3.14 to approximate π.

$V = \frac{175\pi}{3}$	Start with the exact volume.
$\approx \frac{175 \bullet 3.14}{3}$	Use 3.14 for π.
$\approx \frac{549.5}{3}$	Multiply.
≈ 183	Divide.

The volume of the cone is approximately 183 ft^3. ■

Application: Problems Involving Cones

EXAMPLE 2

A candy dish has the shape of a cone with a diameter of 8 in. and a height of 6 in. What is the volume of the dish? Round to the nearest whole number.

SOLUTION

Since the dish's diameter is 8 in., its radius is 4 in. Apply the volume formula. Let $r = 4$ and $h = 6$.

$$\begin{aligned} V &= \frac{1}{3}\pi r^2 h \\ &= \frac{1}{3} \bullet \pi \bullet 4^2 \bullet 6 \\ &= \frac{1}{3} \bullet \pi \bullet 16 \bullet 6 \\ &= 32\pi \\ &\approx 32 \bullet 3.14 \\ &\approx 100 \end{aligned}$$

The volume of the dish is about 100 in^3. ■

EXAMPLE 3

A cone-shaped pile of sand has a diameter 6 m and a volume of 47.1 m^3. What is the height of the pile?

SOLUTION

Since the diameter of the pile is 6 m, the radius is 3 m. Substitute 3 for *r* and 47.1 for *V* in the volume formula, and solve for *h*.

$$V = \frac{1}{3}\pi r^2 h$$

$$47.1 = \frac{1}{3} \bullet \pi \bullet 3^2 \bullet h$$

$$47.1 = \frac{1}{3} \bullet \pi \bullet 9 \bullet h$$

$$47.1 = 3\pi h$$

$$\frac{47.1}{3\pi} = \frac{3\pi h}{3\pi}$$

$$\frac{47.1}{3 \bullet 3.14} \approx h$$

$$5 \approx h$$

The height of the pile is about 5 m. ■

Applications of Cones

Many real-world problems involve volumes of cones.

Solving Problems Involving Volumes of Cones

You can use the formula for finding the volume of a cone to solve many real-world problems.

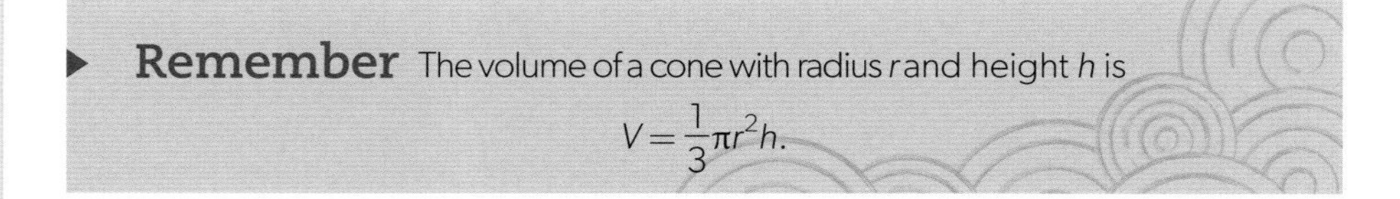

▶ **Remember** The volume of a cone with radius r and height h is

$$V = \frac{1}{3}\pi r^2 h.$$

EXAMPLE 1

A city sands its roads in icy weather. At the end of winter, the remaining sand is in a pile in the shape of a cone with a diameter of 50 ft and a height of 15 ft. Can all the sand be moved into a silo in the shape of a cylinder with a radius of 12 ft and a height of 18 ft for summer storage?

SOLUTION

Find the volume of sand in the cone. Compare it to the volume of the silo.

$V_{\text{cone}} = \frac{1}{3}\pi r^2 h$	Write the volume formula.
$= \frac{1}{3}\pi \cdot \mathbf{25}^2 \cdot \mathbf{15}$	If the diameter is 50 ft, then the radius is 25 ft. Substitute 25 for r and 15 for h.
$= 3125\pi$	Simplify to find the exact volume.

The volume of sand in the cone-shaped pile is 3125π ft^3.

$V_{silo} = \pi r^2 h$	Write the volume formula.
$= \pi \cdot \mathbf{12}^2 \cdot \mathbf{18}$	Substitute 12 for r and 18 for h.
$= 2592\pi$	Simplify to find the exact volume.

The volume of the silo is 2592π ft^3.

Since 3125π ft$^3 > 2592\pi$ ft^3, all the remaining sand will not fit in the silo. ■

▶ **Think About It** Using subscripts like in V_{cone} and V_{silo} helps you identify which figure you are working with in each part of the problem.

EXAMPLE 2

Sand is poured to create a cone-shaped pile. After some time, the diameter of the pile is 12 cm and the height is 10 cm. A little while later, the volume of the pile increases by 80% and the diameter is 18 cm.

A What is the exact volume of the pile of sand before the increase?

SOLUTION

The height of the pile is 10 cm and the diameter is 12 cm. Since the diameter is 12 cm, the radius is 6 cm. Let $r = 6$ and $h = 10$.

$$\begin{aligned} V_1 &= \frac{1}{3}\pi r^2 h \\ &= \frac{1}{3} \cdot \pi \cdot 6^2 \cdot 10 \\ &= \frac{1}{3} \cdot \pi \cdot 36 \cdot 10 \\ &= 120\pi \end{aligned}$$

The volume of the pile before the increase is 120π cm^3.

B What is the exact volume of the pile after the increase?

> ▶ **Think About It** If you want to find the result of increasing a value by $a\%$, you can multiply the value by $(100 + a)\%$. In Example 2B, that means multiplying by 180%, which equals 1.80.

SOLUTION

Multiply 120π by 1.8.

$$120\pi \bullet 1.8 = 216\pi$$

The volume of the pile after the increase is 216π cm^3.

C What is the height of the pile after the increase?

SOLUTION

The diameter is 18 cm, so the radius is 9 cm. Let $r = 9$ and $V_2 = 216\pi$.

$$V_2 = \frac{1}{3}\pi r^2 h$$

$$216\pi = \frac{1}{3} \bullet \pi \bullet 9^2 \bullet h$$

$$216\pi = \frac{1}{3} \bullet \pi \bullet 81 \bullet h$$

$$216\pi = 27\pi h$$

$$\frac{216\pi}{27\pi} = \frac{27\pi h}{27\pi}$$

$$8 = h$$

The height of the pile after the increase is 8 cm. It is not as high as before the increase, but its diameter is wider.

Volumes of Spheres

Many objects, both natural and man-made, are spherical in shape.

Finding the Volume of a Sphere

A **sphere** is the set of all points in space that are a given distance from a point called the center. A **radius** of a sphere is a line segment joining the center of the sphere and a point on the surface of the sphere. Every radius of a given sphere has the same length, so the term *radius* also means the length of any radius of a given sphere.

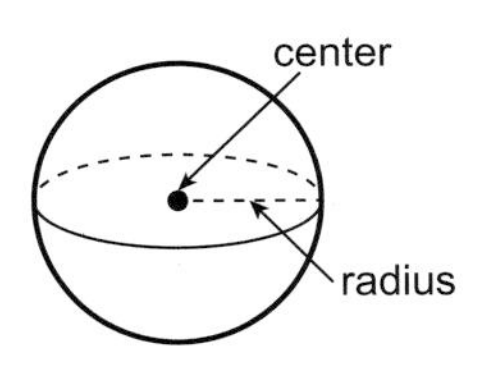

A **diameter** is a line segment passing through the center that joins two points on the sphere. Every diameter of a given sphere has the same length, so the term *diameter* also means the length of any diameter of a given sphere.

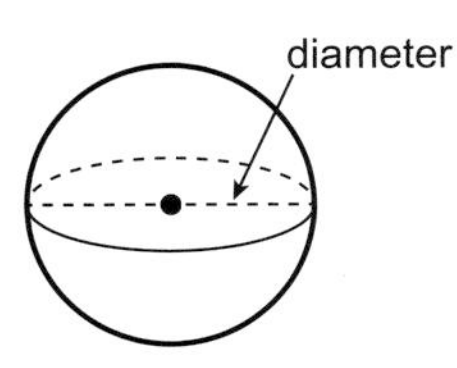

The volume of a sphere can be found by multiplying $\frac{4}{3}\pi$ by the radius cubed.

Make sure to use the radius of the sphere, not the diameter.

Volume of a Sphere

The formula for the volume V of a sphere with radius r is

$$V = \frac{4}{3}\pi r^3.$$

You can use 3.14 to approximate π or you can keep the symbol π to show an exact answer.

EXAMPLE

Find the exact volume of the sphere. Then find the approximate volume. Round to the nearest whole number.

A

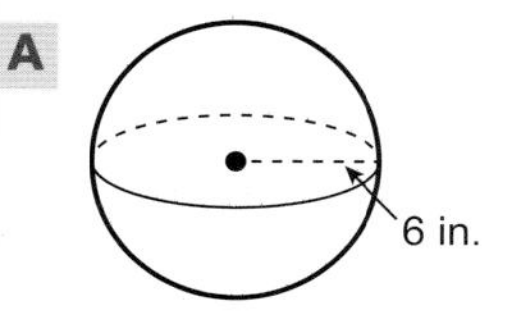

SOLUTION

The radius of the sphere is 6 in. Apply the volume formula. Let $r = 6$.

$$\begin{aligned} V &= \frac{4}{3}\pi r^3 \\ &= \frac{4}{3} \bullet \pi \bullet 6^3 \\ &= \frac{4}{3} \bullet \pi \bullet 216 \\ &= 288\pi \end{aligned}$$

The exact volume of the sphere is 288π in^3.

To find the approximate volume, replace π with 3.14 and simplify.

$$288 \bullet 3.14 = 904.32$$

The volume of the sphere is approximately 904 in^3.

B

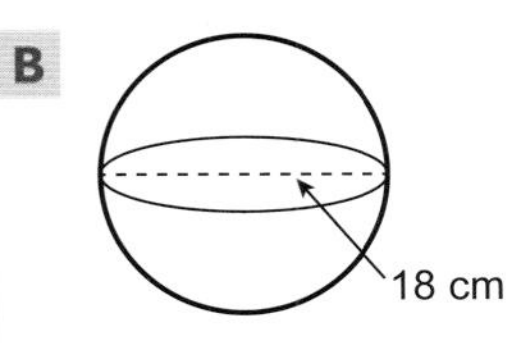

SOLUTION

The diameter of the sphere is 18 cm. Therefore, the radius is 9 cm. Apply the volume formula. Let $r = 9$.

$$\begin{aligned} V &= \frac{4}{3}\pi r^3 \\ &= \frac{4}{3} \bullet \pi \bullet 9^3 \\ &= \frac{4}{3} \bullet \pi \bullet 729 \\ &= 972\pi \end{aligned}$$

The exact volume of the sphere is 972π cm^3.

To find the approximate volume, replace π with 3.14 and simplify.

$$972 \bullet 3.14 = 3052.08$$

The volume of the sphere is approximately 3052 cm^3. ■

Applications of Spheres

Many real-world problems involve finding the volumes of spheres.

Solving Problems Involving the Volumes of Spheres

Real-world situations may involve finding the volume of spheres or finding the volume of figures that are combinations of spheres and other solids.

▶ **Remember** The volume of a sphere with radius r is $V = \frac{4}{3}\pi r^3$.

The volume of a cylinder with radius r and height h is $V = \pi r^2 h$.

EXAMPLE 1

A silo is constructed as a cylinder topped with a half-sphere. The silo is 48 ft tall and has a diameter of 24 ft. What is the volume of the silo? Round your answer to the nearest tenth of a cubic foot.

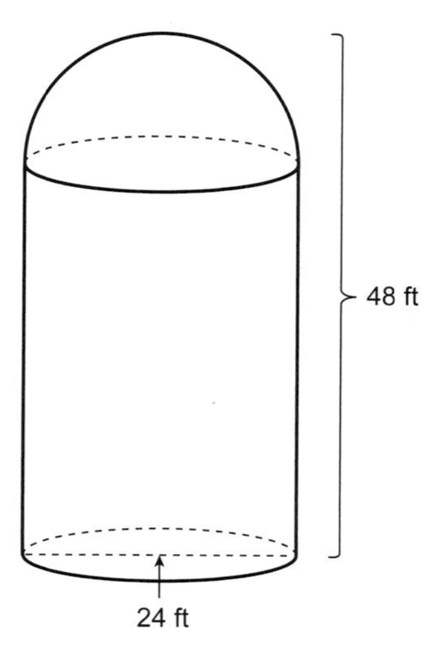

SOLUTION

The volume of the silo is the sum of the volume of the cylinder and the volume of the half-sphere. Begin by finding the volume of the half-sphere. The diameter of the half-sphere is equal to the diameter of the cylinder. Therefore, its diameter is 24 ft. Since the diameter is 24 ft, the radius is 12 ft. Find the volume of a sphere with a radius of 12 ft and then divide the volume by 2.

$$\begin{aligned} V_{\text{sphere}} &= \frac{4}{3}\pi r^3 \\ &= \frac{4}{3} \bullet \pi \bullet 12^3 \\ &= \frac{4}{3} \bullet \pi \bullet 1728 \\ &= 2304\pi \\ &\approx 2304 \bullet 3.14 \\ &\approx 7234.6 \end{aligned}$$

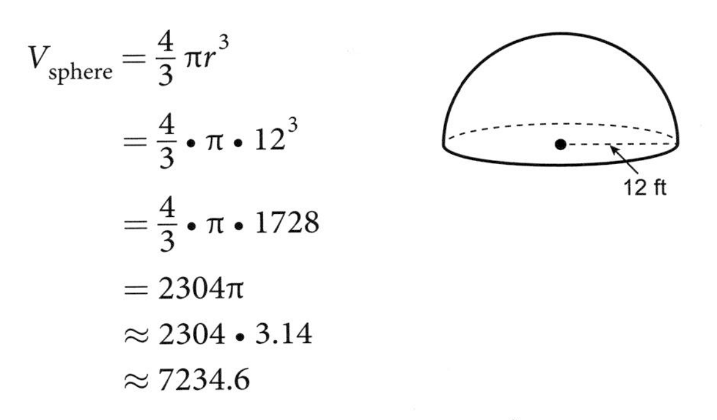

The volume of a sphere with a radius of 12 ft is about 7234.6 ft^3, so the volume of the half-sphere is $7234.6 \div 2$, or 3617.3 ft^3.

Now find the volume of cylinder. First determine the height. The height of the entire silo is 48 ft. Since the radius of the half sphere is 12 ft, the height of the cylinder is $48 - 12$, or 36 ft.

Apply the formula for finding the volume of a cylinder. Let $r = 12$ and $h = 36$.

$$\begin{aligned} V_{\text{cylinder}} &= \pi r^2 h \\ &= \pi \bullet 12^2 \bullet 36 \\ &= \pi \bullet 144 \bullet 36 \\ &= 5184\pi \\ &\approx 5184 \bullet 3.14 \\ &\approx 16{,}277.8 \end{aligned}$$

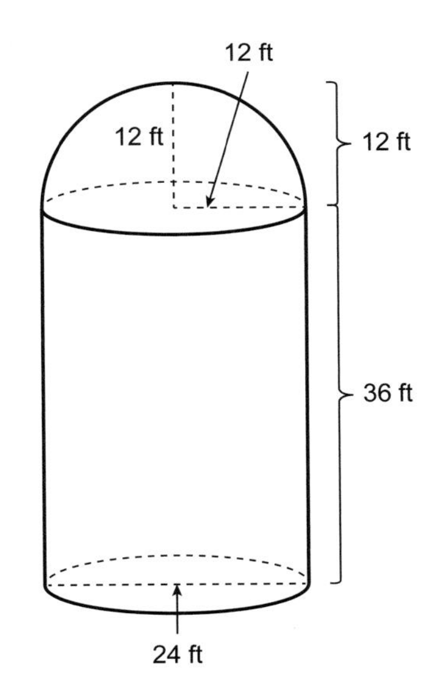

The volume of the cylinder is about 16,300 ft^3.

To find the volume of the silo, add the volume of the half-sphere and the volume of the cylinder.

$$\begin{aligned} V_{\text{silo}} &= V_{\text{half-sphere}} + V_{\text{cylinder}} \\ &\approx 3617.3 + 16{,}277.8 \\ &\approx 19{,}895.1 \end{aligned}$$

The volume of the silo is about 19,895.1 ft^3.

EXAMPLE 2

An ice-cream cone is made up of a cone topped with a half-sphere. The total height of the ice-cream cone is 11 cm, and the base of the cone has a radius of 3 cm. What is the volume of the ice-cream cone? Round your answer to the nearest tenth of a cubic centimeter.

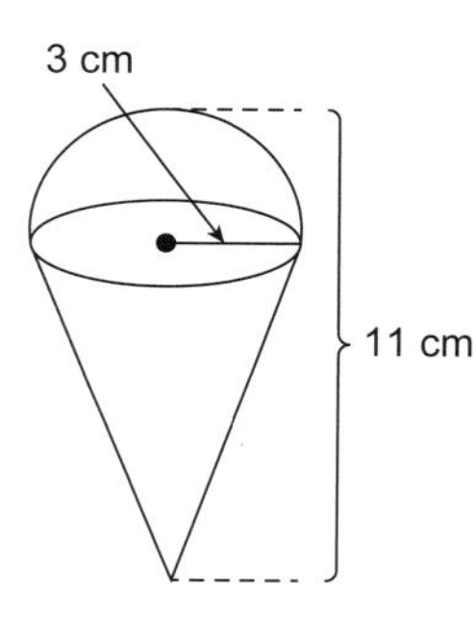

SOLUTION

The volume of the ice-cream cone is the sum of the volume of the cone and the volume of the half-sphere. Begin by finding the volume of the half-sphere. The radius of the half-sphere is equal to the radius of the cone. Therefore, the half-sphere's radius is 3 cm. Find the volume of a sphere with a radius of 3 cm and then divide the volume by 2.

$$\begin{aligned} V_{\text{sphere}} &= \frac{4}{3}\pi r^3 \\ &= \frac{4}{3} \bullet \pi \bullet 3^3 \\ &= \frac{4}{3} \bullet \pi \bullet 27 \\ &= 36\pi \\ &\approx 36 \bullet 3.14 \\ &\approx 113.0 \end{aligned}$$

The volume of a sphere with a radius of 3 cm is about 113.0 cm^3, so the volume of the half-sphere is 113.0 ÷ 2, or 56.5 cm^3.

Now find the volume of the cone. First determine the height. The height of the entire ice-cream cone is 11 cm. Since the radius of the half-sphere is 3 cm, the height of the cone is 11 − 3, or 8 cm.

Apply the formula for finding the volume of a cone. Let $r = 3$ and $h = 8$.

$$\begin{aligned} V_{cone} &= \frac{1}{3}\pi r^2 h \\ &= \frac{1}{3}\pi \bullet 3^2 \bullet 8 \\ &= \frac{1}{3}\pi \bullet 9 \bullet 8 \\ &= 24\pi \\ &\approx 24 \bullet 3.14 \\ &\approx 75.4 \end{aligned}$$

The volume of the cone is about 75.4 cm^3.

To find the volume of the ice-cream cone, add the volume of the half-sphere and the volume of the cone.

$$\begin{aligned} V_{\text{ice-cream cone}} &= V_{\text{half-sphere}} + V_{\text{cone}} \\ &\approx 56.5 + 75.4 \\ &\approx 131.9 \end{aligned}$$

The volume of the ice-cream cone is about 131.9 cm^3. ■

Transformation, Congruence, and Similarity

Topic List

- Transformations
- Congruence and Similarity
- Sequences of Transformations
- Properties of Transformations
- Transformations and Coordinates
- Similarity and Scale
- Transformations and Similarity
- The AA Criterion

Many artists use a few shapes repeated over and over. Each new version of the shape is shifted to a new location and might be rotated, flipped, or resized. The language of geometry can describe many ways in which shapes can be moved, reduced, or enlarged to make new shapes.

Transformations

A transformation is a change. With transformations, geometric figures can be moved around and altered.

A **transformation** is a change in the position, orientation, or size of a figure. There are three types of transformations that change the position, but not the size, of a figure.

▶ **Think About It** A transformation can also be defined as a mapping between two sets of points.

Reflections

Definition

A **reflection** is a transformation of a figure by flipping it across a line or line segment, creating a mirror image of the figure.

The line or line segment that the image is flipped across is called a **line of reflection**. It can also be called a line of symmetry.

EXAMPLE 1

Draw the reflection over the given line.

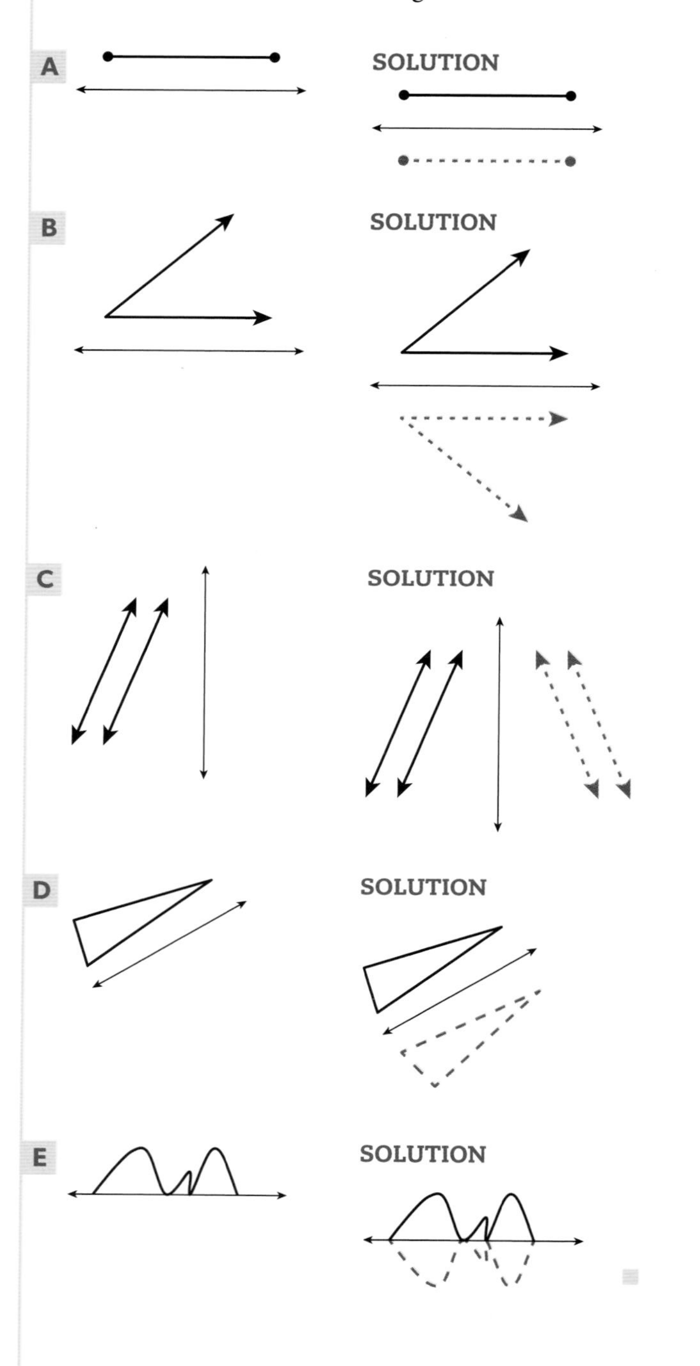

EXAMPLE 2

The figure was created by drawing the reflection of a figure over a given line. Draw all the lines of reflection that could have been used.

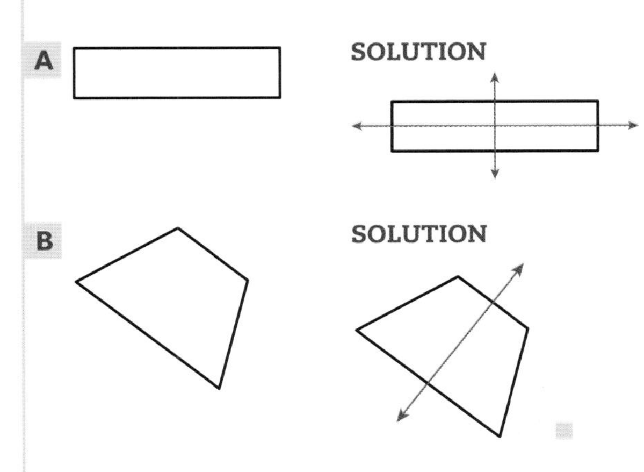

Rotations

Definition

A **rotation** is the turning of a figure around a given point.

The point the figure is rotated about is called the **center of rotation**. It can be located in, on, or outside the figure.

The number of degrees the figure is rotated is called the **angle of rotation**. It can be anywhere from 0° to 360° (a full circle). Figures can be rotated clockwise or counterclockwise.

EXAMPLE 3

Draw the rotation image about the given point.

A clockwise 90°

SOLUTION

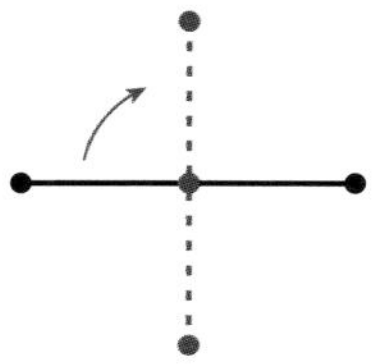

B counterclockwise 180°

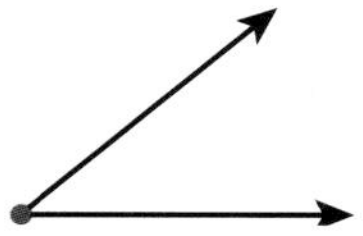

SOLUTION

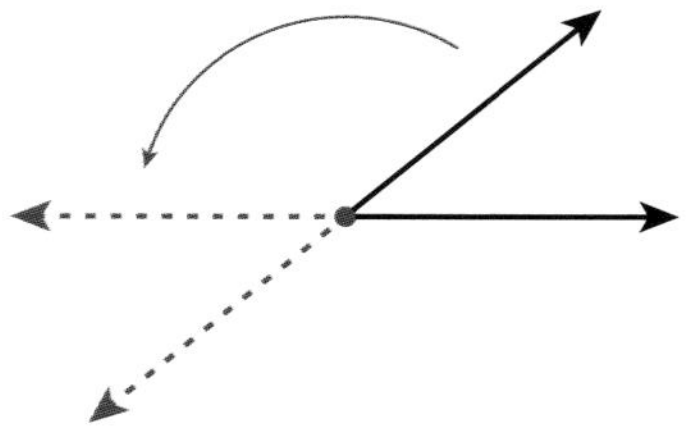

C clockwise 90°

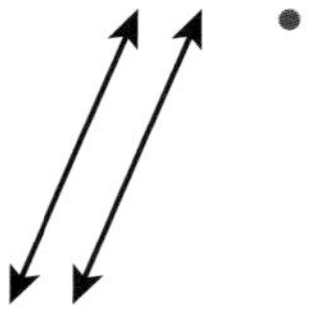

SOLUTION

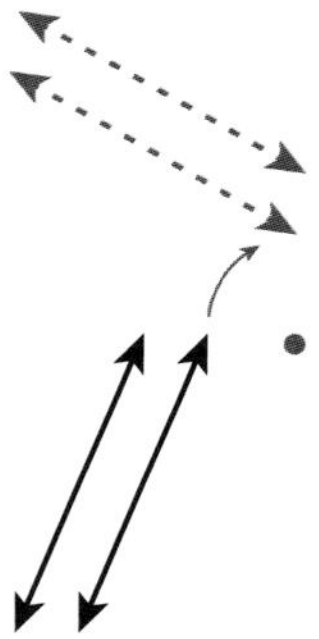

EXAMPLE 4

Draw the rotation image about the given point.

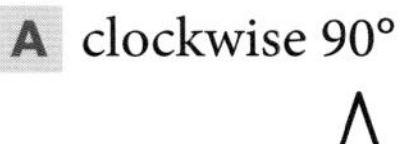

A clockwise 90°

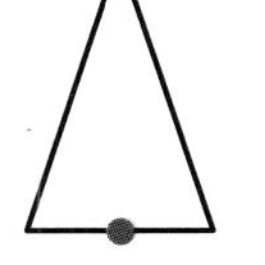

SOLUTION

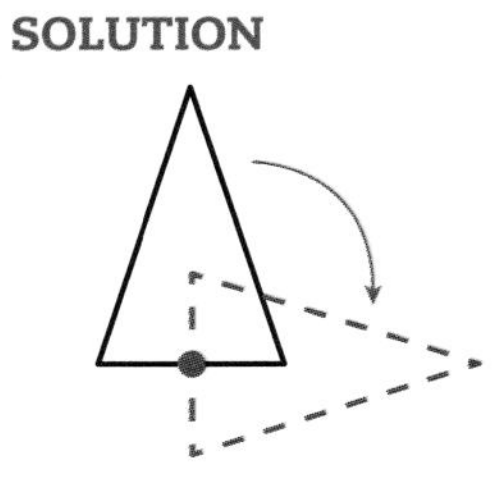

B counterclockwise 270°

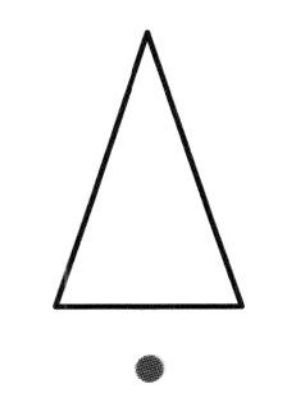

SOLUTION

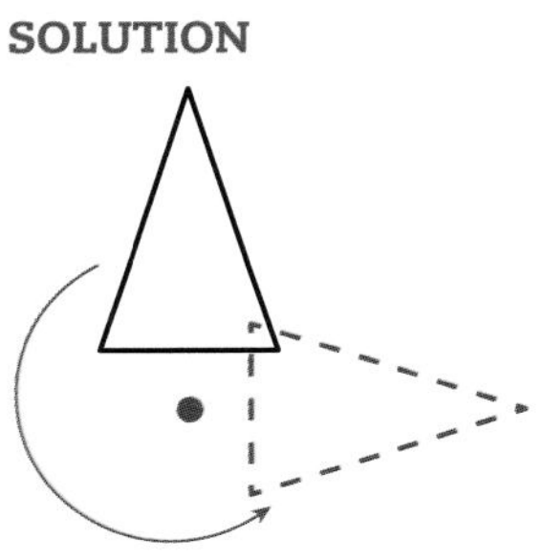

C clockwise 180°

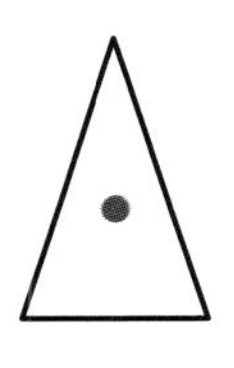

SOLUTION

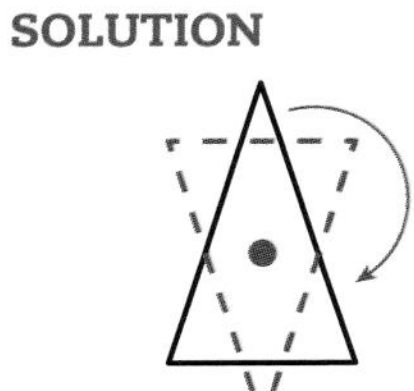

▶ **Think About It** A quarter turn (15 min on a clock) is a 90° turn. A 180° turn is halfway around a circle.

▶ **Think About It** A 180° rotation clockwise and a 180° rotation counterclockwise produce the same result.

D counterclockwise 45°

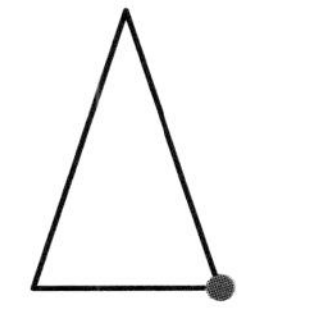

SOLUTION

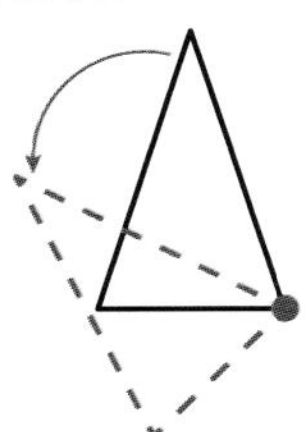

Describing Rotations

EXAMPLE 5

A The dashed figure was produced by rotating the other figure about the given point. What angle of rotation and direction could have been used?

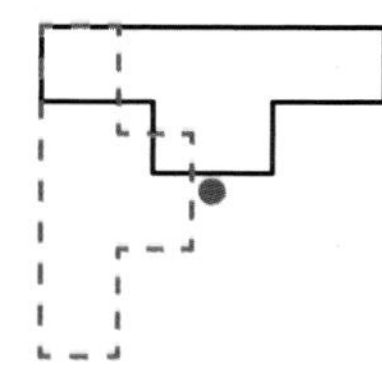

SOLUTION

The dashed figure was produced by rotating the other figure either 90° counterclockwise or 270° clockwise about the point.

B The dashed figure was produced by rotating the other figure 90° clockwise. Draw the point that was used as the center of rotation.

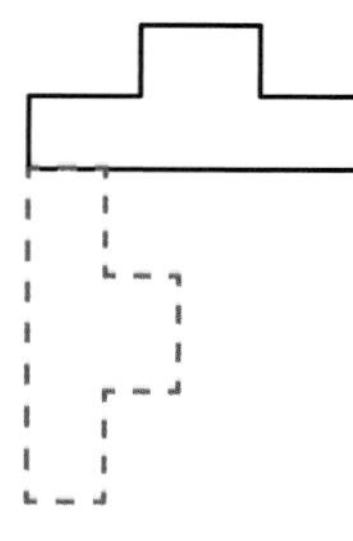

SOLUTION

Notice that the lower left point of the figure never moves.

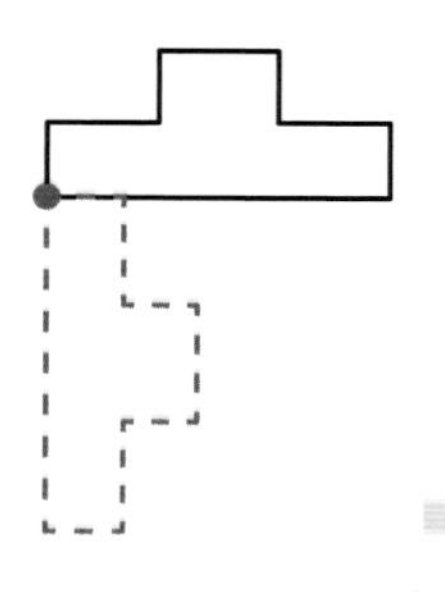

Translations

Definition

A **translation** is a sliding of a figure in a straight path without rotation or reflection.

You can use a segment with an arrow (also called a **vector**) to indicate the direction and length of a translation.

EXAMPLE 6

Draw the translation image as indicated by the vector.

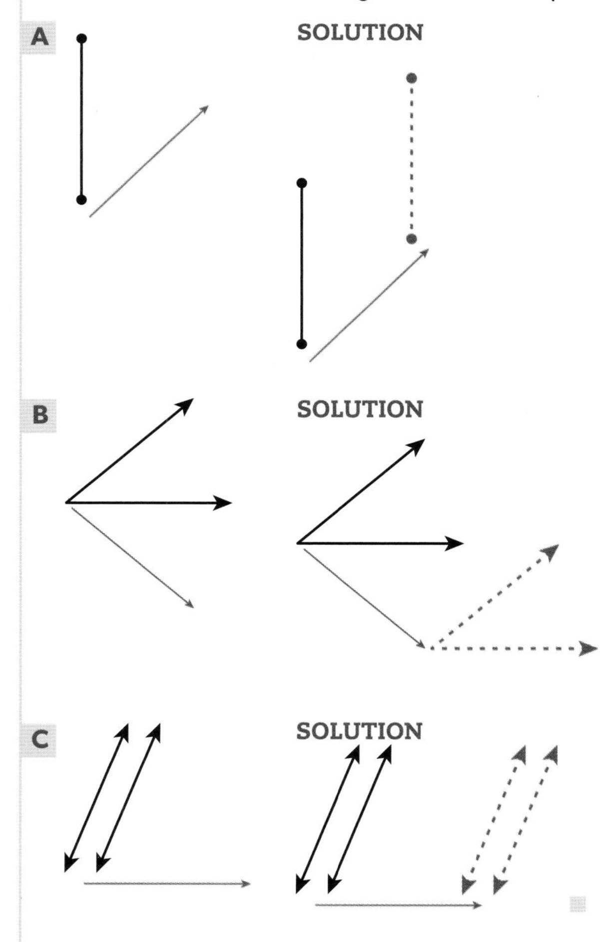

EXAMPLE 7

Draw the translation image as indicated by the vector.

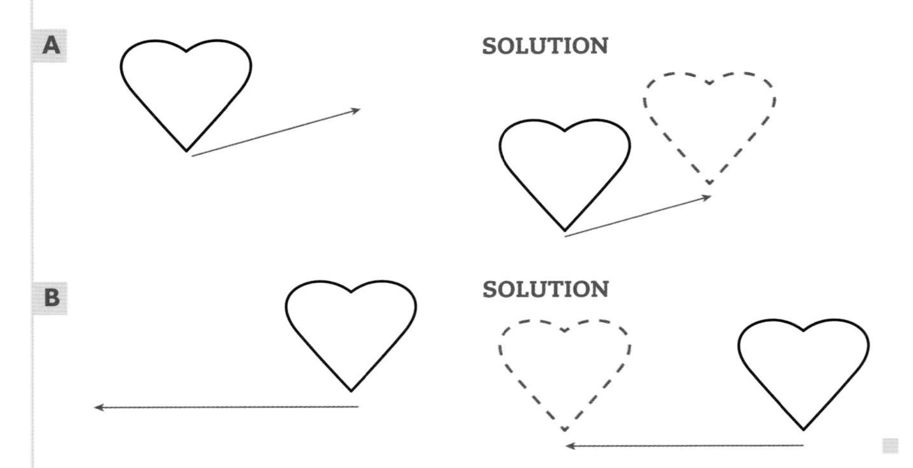

Identifying Transformations

Definitions

In a transformation, the original figure is the **pre-image**. The new figure that results from the transformation is the **image**.

EXAMPLE 8

Determine what type of transformation was done to the pre-image to result in the image shown. Write *reflection*, *rotation*, *translation*, or *none of these*.

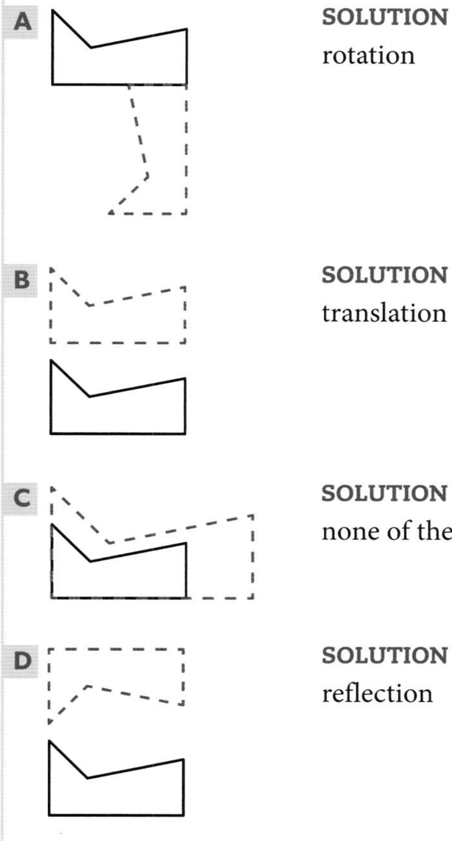

A

SOLUTION

rotation

B

SOLUTION

translation

C

SOLUTION

none of these

D

SOLUTION

reflection ■

Application: Graphic Design

EXAMPLE 9

A designer is working with logos on a grid. He is told to translate this logo 1 unit down and 3 units to the right, and then to perform a 90° clockwise rotation about the point that is at the center of the X. Draw the resulting figure.

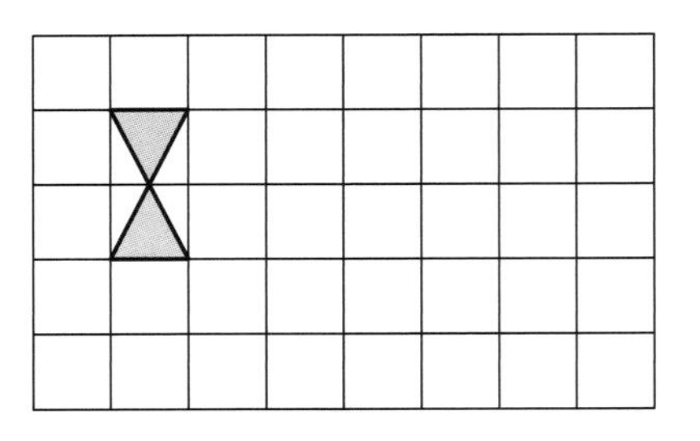

SOLUTION

Slide 1 down and 3 right.

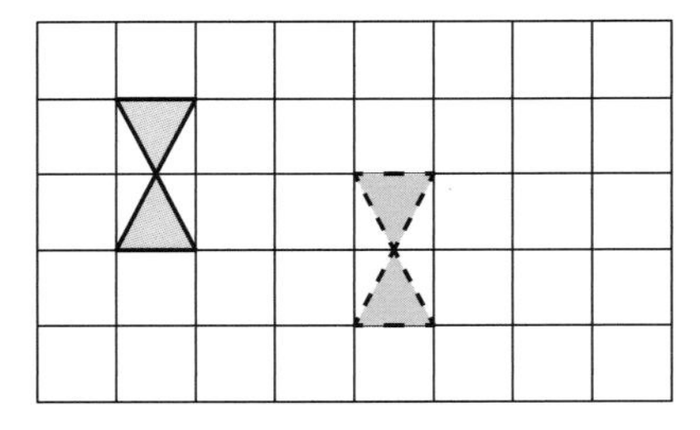

Then rotate 90° clockwise.

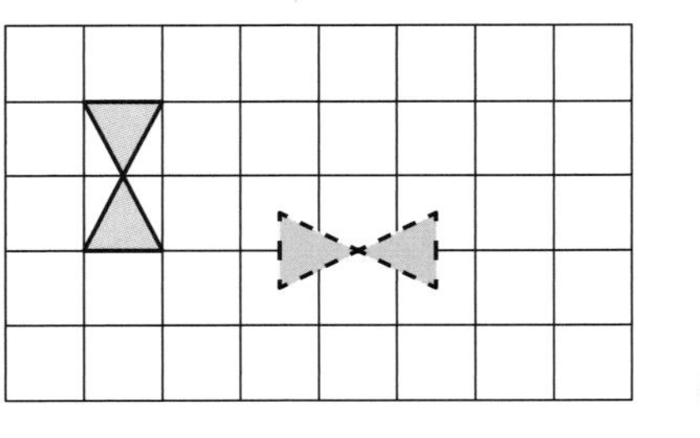

▶ **Think About It** A 90° counterclockwise rotation would have produced the same result.

Congruence and Similarity

If you can flip, turn, or slide one figure to make it look exactly like another, then the figures are **congruent**. If you can throw a shrink or stretch in there and make two figures the same, then they are **similar**.

Congruent polygons have the same size and shape. If one polygon is placed on top of the other, the polygons match up exactly.

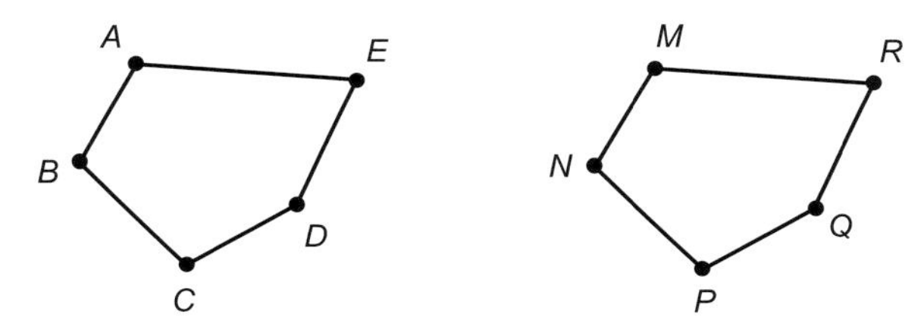

When polygons are congruent, all pairs of corresponding angles are congruent and all pairs of corresponding sides are congruent.

▶ **Think About It** The corresponding parts are the parts that match up with each other.

Determining Whether Two Polygons Are Congruent

EXAMPLE 1

Determine whether the polygons are congruent.

A

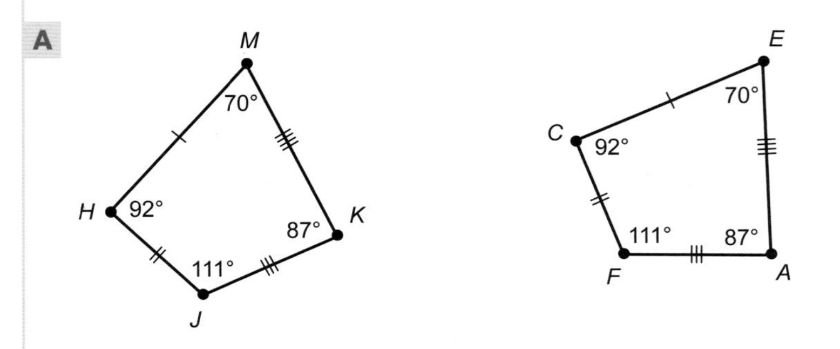

SOLUTION

Yes, every angle and side in *MHJK* has a corresponding congruent part in *ECFA*.

B

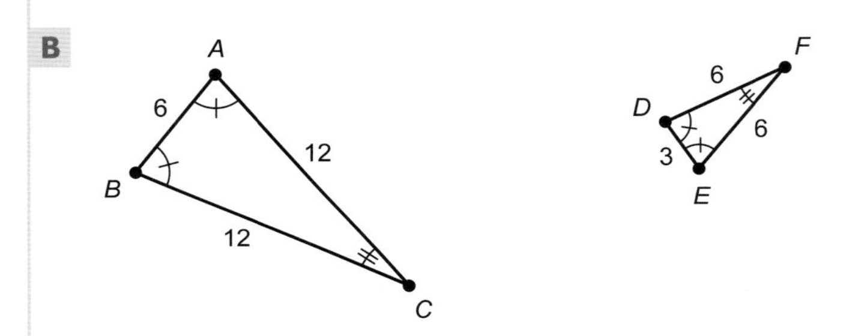

SOLUTION

No, there are three pairs of congruent angles, but the corresponding segments are not congruent.

Interpreting Congruence Statements

A congruence statement gives the names of two congruent polygons. The order of the vertices in the names shows which angles correspond to each other. Possible congruence statements for the congruent quadrilaterals in Example 1A are $MHJK \cong ECFA$ and $JHMK \cong FCEA$.

EXAMPLE 2

Given that $\triangle WKM \cong \triangle APR$, name all pairs of congruent angles and sides in the polygons.

SOLUTION

To list the corresponding angles, match the first vertex in the first name with the first vertex in the second name, and so on.

$\angle W \cong \angle A \qquad \angle K \cong \angle P \qquad \angle M \cong \angle R$

To list the corresponding sides, match the endpoints of the sides.

$\overline{WK} \cong \overline{AP} \qquad \overline{WM} \cong \overline{AR} \qquad \overline{KM} \cong \overline{PR}$ ■

▶ **Think About It** To list congruent sides of polygons with many sides, sketch and label the polygons.

Finding Missing Measures in Congruent Polygons

EXAMPLE 3

Find each missing measure.

A Given $ABCD \cong PQRS$, find $m\angle Q$ and $m\angle R$.

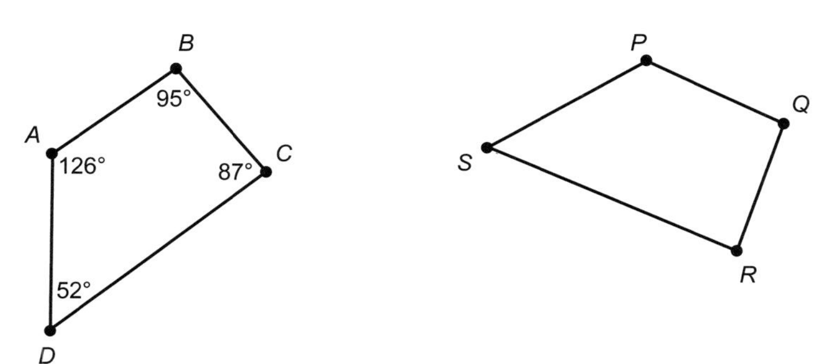

SOLUTION

Use the congruence statement to determine which angles in $ABCD$ correspond to angles Q and R.

Since $\angle Q \cong \angle B$, $m\angle Q = m\angle B = 95°$.

Since $\angle R \cong \angle C$, $m\angle R = m\angle C = 87°$.

B $MNPR \cong CEDH$, $MN = 3.2$, $NP = 6.5$, $PR = 4.5$, and $RM = 9$
Find CE and DH.

SOLUTION

Use the congruence statement to determine which sides in $MNPR$ correspond to sides $\overline{CE}$ and $\overline{DH}$.

Since $\overline{CE} \cong \overline{MN}$, $CE = MN = 3.2$.

Since $\overline{DH} \cong \overline{PR}$, $DH = PR = 4.5$.

Determining Whether Two Polygons Are Similar

Similar polygons are the same shape but not necessarily the same size. If they are not the same size, reducing or enlarging one of the polygons proportionally would make them so. The symbol for similarity is $\sim$.

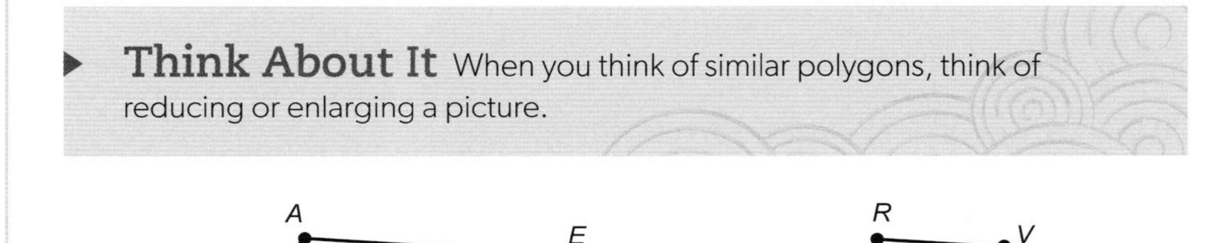

▶ **Think About It** When you think of similar polygons, think of reducing or enlarging a picture.

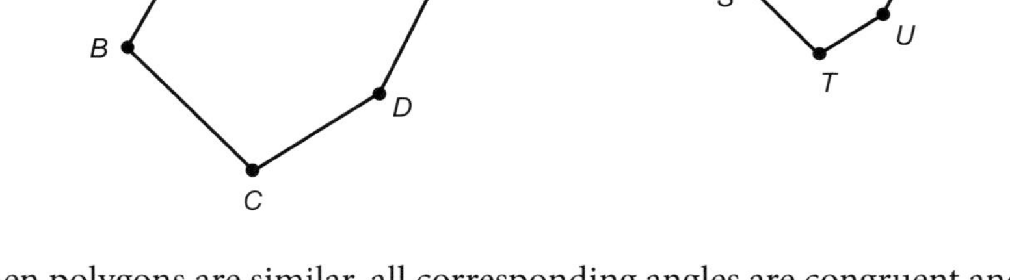

When polygons are similar, all corresponding angles are congruent and all corresponding sides are proportional. Congruent polygons are similar polygons with sides in a 1 : 1 ratio.

EXAMPLE 4

Determine whether the polygons are similar.

A

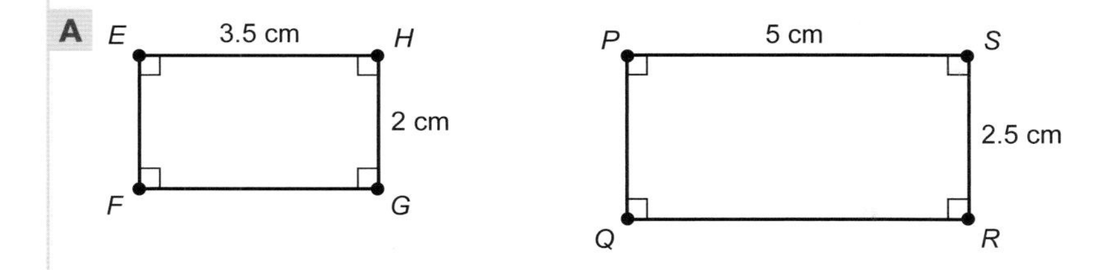

SOLUTION

The corresponding angles are congruent. Check whether the sides are proportional.

$$\frac{EH}{PS} = \frac{3.5}{5} = 0.7 \text{ and } \frac{HG}{SR} = \frac{2}{2.5} = 0.8$$

The sides are not proportional. The polygons are not similar.

B

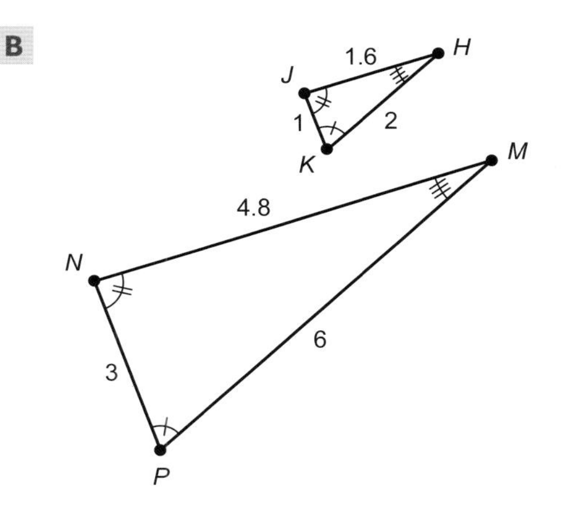

SOLUTION

The corresponding angles are congruent. Check whether the sides are proportional.

$$\frac{NM}{JH} = \frac{4.8}{1.6} = 3 \text{ and } \frac{NP}{JK} = \frac{3}{1} = 3 \text{ and } \frac{PM}{KH} = \frac{6}{2} = 3$$

The sides are proportional. The polygons are similar.

Writing and Interpreting Similarity Statements

A similarity statement names two similar polygons, and the order of the vertices shows which angles are congruent.

EXAMPLE 5

Write a similarity statement for the similar polygons.

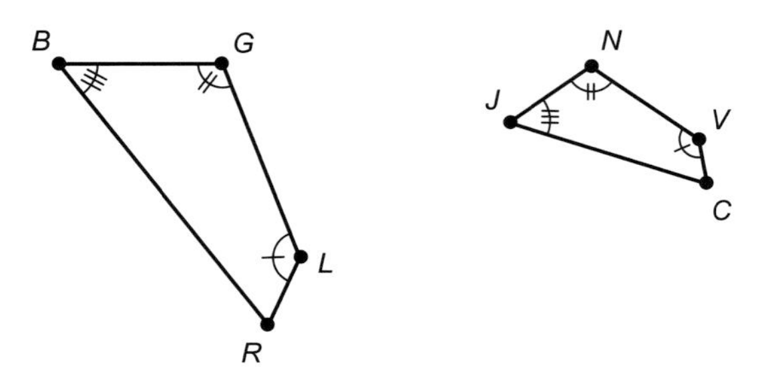

SOLUTION

Name the second polygon in the same order you name the first. One possible similarity statement is $BGLR \sim JNVC$.

EXAMPLE 6

Given that $\triangle ADP \sim \triangle RBK$, name all the pairs of congruent angles, and write a proportionality statement for the sides.

SOLUTION

Use the order of the vertices to list the corresponding angles.

$$\angle A \cong \angle R \qquad \angle D \cong \angle B \qquad \angle P \cong \angle K$$

To write the proportionality statement, set the ratios of the corresponding sides equal to each other.

$$\frac{AD}{RB} = \frac{DP}{BK} = \frac{AP}{RK}$$

Finding Missing Measures in Similar Polygons

EXAMPLE 7

Given $ESMT \sim CRGP$, find ET and PG.

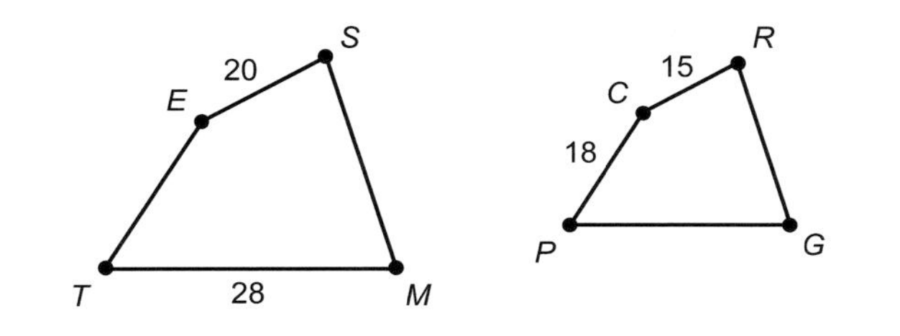

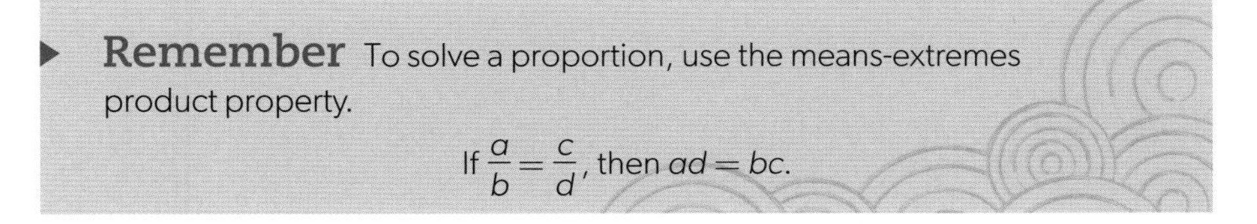

SOLUTION

Write proportions so that each has one ratio with two known corresponding side lengths and one ratio with one unknown length.

$$\frac{ET}{CP} = \frac{ES}{CR} \qquad \frac{ES}{CR} = \frac{TM}{PG}$$

$$\frac{ET}{18} = \frac{20}{15} \qquad \frac{20}{15} = \frac{28}{PG}$$

$$15 \bullet ET = 360 \qquad 20 \bullet PG = 420$$

$$ET = 24 \qquad PG = 21$$

Application: Photography

EXAMPLE 8

A photographer reduces a photograph that is 16 in. wide by 20 in. long so that it is 10 in. wide. What is the length of the reduced photograph if it is similar to the original photograph?

SOLUTION

Write and solve a proportion.

$$\frac{\text{width original}}{\text{width reduced}} = \frac{\text{length original}}{\text{length reduced}}$$

$$\frac{16}{10} = \frac{20}{x}$$

$$16x = 200$$

$$x = 12.5$$

The length of the reduced photograph is 12.5 in. ■

Sequences of Transformations

Reflections, rotations, and translations produce congruent figures.

Showing Multiple Transformations and Congruence

Two figures are congruent if one of the figures can be obtained by translating, reflecting, and/or rotating the other figure.

EXAMPLE

What sequence of transformations results in the transformation of parallelogram $ABCD$ to parallelogram $A''B''C''D''$?

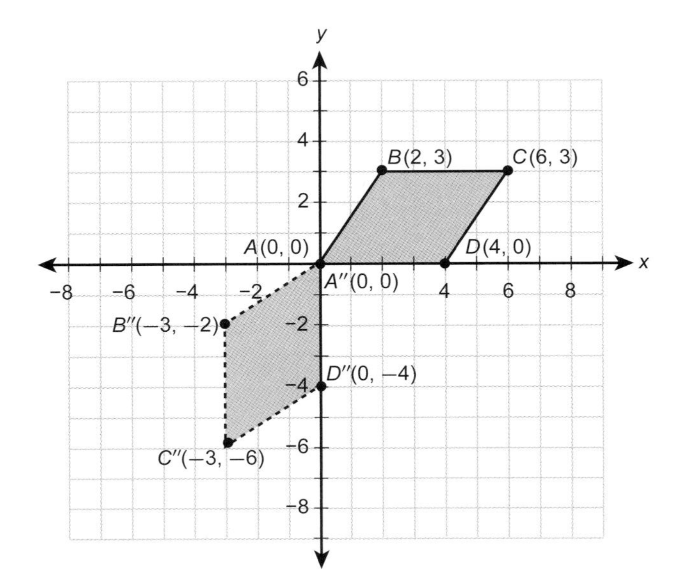

SOLUTION

Reflecting parallelogram $ABCD$ across the x-axis results in parallelogram $A'B'C'D'$.

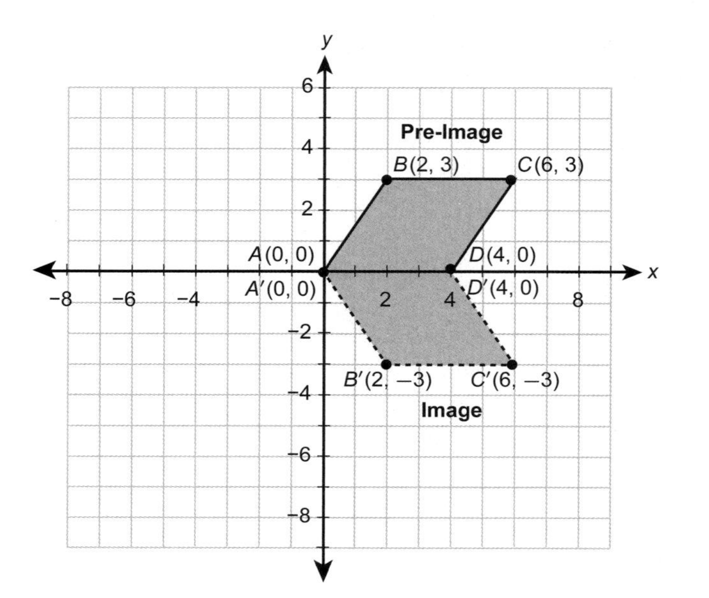

Rotating parallelogram $A'B'C'D'$ clockwise 90° about the origin results in parallelogram $A''B''C''D''$.

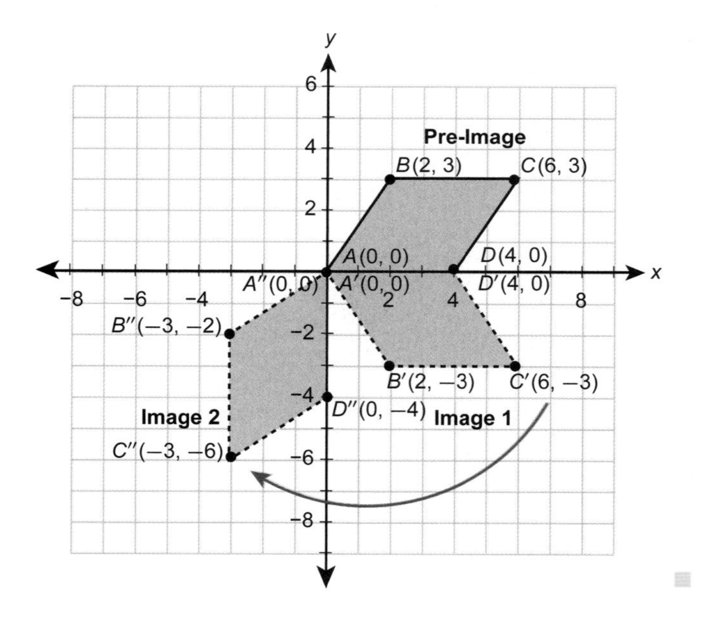

Properties of Transformations

Reflections, rotations, and translations are transformations that result in images that are congruent to the pre-image.

Verifying Rigid Transformations

Properties of Rigid Transformations

When a figure is reflected, rotated, or translated,

- A line in the pre-image has a corresponding line in the image.
- A line segment in the pre-image has a corresponding congruent line segment in the image.
- An angle in the pre-image has a corresponding congruent angle in the image.
- Parallel lines in the pre-image have corresponding parallel lines in the image.

Reflections, rotations, and translations are called **rigid transformations** because they do not change the size or shape of a figure. They only change a figure's location or orientation. You can experiment with paper folding to verify these properties.

EXAMPLE

Jacob has a rectangular piece of paper that he folded. The folds are indicated by dashed lines.

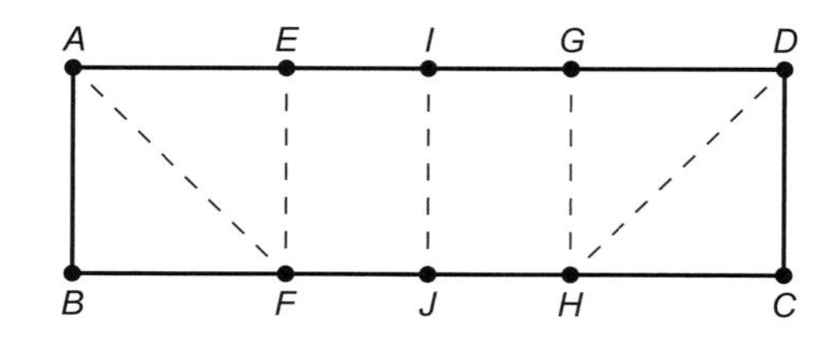

A Jacob concluded that $\overline{AB}$ is congruent to $\overline{AE}$. Why was he able to draw this conclusion?

SOLUTION

When he folded the paper along $\overline{AF}$, $\overline{AB}$ lay directly over $\overline{AE}$.

Folding the paper along $\overline{AF}$ allowed Jacob to reflect $\overline{AB}$ about $\overline{AF}$.

Reflecting a segment about a line results in another segment of equal length.

You can think of $\overline{AE}$ as the image of the reflection of $\overline{AB}$.

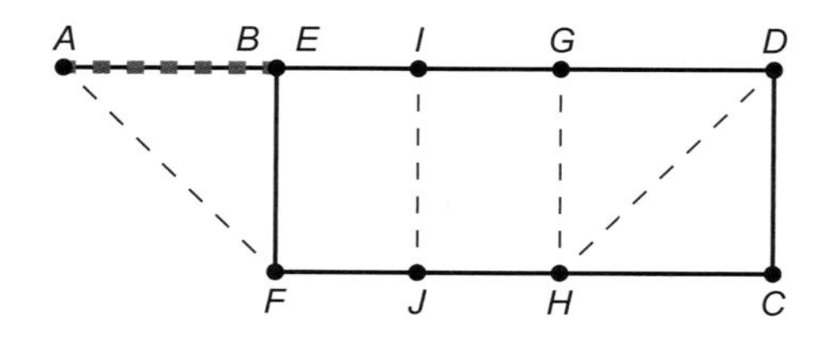

B Is $\overline{AF}$ congruent to $\overline{DH}$? How do you know?

SOLUTION

Yes, $\overline{AF}$ is congruent to $\overline{DH}$. Jacob began with the original paper.

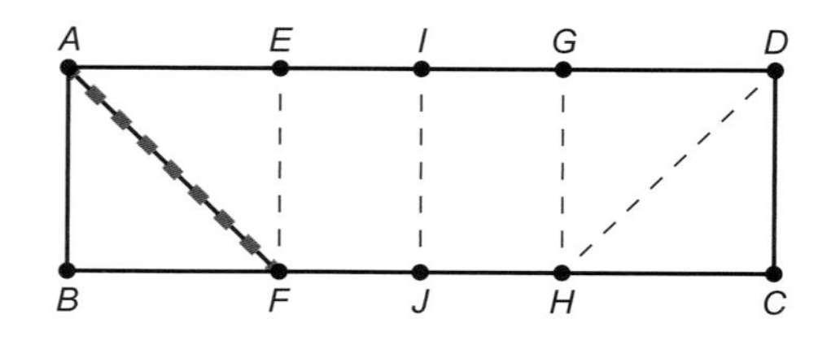

When he folded the paper along $\overline{IJ}$, $\overline{AF}$ lay directly on top of $\overline{DH}$, with point A corresponding directly with point D and point F corresponding directly with point H.

Folding the paper along $\overline{IJ}$ allowed Jacob to reflect $\overline{AF}$ about $\overline{IJ}$.

You can think of $\overline{DH}$ as the image of the reflection of $\overline{AF}$.

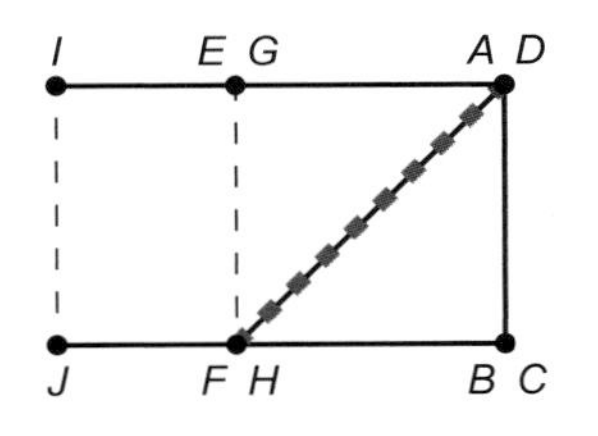

C How can Jacob fold the paper to show that $\triangle BFA$ is congruent to $\triangle GHD$?

SOLUTION

Jacob should start with the original paper and shade $\triangle BFA$.

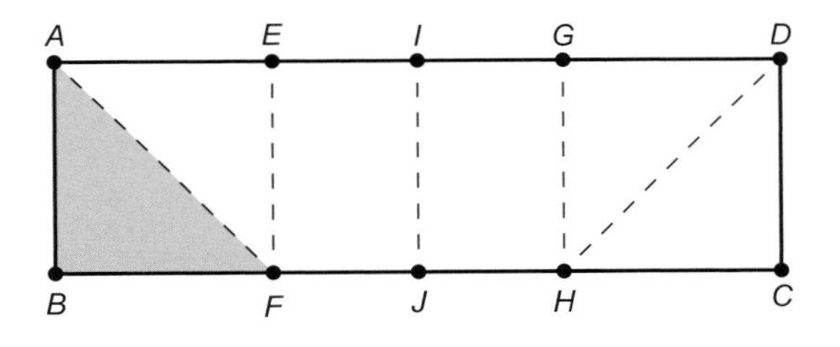

Next he should fold the paper along $\overline{AF}$.

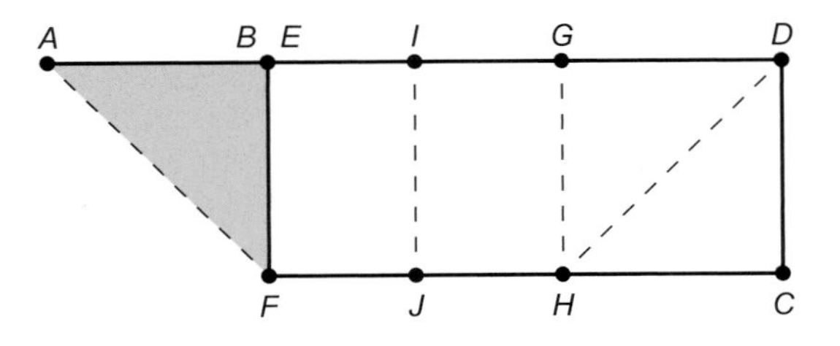

Then he should fold the paper again along $\overline{IJ}$.

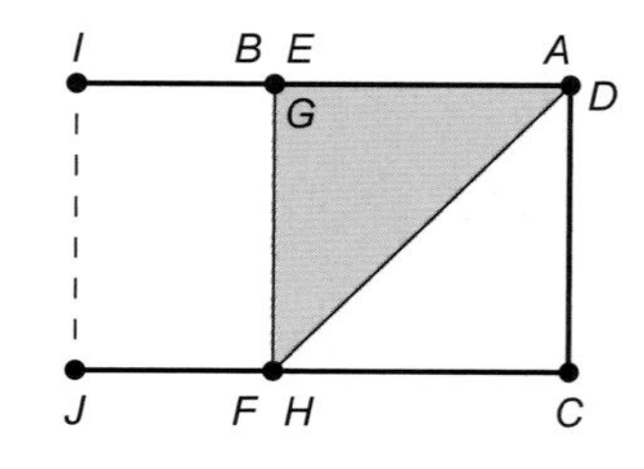

D Describe the transformations that took place in Example C.

SOLUTION

Triangle ABF was reflected about $\overline{AF}$, and then $\triangle ABF$ was reflected about $\overline{IJ}$. ■

Transformations and Coordinates

Compare the coordinates of a figure's pre-image and image to determine how it was transformed.

Translations with Coordinates

When a point (x, y) is translated a units horizontally and b units vertically, the coordinates of the image are $(x + a, y + b)$.

EXAMPLE 1

Triangle ABC has vertices $A(1, 3)$, $B(4, 2)$, and $C(2, -1)$. What are the vertices of triangle $A'B'C'$ when triangle ABC is translated 4 units to the right and 3 units down?

SOLUTION

Add 4 to each x-coordinate and add -3 to each y-coordinate of each vertex of the triangle.

$$A(1, 3) \rightarrow A'(1 + 4, 3 + (-3)) \text{ or } A'(5, 0)$$
$$B(4, 2) \rightarrow B'(4 + 4, 2 + (-3)) \text{ or } B'(8, -1)$$
$$C(2, -1) \rightarrow B'(2 + 4, -1 + (-3)) \text{ or } C'(6, -4)$$

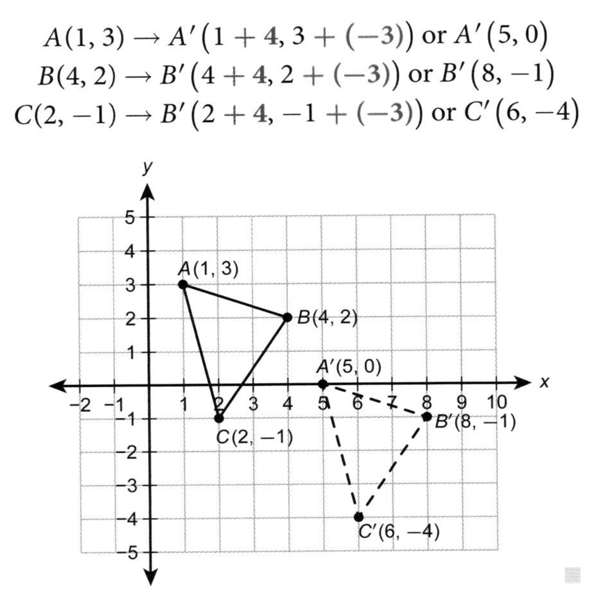

EXAMPLE 2

Rectangle $WXYZ$ has vertices $W(-1, 2)$, $X(2, 2)$, $Y(2, -3)$, and $Z(-1, -3)$. The rectangle is translated so that the vertices of the image are $W'(-3, 6)$, $X'(0, 6)$, $Y'(0, 1)$, and $Z'(-3, 1)$. Describe the translation.

SOLUTION

Choose a point in the pre-image and its corresponding point in the image, such as point $W(-1, 2)$ and point $W'(-3, 6)$.

Find the number of units the rectangle moved horizontally by subtracting the x-coordinate of the point in the pre-image from the x-coordinate of the corresponding point in the image. So subtract the x-coordinate of point W from the x-coordinate of point W'.

$$-3 - (-1) = -3 + 1 = -2$$

The rectangle was translated 2 units to the left.

Next find the number of units the rectangle moved vertically by subtracting the y-coordinate of the point in the pre-image from the y-coordinate of the corresponding point in the image. So subtract the y-coordinate of point W from the y-coordinate of point W'.

$$6 - 2 = 4$$

The rectangle was translated 4 units up. ■

Reflections with Coordinates

When a point (x, y) is reflected about the x-axis, the coordinates of the image are $(x, -y)$.

When a point (x, y) is reflected about the y-axis, the coordinates of the image are $(-x, y)$.

EXAMPLE 3

Triangle ABC has vertices $A(-5, 4)$, $B(-1, 1)$, and $C(-3, -2)$. The triangle is reflected about the y-axis. What are the coordinates of the vertices in the image?

SOLUTION

When a point is reflected about the y-axis, the x-coordinates of the pre-image and image are opposites and the y-coordinates are the same.

$$A(-5, 4) \rightarrow A'(5, 4)$$
$$B(-1, 1) \rightarrow B'(1, 1)$$
$$C(-3, -2) \rightarrow C'(3, -2)$$

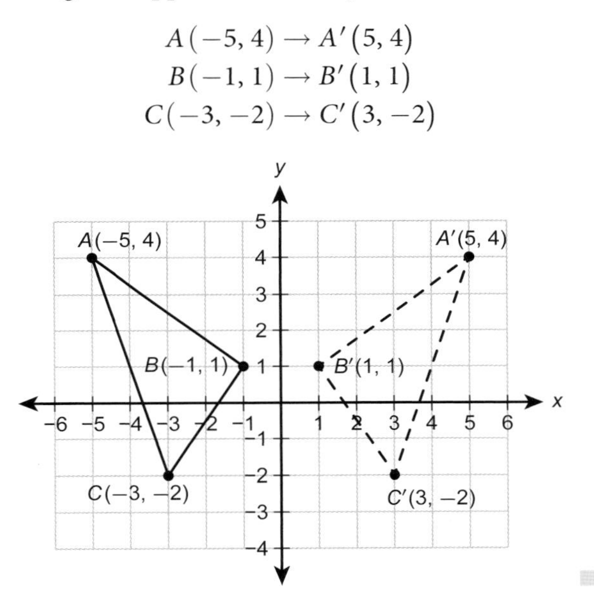

EXAMPLE 4

Triangle DEF has vertices $D(1, 6)$, $E(4, 3)$, and $F(2, 1)$. The triangle is transformed so that the vertices of the image have coordinates $D'(1, -6)$, $E'(4, -3)$, and $F'(2, -1)$. Describe the transformation.

SOLUTION

The vertices in the pre-image and image have the same x-coordinates, but their y-coordinates are opposites. Therefore, triangle DEF was reflected about the x-axis.

Rotations with Coordinates

When a point (x, y) is rotated 90° counterclockwise about the origin, the coordinates of the image are $(-y, x)$.

When a point (x, y) is rotated 90° clockwise about the origin, the coordinates of the image are $(y, -x)$.

When a point (x, y) is rotated 180° counterclockwise or clockwise about the origin, the coordinates of the image are $(-x, -y)$.

EXAMPLE 5

Parallelogram $LMNO$ has vertices $L(1, 5)$, $M(3, 5)$, $N(4, 1)$, and $O(2, 1)$.

A The parallelogram is rotated counterclockwise about the origin. What are the coordinates of the vertices in the image?

SOLUTION

When a point is rotated 90° counterclockwise about the origin, the x-coordinate of the image is the opposite of the y-coordinate in the pre-image, and the y-coordinate of the image is the same as the x-coordinate in the pre-image.

$$\begin{array}{c} \quad (x, y) \qquad (-y, x) \\ L(1, 5) \rightarrow L'(-5, 1) \\ M(3, 5) \rightarrow M'(-5, 3) \\ N(4, 1) \rightarrow N'(-1, 4) \\ O(2, 1) \rightarrow O'(-1, 2) \end{array}$$

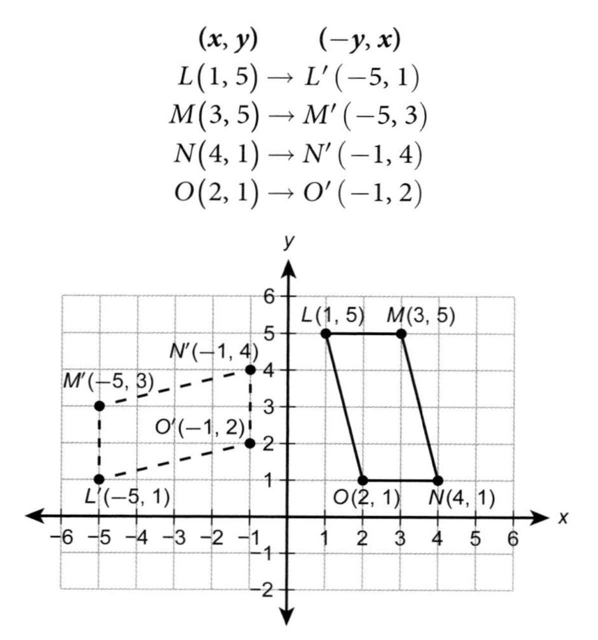

B Parallelogram *LMNO* is rotated 180° clockwise about the origin. What are the coordinates of the vertices in the image?

SOLUTION

When a point is rotated 180° in either a clockwise or counterclockwise direction about the origin, the *x*- and *y*-coordinates of the image are the opposite of the *x*- and *y*-coordinates of the pre-image.

$$
\begin{aligned}
&(x, y) \qquad (-x, -y)\\
&L(1, 5) \rightarrow L'(-1, -5)\\
&M(3, 5) \rightarrow M'(-3, -5)\\
&N(4, 1) \rightarrow N'(-4, -1)\\
&O(2, 1) \rightarrow O'(-2, -1)
\end{aligned}
$$

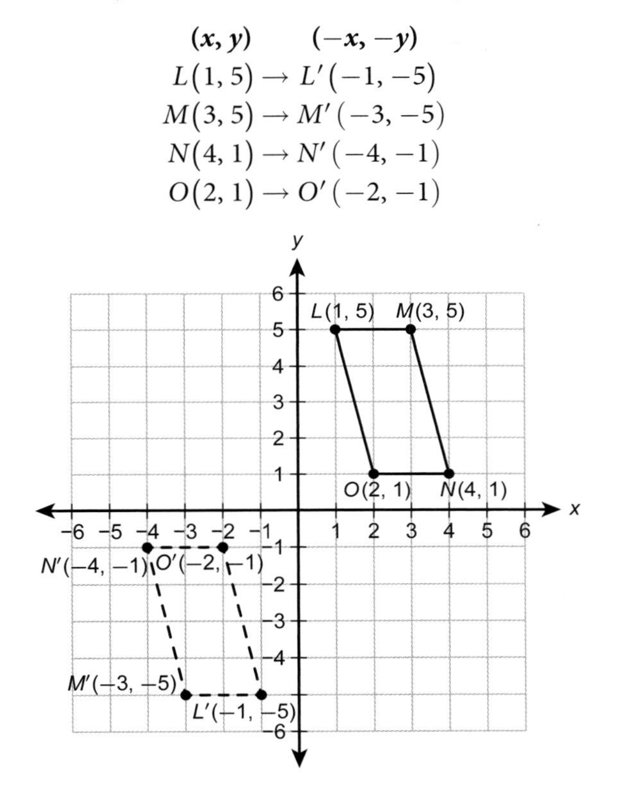

C Parallelogram *LMNO* is transformed so that the coordinates of the vertices in the image are $L'(5, -1)$, $M'(5, -3)$, $N'(1, -4)$, and $O'(1, -2)$. Describe the transformation.

SOLUTION

The x-coordinates in the image are the same as the y-coordinates in the pre-image. The y-coordinates in the image are the opposite of the x-coordinates in the pre-image.

$$\begin{array}{rcl} (x, y) & & (y, -x) \\ L(1, 5) & \rightarrow & L'(5, -1) \\ M(3, 5) & \rightarrow & M'(5, -3) \\ N(4, 1) & \rightarrow & N'(1, -4) \\ O(2, 1) & \rightarrow & O'(1, -2) \end{array}$$

Therefore, parallelogram *LMNO* is rotated 90° clockwise about the origin. ■

Dilations with Coordinates

When a figure is dilated by a scale factor of a with the origin as the center of dilation, the image of any point (x, y) on the figure is (ax, ay).

EXAMPLE 6

Trapezoid *PQRS* has vertices $P(1, 1)$, $Q(2, 3)$, $R(4, 3)$, and $S(5, 1)$.

A The trapezoid is dilated by a scale factor of 2 with the origin as the center of dilation. What are the coordinates of the vertices in the image?

SOLUTION

Multiply the coordinates of each vertex by the scale factor.

$$P(1, 1) \rightarrow P'(1 \bullet 2, 1 \bullet 2) \text{ or } P'(2, 2)$$
$$Q(2, 3) \rightarrow Q'(2 \bullet 2, 3 \bullet 2) \text{ or } Q'(4, 6)$$
$$R(4, 3) \rightarrow R'(4 \bullet 2, 3 \bullet 2) \text{ or } R'(8, 6)$$
$$S(5, 1) \rightarrow S'(5 \bullet 2, 1 \bullet 2) \text{ or } S'(10, 2)$$

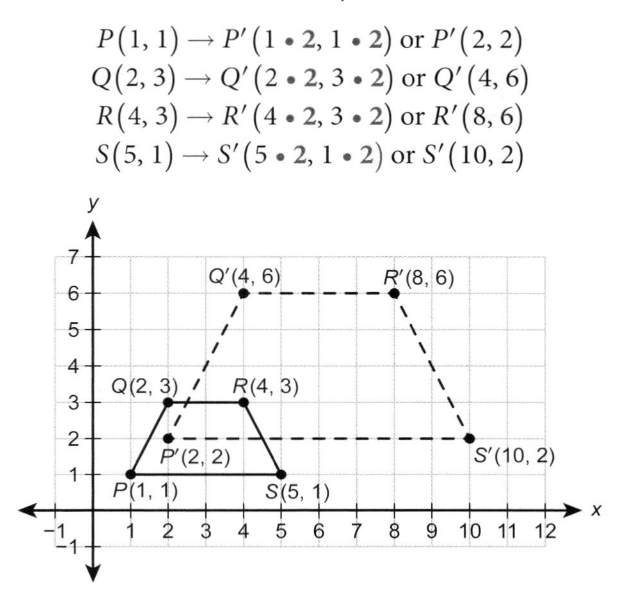

B Trapezoid *PQRS* is transformed so that the vertices of the image are $P'\left(\frac{1}{4}, \frac{1}{4}\right)$, $Q'\left(\frac{1}{2}, \frac{3}{4}\right)$, $R'\left(1, \frac{3}{4}\right)$, and $S'\left(\frac{5}{4}, \frac{1}{4}\right)$. Describe the transformation.

SOLUTION

The coordinates of the vertices in the image are the result of multiplying the coordinates of the vertices in the pre-image by $\frac{1}{4}$. Therefore, trapezoid *PQRS* is dilated by a scale factor of $\frac{1}{4}$.

Similarity and Scale

Similar figures are figures that have the exact same shape but not necessarily the same size.

Figures are similar if corresponding angles are congruent and corresponding sides are proportional.

▶ **Remember** Congruent angles are angles having equal measures.

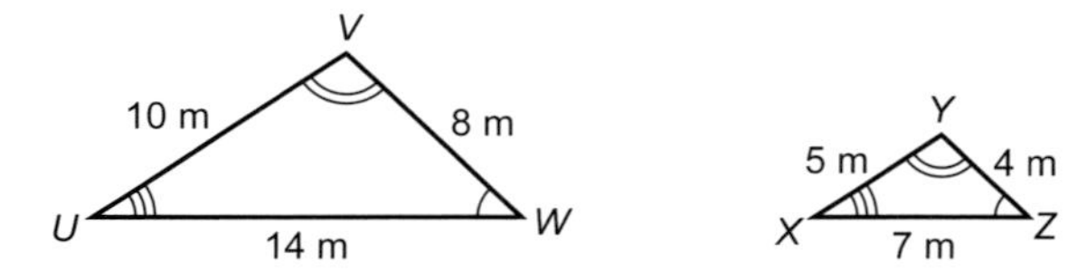

$\triangle UVW$ is similar to $\triangle XYZ$.

$\angle U \cong \angle X$	$\angle V \cong \angle Y$	$\angle W \cong \angle Z$	
$\frac{UV}{XY} = \frac{VW}{YZ}$	$\frac{UV}{XY} = \frac{WU}{ZX}$	$\frac{VW}{YZ} = \frac{WU}{ZX}$	
$\frac{10}{5} \stackrel{?}{=} \frac{8}{4}$	$\frac{10}{5} \stackrel{?}{=} \frac{14}{7}$	$\frac{8}{4} \stackrel{?}{=} \frac{14}{7}$	Cross multiply to compare.
$10 \cdot 4 \stackrel{?}{=} 5 \cdot 8$	$10 \cdot 7 \stackrel{?}{=} 5 \cdot 14$	$8 \cdot 7 \stackrel{?}{=} 4 \cdot 14$	
$40 = 40$ ✓	$70 = 70$ ✓	$56 = 56$ ✓	

▶ **Think About It** UV means the length of $\overline{UV}$.

Determining Whether Two Figures Are Similar

EXAMPLE 1

Determine whether *ABCD* and *EFGH* are similar.

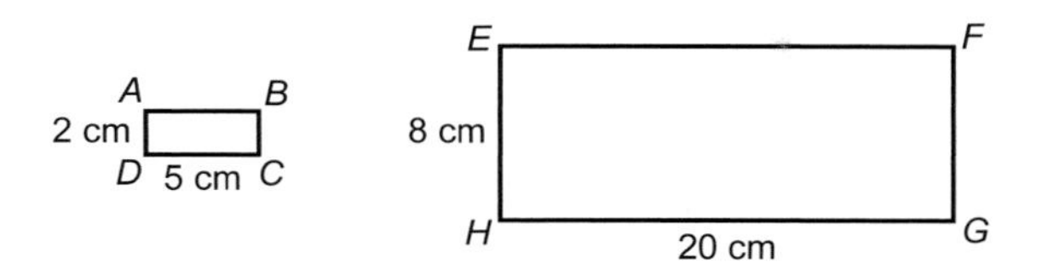

SOLUTION

Step 1 Check corresponding angles.

Because both figures are rectangles, all angles measure 90°.

$$\angle A \cong \angle E,\ \angle B \cong \angle F, \angle C \cong \angle G, \angle D \cong \angle H$$

Therefore, corresponding angles are congruent.

Step 2 Check corresponding sides.

If corresponding sides are proportional, then $\frac{AD}{EH} = \frac{DC}{HG}$.

$\frac{2}{8} \stackrel{?}{=} \frac{5}{20}$ Write the measures of the side lengths as a proportion, and check if the proportion is true.

$2 \bullet 20 \stackrel{?}{=} 8 \bullet 5$ Cross multiply to see whether the fractions are equal.

$40 = 40$ ✓

Because corresponding angles are congruent and corresponding sides are proportional, the rectangles are similar. ■

Using Similarity to Find Missing Side Lengths

You can use the properties of similar figures to find a missing side.

EXAMPLE 2

$\triangle GHI$ and $\triangle JKL$ are similar. What is the length of $\overline{JK}$?

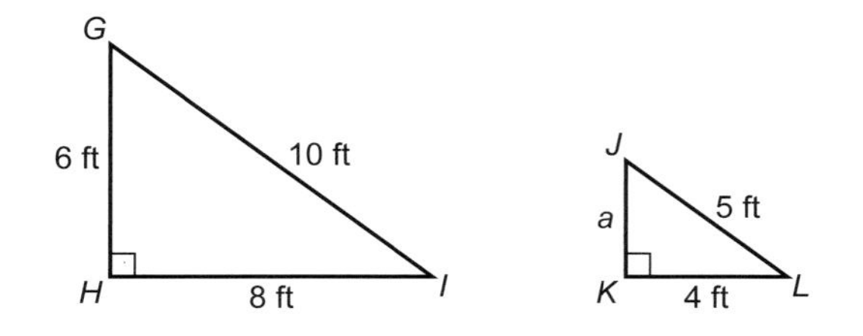

SOLUTION

$\overline{GH}$ corresponds to $\overline{JK}$. $\overline{HI}$ corresponds to $\overline{KL}$. Set up the corresponding sides as a proportion. Then solve for a.

$\frac{6}{a} = \frac{8}{4}$	Write a proportion.
$6 \bullet 4 = 8a$	Cross multiply.
$\frac{24}{8} = \frac{8a}{8}$	Divide both sides by 8.
$3 = a$	Simplify.

The length of $\overline{JK}$ is 3 ft. ■

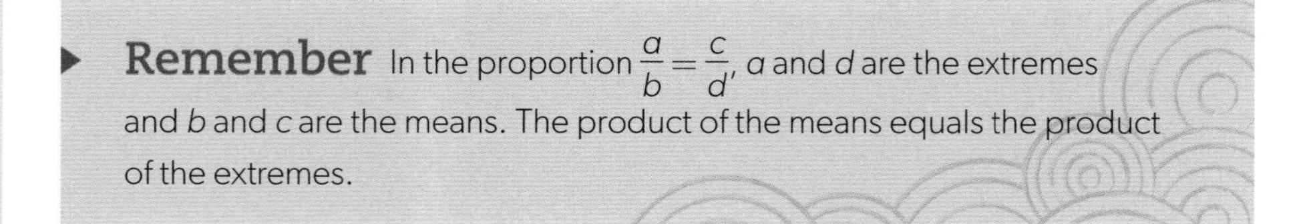

Determining Scale

Scale factor is a ratio of one measure to another. You can find a scale factor from one figure to another by using the ratio of corresponding parts.

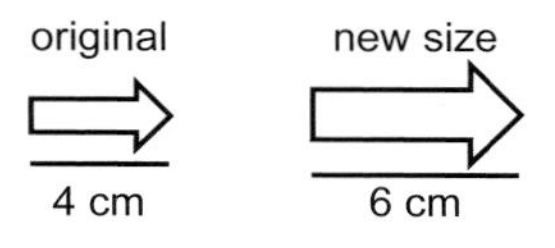

For the two arrows, the new size is an enlargement. To find the scale factor, write a ratio comparing corresponding sides.

$\frac{\text{new size}}{\text{original size}} = \frac{6 \text{ cm}}{4 \text{ cm}} = \frac{3}{2}$ The scale factor for the arrows is 3 : 2 or 1.5.

EXAMPLE 3

The regular pentagons shown are similar. What is the scale factor?

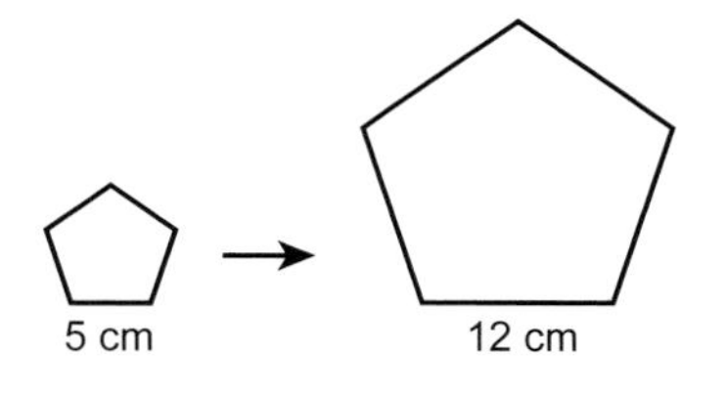

▶ **Think About It** All regular pentagons are similar to each other.

SOLUTION

The new size is an enlargement, so the scale factor is greater than 1.

The scale factor is $\frac{12}{5}$. ■

Using Scale Factor

A scale factor greater than 1 indicates an enlargement. A scale factor less than 1 indicates a reduction. A scale factor equal to 1 means there is no change in size.

EXAMPLE 4

An equilateral triangle with side length of 8 cm is multiplied by the scale factors. State whether the new triangle is an enlargement or a reduction. Then find the side length of the new size.

A $\frac{3}{4}$

SOLUTION

This scale factor is a reduction because it is less than 1.

Multiplying by the scale factor, $\frac{3}{4} \bullet 8 = 6$. The new side measure is 6 cm.

B 8 : 1

SOLUTION

The scale factor is $\frac{8}{1} = 8$. This scale factor is an enlargement because 8 is greater than 1. Multiplying by the scale factor, $8 \bullet 8 = 64$. The new side measure is 64 cm.

C 2.2

SOLUTION

This scale factor is an enlargement because it is greater than 1. Multiplying by the scale factor, $2.2 \bullet 8 = 17.6$. The new side measure is 17.6 cm.

Application: Photography

EXAMPLE 5

A rectangular picture is 2.5 in. wide and 4 in. long. If the picture is enlarged so that it is 10 in. long, what is the new width?

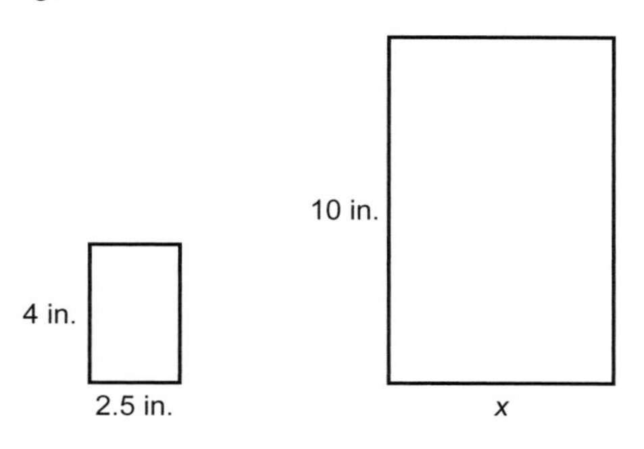

SOLUTION

Because the new size is an enlargement, the pictures will be similar.

$\frac{2.5}{x} = \frac{4}{10}$	Set up a proportion using corresponding sides.
$2.5 \cdot 10 = 4x$	Cross multiply.
$\frac{25}{4} = \frac{4x}{4}$	Divide both sides by 4.
$6.25 = x$	Simplify.

The width of the enlarged picture is 6.25 in. ■

Transformations and Similarity

Figures are similar if one figure is the result of dilating the other figure.

Multiple Transformations with Dilations

Translations, reflections, and rotations are rigid transformations, meaning they do not change the size or shape of a figure. Therefore, when you translate, reflect, or rotate a figure, the image and pre-image are congruent. A dilation is not a rigid transformation. When you dilate a figure, the shape of the figure doesn't change, but the size of the figure does change. Therefore, the image of a dilation is not congruent to the pre-image. Instead, it is similar to the pre-image.

When a sequence of transformations includes a dilation, the image and pre-image are similar.

EXAMPLE 1

Use transformations to determine whether triangles *ABC* and *DEF* are similar. Explain how you know.

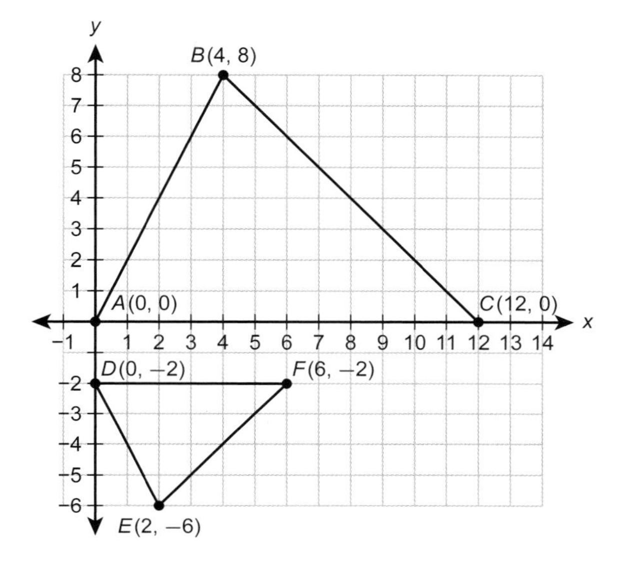

SOLUTION

Triangles *ABC* and *DEF* are similar if you can perform a sequence of transformations on one triangle to produce the other triangle. Therefore, try to find a sequence of transformations that you can perform on triangle *ABC* to produce triangle *DEF*.

Step 1 Notice that the side *AC* is 12 units and side *DF* is 6 units. Since *DF* is half the length of *AC*, dilate triangle *ABC* by a scale factor of $\frac{1}{2}$.

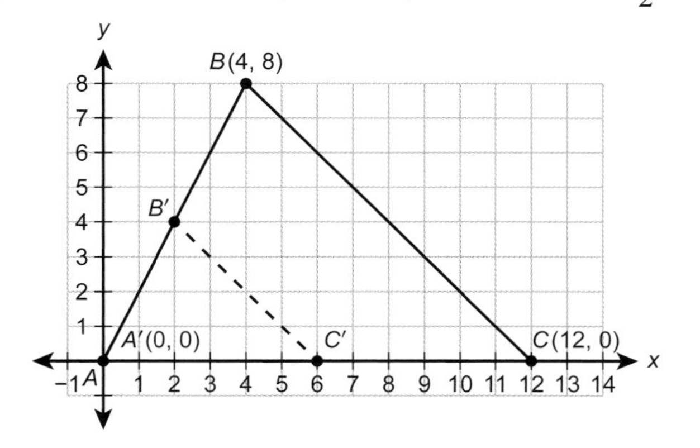

Step 2 Reflect triangle $A'B'C'$ about the x-axis.

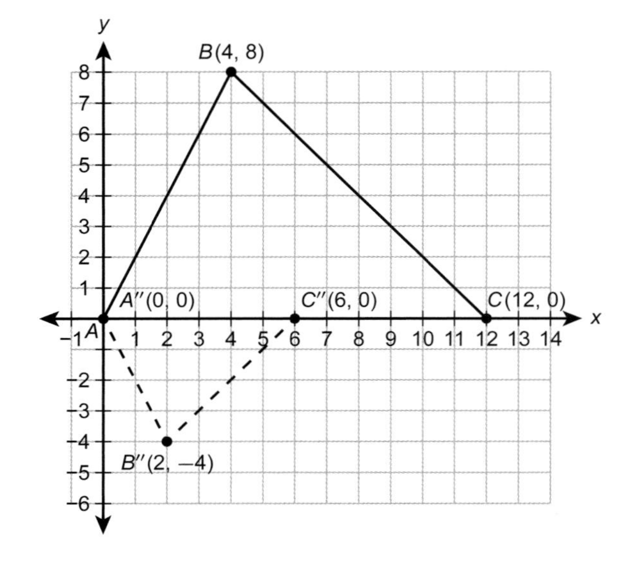

Step 3 Translate triangle $A''B''C''$ down 2 units.

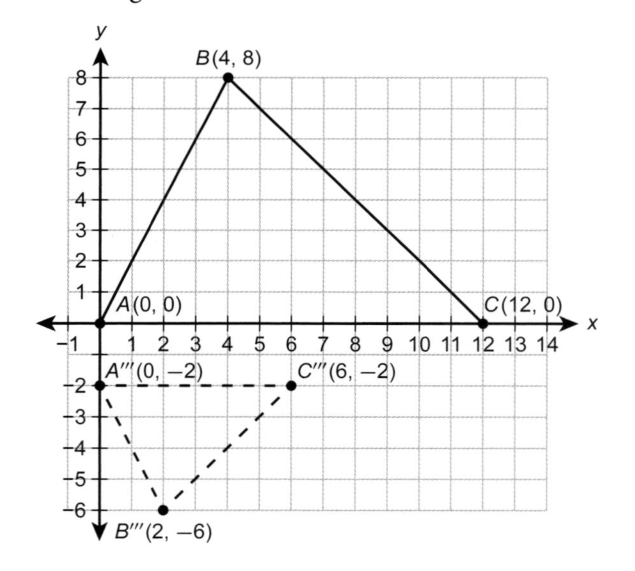

Triangle $A'''B'''C'''$ is similar to triangle ABC. Notice that the vertices of triangle $A'''B'''C'''$ are the same as the vertices of triangle DEF. Therefore, triangles $A'''B'''C'''$ and DEF are congruent. Since triangle ABC is similar to triangle $A'''B'''C'''$ and triangle DEF is congruent to triangle $A'''B'''C'''$, triangle ABC is similar to triangle DEF. ■

EXAMPLE 2

Use transformations to determine whether rectangles *RSTU* and *LMNO* are similar. Explain how you know.

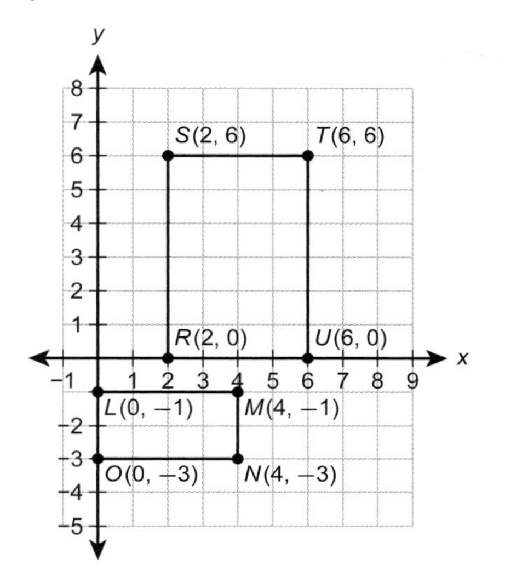

SOLUTION

Try to find a sequence of transformations that you can perform on rectangle *RSTU* to produce rectangle *LMNO*.

Step 1 Side *MN* is half the length of side *ST*. Therefore, dilate rectangle *RSTU* by a scale factor of $\frac{1}{2}$.

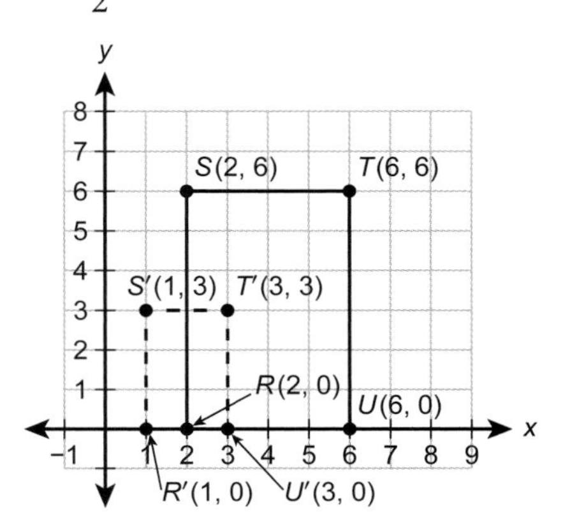

Step 2 Rotate rectangle $R'S'T'U'$ clockwise about the origin.

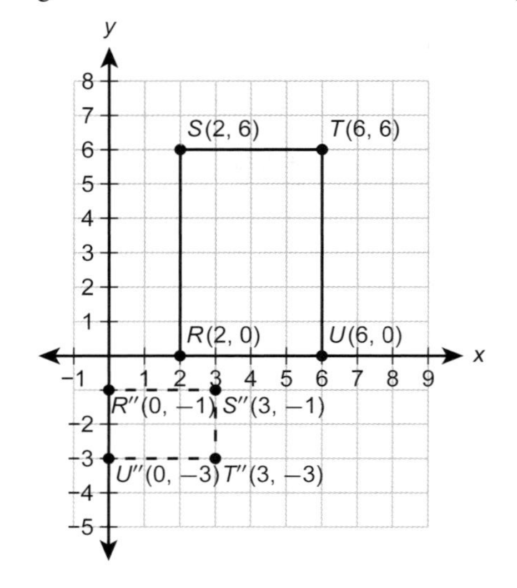

Rectangle $R''S''T''U''$ is similar to rectangle $RSTU$.

Now compare rectangle $R''S''T''U''$ to rectangle $LMNO$. Notice that although vertices R'' and U'' have the same coordinates as vertices L and O, vertices S'' and T'' have different coordinates than vertices M and N.

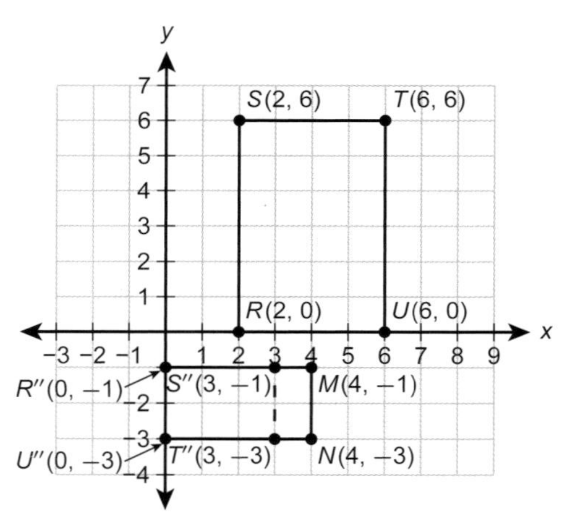

Since only some of the vertices of rectangle $LMNO$ match up with the four vertices of rectangle $R''S''T''U''$, rectangle $LMNO$ is not congruent to rectangle $R''S''T''U''$ and not similar to rectangle $RSTU$.

The AA Criterion

To show that two triangles are similar, it is sufficient to show that two angles of one triangle are congruent to two angles of the other triangle.

Similar Triangles

The Angle-Angle (AA) Criterion

If two angles of one triangle are congruent to two angles of another triangle, then the triangles are similar.

When two triangles are similar, all the angles of one triangle are congruent to all the angles of the other triangle. For example, triangle ABC is similar to triangle DEF.

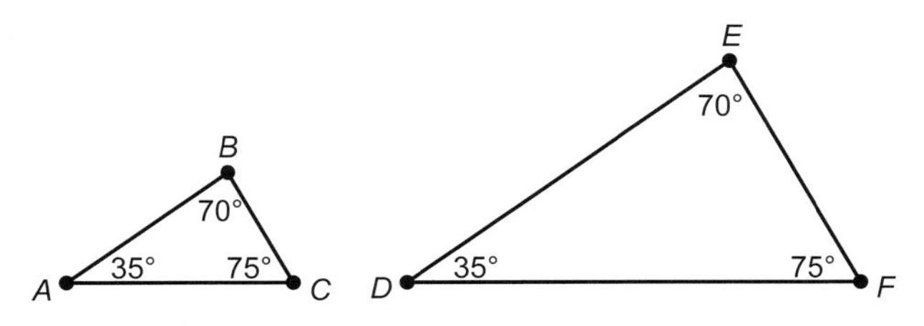

Notice that $\angle A \cong \angle D$, $\angle B \cong \angle E$, and $\angle C \cong \angle F$.

The AA criterion states that it is only necessary to show that two angles of one triangle are congruent to two angles of the other triangle to show that the triangles are similar. Why is this so?

Suppose you have triangles LMN and RST.

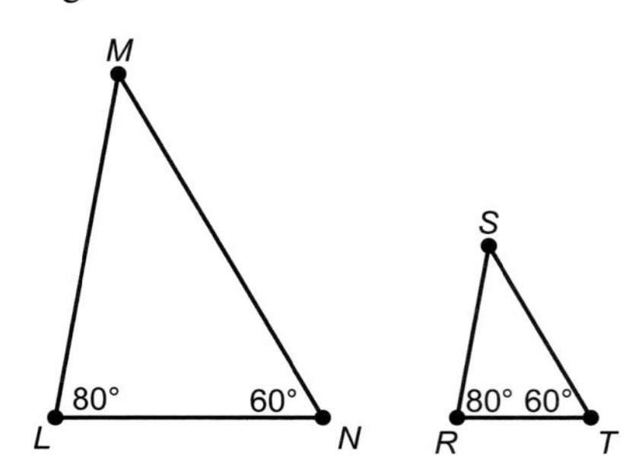

By looking at the triangles, you can see that $\angle L$ is congruent to $\angle R$ and $\angle N$ is congruent $\angle T$.

What does this tell you about $\angle M$ and $\angle S$? Solve for the measures of these angles.

$$\begin{aligned} m\angle M &= 180° - (m\angle L + m\angle N) \\ &= 180° - (80° + 60°) \\ &= 180° - 140° \\ &= 40° \end{aligned}$$

$$\begin{aligned} m\angle S &= 180° - (m\angle R + m\angle T) \\ &= 180° - (80° + 60°) \\ &= 180° - 140° \\ &= 40° \end{aligned}$$

$\angle M$ is congruent to $\angle S$.

When two angles of one triangle are congruent to two angles of another triangle, the third angle of both triangles must also be congruent. Therefore, showing that the two angles of one triangle are congruent to the two angles of another triangle is sufficient to show that the triangles are similar.

EXAMPLE

Determine whether the triangles are similar.

A

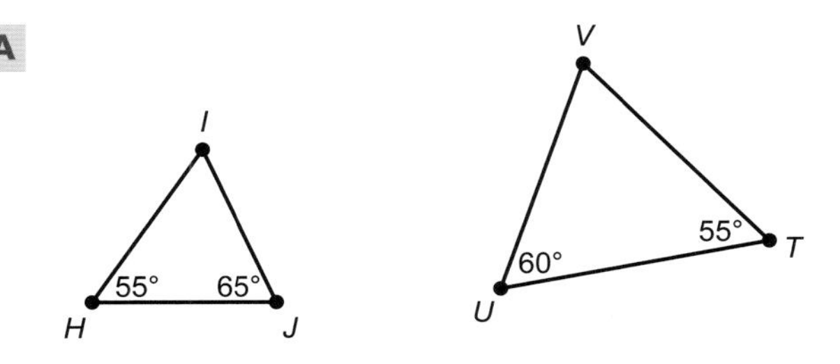

SOLUTION

Determine whether two angles of triangle *HIJ* are congruent to two angles of triangle *TUV*. Immediately, you can see that $\angle H$ is congruent to $\angle T$, so you already know that one angle of triangle *HIJ* is congruent to one angle of triangle *TUV*.

Look at the remaining angles. Angles *J* and *U* are not congruent, and angles *I* and *V* are unknown. For the triangles to be similar, you must show that at least one more angle of triangle *HIJ* is congruent to one more angle of triangle *TUV*. Solve for the measure of one of the unknown angles.

$$\begin{aligned} m\angle I &= 180° - (m\angle H + m\angle J) \\ &= 180° - (55° + 65°) \\ &= 180° - 120° \\ &= 60° \end{aligned}$$

The measure of angle *I* is 60°, which is equal to the measure of angle *U*. Therefore, angle *I* is congruent to angle *U*. Since $\angle H \cong \angle T$ and $\angle I \cong \angle U$, you can conclude by the AA criterion that the triangles are similar.

▶ **Think About It** Instead of solving for the measure of $\angle I$, you can also solve for the measure of angle *V* to show that $\angle J \cong \angle V$.

$$\begin{aligned} m\angle V &= 180° - (m\angle T + m\angle U) \\ &= 180° - (55° + 60°) \\ &= 180° - 115° \\ &= 65° \end{aligned}$$

B

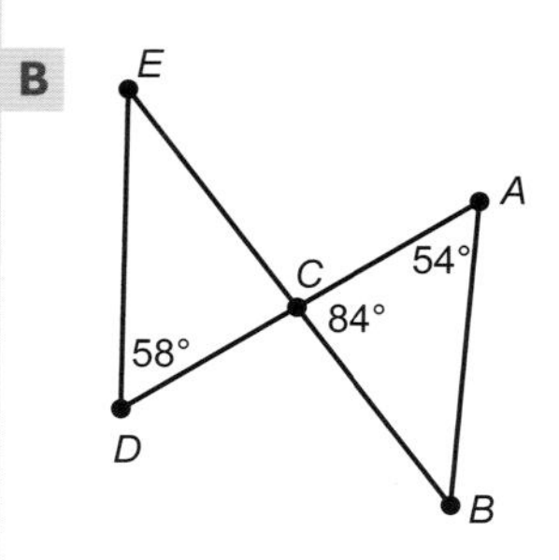

SOLUTION

Determine whether two angles of triangle *DEC* are congruent to two angles of triangle *ABC*.

To begin, notice that angles *ECD* and *BCA* are vertical angles. Therefore, they are congruent. The measure of angle *ECD* is 84°.

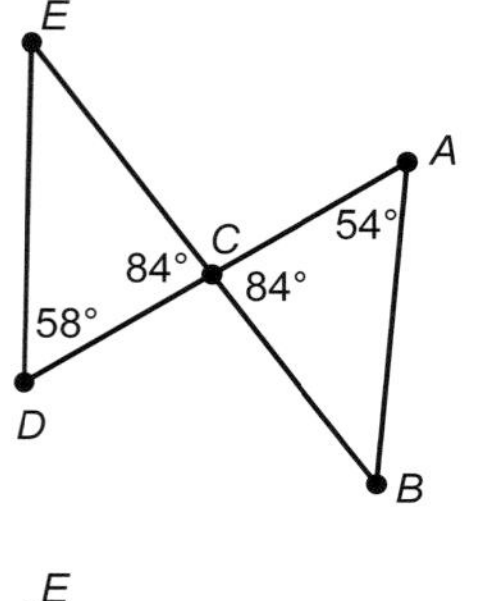

Solve for the unknown angle in each triangle.

$$\begin{aligned} m\angle E &= 180° - (m\angle ECD + m\angle D) \\ &= 180° - (84° + 58°) \\ &= 180° - 142° \\ &= 38° \end{aligned}$$

$$\begin{aligned} m\angle B &= 180° - (m\angle A + m\angle BCA) \\ &= 180° - (54° + 84°) \\ &= 180° - 138° \\ &= 42° \end{aligned}$$

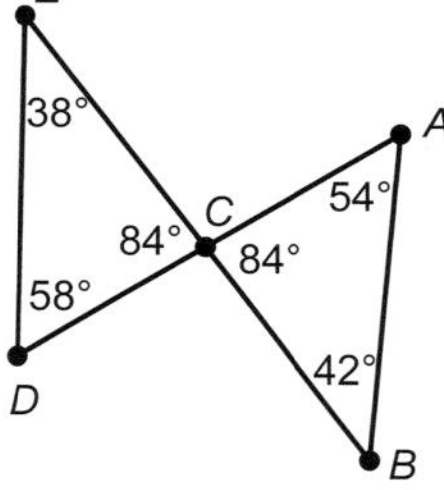

The measure of angle *E* neither equals the measure of angle *A*, nor does it equal the measure of angle *B*, and the measure of angle *B* does not equal the measure of angle *D*. Therefore, there is only one angle in triangle *DEC* that is congruent to one angle in triangle *ABC*. The triangles are not similar. ■

Real Numbers

Topic List

Ancient Egyptians, Indians, and Chinese discovered irrational numbers. For example, in the seventeenth century B.C., an ancient Egyptian scholar showed how to approximate areas of circles and volumes of spheres, both of which involve irrational numbers.

Rational Numbers

The rational numbers are a subset of the real numbers. Examples of rational numbers include $\frac{1}{2}$, 5, −3, 0.25, $10\frac{3}{4}$, and 23.78.

Definition

A **rational number** is any number that can be expressed as a ratio $\frac{a}{b}$, where a and b are integers and $b \neq 0$.

The letter $\mathbb{Q}$ represents the set of rational numbers. Every integer is rational because you can write each integer as a fraction (a ratio) with a denominator of 1. For example, $-6 = \frac{-6}{1}$.

Think About It

NOTATION The letter $\mathbb{Q}$ denotes the set of rational numbers. The "Q" stands for *quoziente*, which is the Italian word for "quotient."

A **proper fraction** is a fraction in which the numerator is less than the denominator. An **improper fraction** is a fraction in which the numerator is greater than or equal to the denominator. Improper fractions have values greater than or equal to 1 and can be written as mixed numbers or integers. A **mixed number** is a number consisting of both a whole number and a fraction or the opposite of such a number.

Proper fractions	Improper fractions	Mixed numbers
$-\frac{7}{8}, \frac{1}{3}, \frac{1}{2}, \frac{3}{4}$	$-\frac{26}{5}, \frac{4}{4}, \frac{16}{8}, \frac{12}{5}$	$-3\frac{2}{3}, 1\frac{1}{4}, 5\frac{7}{8}$

Writing Rational Numbers

EXAMPLE 1

A Write $-\frac{25}{8}$ as a mixed number.

SOLUTION

Write the improper fraction as a mixed number by dividing the numerator by the denominator. Because a mixed number has a whole number part, and whole numbers are not negative, consider $-\frac{25}{8}$ as the opposite of $\frac{25}{8}$.

$-\left(\frac{25}{8}\right) = -\left(3\frac{1}{8}\right)$ Divide.

$= -3\frac{1}{8}$ Simplify.

B Write 4.25 as a percent, a mixed number, and an improper fraction.

SOLUTION

percent: $4.25 = 425\%$

mixed number:

$4.25 = 4\frac{25}{100}$ Write 0.25 as a fraction.

$= 4\frac{1}{4}$ Simplify.

improper fraction:

$4.25 = 4\frac{1}{4}$ Write the decimal as a mixed number.

$= \frac{4 \cdot 4 + 1}{4}$ Multiply the whole number by the denominator and add it to the numerator.

$= \frac{16 + 1}{4}$ Multiply.

$= \frac{17}{4}$ Add.

Comparing Rational Numbers

Two rational numbers are either equal or not equal to each other. If they are not equal, then one of the numbers is greater than the other number.

Comparison Property of Rational Numbers

For positive integers a and c and nonzero integers b and d,

$$\frac{a}{b} > \frac{c}{d} \text{ if and only if } ad > bc.$$

$$\frac{a}{b} < \frac{c}{d} \text{ if and only if } ad < bc.$$

$$\frac{a}{b} = \frac{c}{d} \text{ if and only if } ad = bc.$$

EXAMPLE 2

Write <, =, or > to make a true statement.

A $\frac{3}{4} \blacksquare \frac{7}{9}$

SOLUTION

Compare the rational numbers $\frac{3}{4}$ and $\frac{7}{9}$. Use the comparison property of rational numbers, with $\frac{a}{b} = \frac{3}{4}$ and $\frac{c}{d} = \frac{7}{9}$.

$$ad = 3 \bullet 9 = 27 \text{ and } bc = 4 \bullet 7 = 28$$

Since $27 < 28$, $\frac{3}{4} < \frac{7}{9}$.

B $-\frac{23}{9} \blacksquare -\frac{18}{7}$

SOLUTION

Write each fraction as a mixed number.

$$-\left(\frac{23}{9}\right) = -\left(2\frac{5}{9}\right) = -2\frac{5}{9} \text{ and } -\left(\frac{18}{7}\right) = -\left(2\frac{4}{7}\right) = -2\frac{4}{7}$$

▶ **Think About It** On a number line, a number to the right of another number is the greater of the two numbers.

Compare $\frac{5}{9}$ and $\frac{4}{7}$. Multiply so you can use the comparison property of rational numbers, $ad = 5 \bullet 7 = 35$ and $bc = 9 \bullet 4 = 36$. Since $35 < 36$, $\frac{5}{9} < \frac{4}{7}$. That means $-2\frac{5}{9}$ is closer to 0 on the number line than $-2\frac{4}{7}$ is and $-2\frac{5}{9} > -2\frac{4}{7}$. Therefore, $-\frac{23}{9} > -\frac{18}{7}$. ■

Finding a Rational Number Between Two Rational Numbers

The density property of rational numbers states that there are infinitely many numbers between any two rational numbers.

EXAMPLE 3

Find a rational number between $\frac{3}{4}$ and $\frac{3}{5}$.

SOLUTION

One solution is to find the average, the number that is halfway between the two numbers. Find the average of the two numbers by finding their sum and dividing by 2.

Step 1 Add the numbers.

$$\frac{3}{4} + \frac{3}{5} = \frac{3}{4} \bullet \frac{5}{5} + \frac{3}{5} \bullet \frac{4}{4}$$
$$= \frac{15}{20} + \frac{12}{20}$$
$$= \frac{27}{20}$$

Step 2 Divide the sum by 2.

$$\frac{27}{20} \div 2 = \frac{27}{20} \div \frac{2}{1}$$
$$= \frac{27}{20} \bullet \frac{1}{2}$$
$$= \frac{27}{40}$$

The rational number $\frac{27}{40}$ is between $\frac{3}{4}$ and $\frac{3}{5}$. ■

▶ **Think About It** Check the answer to Example 3 by writing each fraction as a decimal.

$$\frac{3}{4} = 0.75, \frac{27}{40} = 0.675, \frac{3}{5} = 0.6$$

Proving That the Rational Numbers Are Closed Under a Given Operation

Recall that a set of numbers is closed under an operation if the result of the operation with two numbers in the set is also a member of that set.
The rational numbers are closed under addition, subtraction, multiplication, and division.

EXAMPLE 4

Prove that the rational numbers are closed under multiplication.

SOLUTION

By definition, both the numerator and the denominator of a rational number are integers, and the denominator cannot be zero.

The product of two rational numbers $\frac{a}{b}$ and $\frac{c}{d}$ is $\frac{ac}{bd}$, which is also a rational number. You know that the product is rational because the set of integers is closed under multiplication, so both ac and bd must be integers. ■

Terminating and Repeating Decimals

There are different types of decimals.

Definitions

Terminating decimals are decimals that have a finite number of nonzero digits to the right of the decimal point.

Nonterminating decimals are decimals that do not terminate, or end.

▶ **Think About It** *Terminate* means "stop." Terminating decimals stop; nonterminating decimals do not stop.

There are two types of nonterminating decimals: repeating and nonrepeating. **Repeating decimals** have a repeating pattern of digits, while **nonrepeating decimals** do not. When you write a repeating decimal, place a bar over the block of digits that repeat.

Terminating decimals	Repeating nonterminating decimals	Nonrepeating nonterminating decimals
0.25, 6.1212, −1.5836	$0.\overline{4} = 0.44444\ldots$ $3.\overline{256} = 3.256256\ldots$ $20.76\overline{3} = 20.76333\ldots$	0.356987412569112... 3.1415926535...

▶ **Think About It**
NOTATION A bar placed over digits in a decimal shows that the digits repeat.

Converting Fractions to Decimals

EXAMPLE 1

Express the fraction as a decimal. Determine whether the decimal repeats or terminates.

A $\frac{7}{25}$

SOLUTION

Divide 7 by 25: $7 \div 25 = 0.28$. This decimal terminates.

B $\frac{7}{9}$

SOLUTION

Divide 7 by 9: $7 \div 9 = 0.777777\ldots = 0.\overline{7}$. This decimal repeats and is nonterminating.

▶ **Think About It** On a calculator, the last digit displayed may be rounded up, even when the digits continue to repeat.

C $\frac{5}{12}$

SOLUTION

Divide 5 by 12: $5 \div 12 = 0.41666666\ldots = 0.41\overline{6}$. This decimal repeats and is nonterminating. ■

▶ **Remember** Place the bar over the repeating part of the decimal only.

Expressing Terminating and Repeating Decimals as Fractions

A number is rational if and only if you can write it as a terminating or a repeating decimal. Both terminating and repeating decimals can be written as the quotient of two integers.

EXAMPLE 2

Write the decimal as a quotient of two integers.

A 4.25

SOLUTION

Since the last digit in the decimal part is in the hundredths place, write 0.25 as a fraction with a demonimator of 100.

$$4.25 = 4 + 0.25 = 4 + \frac{25}{100} = 4 + \frac{1}{4} = 4\frac{1}{4} = \frac{17}{4}$$

B $4.\overline{25}$

SOLUTION

Write the number as an equation. Multiply each side of the equation by the power of 10 that has as many zeros as there are digits in the repeating block.

$$x = 4.\overline{25}$$
$$100x = 425.\overline{25}$$

Subtract the first equation from the second to eliminate the repeating part. Then isolate the variable and simplify the fraction, if possible.

$$\begin{aligned} 100x &= 425.\overline{25} \\ -\quad x &= \quad 4.\overline{25} \\ \hline 99x &= 421 \\ \frac{99x}{99} &= \frac{421}{99} \\ x &= \frac{421}{99} \end{aligned}$$

CHECK

$$421 \div 99 = 4.\overline{25} \checkmark$$

So $4.\overline{25}$ is a quotient of 421 and 99.

▶ **Think About It** When multiplying both sides of the equation by a power of 10, it helps to write the repeating decimal without the bar and to display the digits in the repeating block a couple of times.

C $2.02\overline{342}$

SOLUTION

Multiply each side of the equation by 1000.

$$x = 2.02\overline{342}$$
$$1000x = 2023.42\overline{342}$$

Subtract the first equation from the second.

$$\begin{array}{rl} 1000x = & 2023.42\overline{342} \\ - \quad x = & 2.02\overline{342} \\ \hline 999x = & 2021.4 \end{array}$$

Multiply each side by 10 to eliminate the decimal. Then isolate the variable and simplify.

$$999x \bullet 10 = 2021.4 \bullet 10$$
$$9990x = 20{,}214$$
$$\frac{9990x}{9990} = \frac{20{,}214}{9990}$$
$$x = \frac{1123}{555}$$

Finding a Rational Number Between a Fraction and a Repeating Decimal

EXAMPLE 3

Find a rational number between $\frac{8}{11}$ and $0.\overline{81}$.

SOLUTION

Step 1 Write the repeating decimal as a fraction.

$$\begin{array}{rl} 100x = & 81.\overline{81} \\ - \quad x = & 0.\overline{81} \\ \hline 99x = & 81 \end{array}$$

$$x = \frac{81}{99} = \frac{9}{11}$$

Step 2 Find the average of the two fractions.

$\frac{8}{11} + \frac{9}{11} = \frac{17}{11}$ Add the numbers.

$\frac{17}{11} \div 2 = \frac{17}{11} \bullet \frac{1}{2} = \frac{17}{22}$ Divide the sum by 2.

The number $\frac{17}{22}$ is between $\frac{8}{11}$ and $0.\overline{81}$.

Application: Proof with Repeating Decimals

EXAMPLE 4

Prove that $0.\overline{9} = 1$.

SOLUTION

Write $0.\overline{9}$ as a fraction and then simplify. Let $x = 0.\overline{9}$.

$$\begin{aligned} 10x &= 9.\overline{9} \\ - \quad x &= 0.\overline{9} \\ \hline 9x &= 9 \\ x &= \frac{9}{9} = 1 \end{aligned}$$

Since $x = 0.\overline{9}$ from the first assumption, and $x = 1$ from the algebra, $0.\overline{9} = 1$ by the substitution property of equality.

Understanding Irrational Numbers

Real numbers that are not rational numbers are irrational numbers.

Unlike a rational number, an **irrational number** is a real number that cannot be written in the form $\frac{a}{b}$, for any integers a and b. The set of rational numbers $\mathbb{Q}$ and the set of irrational numbers $\mathbb{I}$ together make up the set of real numbers.

▸ **Think About It**

NOTATION The letter $\mathbb{I}$ denotes the set of irrational numbers.

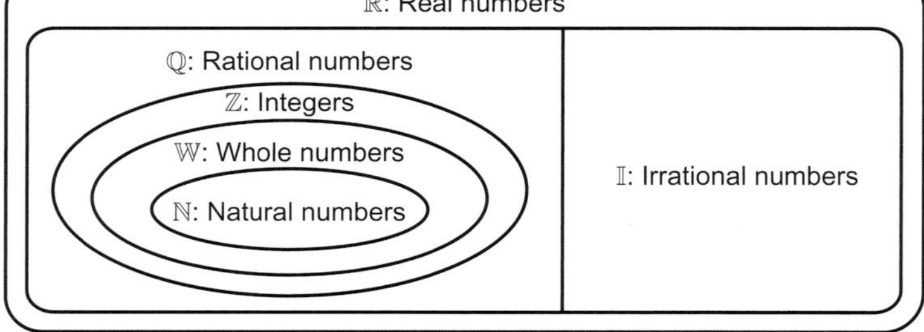

Determining Whether a Number Is Rational or Irrational

Every real number can be written as a decimal. Any decimal that is nonterminating and nonrepeating is an irrational number. The number π is an example of an irrational number. There is no way to convert the decimal into a fraction of integers because there is no repeating block of digits.

Remember $\pi = 3.14159\ldots$

A **perfect square** is a rational number with a rational square root.

Examples of perfect squares are 9, 25, and $\frac{4}{9}$. The square root of any number that is not a perfect square is an irrational number, such as $\sqrt{2}$ and $\sqrt{14}$.

Rational numbers	Irrational numbers
$\sqrt{9} = 3$ $\sqrt{25} = 5$ $\sqrt{36} = 6$	$\sqrt{2} = 1.414213562\ldots$ $\sqrt{14} = 3.741657387\ldots$

Think About It A decimal with a finite number of digits cannot accurately represent an irrational number, but a decimal can approximate its value. $\sqrt{2}$ is an exact value; 1.414 approximates $\sqrt{2}$.

EXAMPLE 1

Determine whether the number is rational or irrational. If the number is rational, determine which other subsets it is in, including integer, whole number, or natural number.

A $\sqrt{90}$

SOLUTION

Because 90 is not a perfect square, $\sqrt{90}$ is irrational.

B $\sqrt{256}$

SOLUTION

Because $16 \bullet 16 = 256$, 256 is a perfect square. So $\sqrt{256}$ is rational. It is also an integer, a whole number, and a natural number.

C $-\sqrt{121}$

SOLUTION

The square root of 121 is 11. The opposite of 11 is -11, which is rational, so $-\sqrt{121}$ is rational. It is also an integer.

D $\sqrt{\frac{1}{5}}$

SOLUTION

Because no number times itself equals 5, there is no number that can be multiplied by itself to equal $\frac{1}{5}$. Therefore, $\sqrt{\frac{1}{5}}$ is irrational.

E $\sqrt{\frac{64}{49}}$

SOLUTION

Both 64 and 49 are perfect squares. Since $\sqrt{\frac{64}{49}} = \frac{8}{7} = 1.\overline{142857}$, $\sqrt{\frac{64}{49}}$ is rational. It is not an integer, a whole number, or a natural number.

Verifying Closure Properties for Irrational Numbers

EXAMPLE 2

Determine whether the set of irrational numbers is closed under multiplication.

SOLUTION

The product of two irrational numbers is not always an irrational number.

$$\sqrt{3} \cdot \sqrt{3} = \sqrt{9} = 3$$

The set of irrational numbers is not closed under multiplication.

Application: Proving That a Square Root Is Irrational

The square of an even number is always an even number and the square of an odd number is always an odd number. Use these facts in Example 3.

▶ **Think About It** You can prove that the square root of a number is irrational by first assuming that it is rational, which leads to a contradiction that proves that the number is irrational.

EXAMPLE 3

Prove that $\sqrt{2}$ is irrational.

SOLUTION

Assume that $\sqrt{2}$ is rational. Then it would be possible to represent the value as a fraction $\frac{a}{b}$, where a and b are integers with no common factors other than 1 and b is not zero.

$$\sqrt{2} = \frac{a}{b}$$

$$\left(\sqrt{2}\right)^2 = \left(\frac{a}{b}\right)^2 \qquad \text{Square both sides of the equation.}$$

$$2 = \frac{a^2}{b^2} \qquad \sqrt{2} \bullet \sqrt{2} = \sqrt{4} = 2 \text{ and } \frac{a}{b} \bullet \frac{a}{b} = \frac{a^2}{b^2}$$

$$2b^2 = a^2 \qquad \text{Means-Extremes Product Property}$$

Since a number with a factor of 2 is an even number, $2b^2$ is an even number. So a^2 is an even number. Since only an even number squared can result in an even number, a must also be even.

Since a is an even number, it can be written as a product with a factor of 2. Let $a = 2c$, where c is an integer.

$2b^2 = a^2$	Last line from above
$2b^2 = (2c)^2$	Substitution Property of Equality
$2b^2 = 4c^2$	$2c \bullet 2c = 4c^2$
$b^2 = 2c^2$	Divide each side by 2.

Now b^2 is shown to be an even number because it is equal to a product with a factor of 2. Since b^2 is even, b is even.

Both a and b have been shown to be even, which means they both have a common factor of 2. However, it was stated in the beginning of the proof that a and b have no common factors other than 1, which is a contradiction.

▶ **Think About It** When an assumption leads to a contradiction (two statements with opposite ideas), the assumption is false.

Therefore, the assumption that $\sqrt{2}$ is rational must be incorrect. A number is either rational or irrational, so $\sqrt{2}$ is irrational. ■

Approximations of Irrationals

You can use a rational number to approximate the value of an irrational number.

Using Number Lines and Integers to Approximate Irrationals

You can use an irrational number's location on a number line relative to the square roots of the nearest perfect squares to help approximate its value.

EXAMPLE 1

Approximate the value of $\sqrt{29}$ to the nearest tenth.

SOLUTION

Step 1 Find the two perfect squares that the radicand 29 lies between.

The radicand lies between the perfect squares 25 and 36.

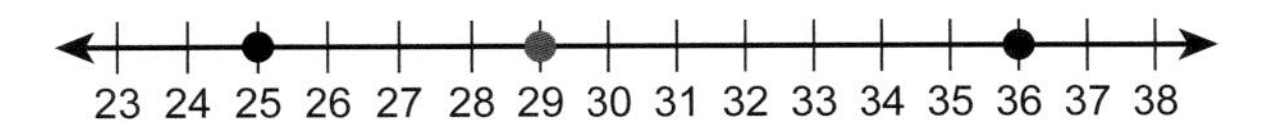

Step 2 Take the square root of each number and simplify.

$$25 < 29 < 36$$
$$\sqrt{25} < \sqrt{29} < \sqrt{36}$$
$$5 < \sqrt{29} < 6$$

So $\sqrt{29}$ lies between the integers 5 and 6. Since 29 is closer to 25 than to 36, you should expect $\sqrt{29}$ to be closer to 5 than to 6.

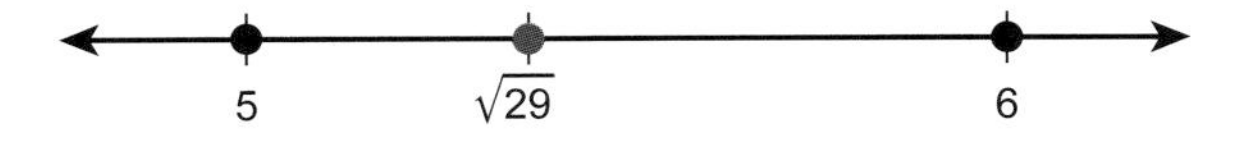

Step 3 Find the distance between 25 and 29, and find the distance between the perfect squares 25 and 36.

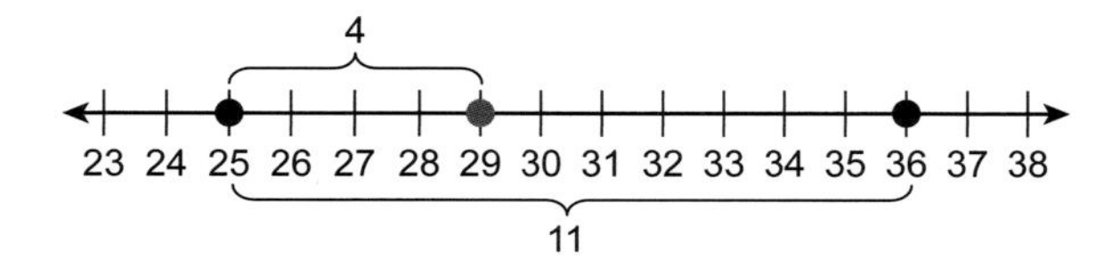

distance from 25 to 29: $29 - 25 = 4$

distance from 25 to 36: $36 - 25 = 11$

Step 4 Find the ratio of the distance from 25 to 29 to the distance from 25 to 36.

$$\frac{\text{distance from 25 to 29}}{\text{distance from 25 to 36}} = \frac{4}{11} \approx 0.4$$

The distance from 25 to 29 is about 0.4 the distance from 25 to 36. Therefore, the distance from 5 to $\sqrt{29}$ is 0.4 of the distance from 5 to 6. The distance from 5 to 6 is 1, so 0.4 of the distance from 5 to 6 is $0.4 \bullet 1 = 0.4$.

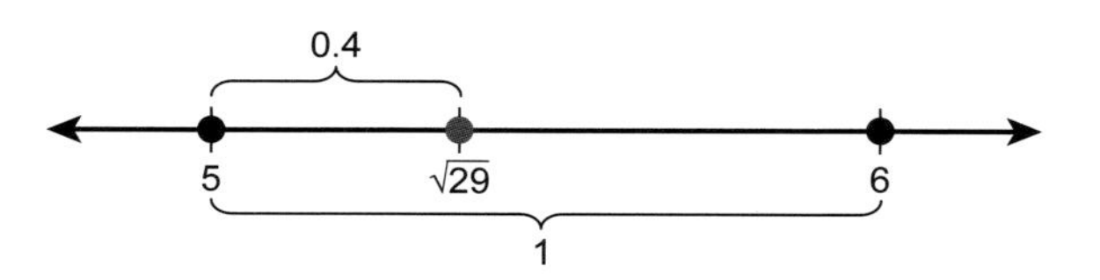

Step 5 Add 0.4 to 5.

$$5 + 0.4 = 5.4$$

CHECK

Using a calculator, you find that the actual value of $\sqrt{29}$ is about 5.4, so the approximation is close.

You can conclude that $\sqrt{29} \approx 5.4$. ■

EXAMPLE 2

Select the symbol ($<$, $>$, or $=$) that makes a true statement.

A $2\sqrt{5}$ ■ $\sqrt{19}$

SOLUTION

Step 1 Approximate the value of $2\sqrt{5}$ to the nearest tenth.

$4 < 5 < 9$	The radicand, 5, lies between the perfect squares 4 and 9.
$\sqrt{4} < \sqrt{5} < \sqrt{9}$	Take the square root of each number.
$2 < \sqrt{5} < 3$	Simplify.

$$\frac{\text{distance from 4 to 5}}{\text{distance from 4 to 9}} = \frac{1}{5} = 0.2$$

$$\sqrt{5} \approx 2 + 0.2 \approx 2.2$$

$$2\sqrt{5} \approx 2 \cdot 2.2 \approx 4.4$$

Step 2 Approximate the value of $\sqrt{19}$ to the nearest tenth.

$16 < 19 < 25$	The radicand, 19, lies between the perfect squares 16 and 25.
$\sqrt{16} < \sqrt{19} < \sqrt{25}$	Take the square root of each number.
$4 < \sqrt{19} < 5$	Simplify.

$$\frac{\text{distance from 16 to 19}}{\text{distance from 16 to 25}} = \frac{3}{9} = \frac{1}{3} \approx 0.3$$

$$\sqrt{19} \approx 4 + 0.3 \approx 4.3$$

Step 3 Compare.

$$4.4 > 4.3$$

$$2\sqrt{5} > \sqrt{19}$$

B $\sqrt{95}$ ■ π^2

SOLUTION

Step 1 Approximate the value of $\sqrt{95}$ to the nearest tenth.

$81 < 95 < 100$	The radicand, 95, lies between the perfect squares 81 and 100.
$\sqrt{81} < \sqrt{95} < \sqrt{100}$	Take the square root of each number.
$9 < \sqrt{95} < 10$	Simplify.

$$\frac{\text{distance from 95 to 100}}{\text{distance from 81 to 100}} = \frac{5}{19} \approx 0.3$$

$$\sqrt{95} \approx 10 - 0.3 \approx 9.7$$

Step 2 Approximate the value of π^2 to the nearest tenth.

$$\pi \approx 3.14$$

$$\pi^2 \approx 3.14 \bullet 3.14 \approx 9.9$$

Step 3 Compare.

$$9.7 < 9.9$$

$$\sqrt{95} < \pi^2$$ ■

Rational Square Roots

Taking a square root is the inverse operation of squaring a number.

The square root of a number is the factor that, when multiplied by itself, results in the number. If a square root of a number is a rational number, it is a **rational square root**.

▶ **Remember** A rational number is any number that can be expressed as a ratio $\frac{a}{b}$, where a and b are integers and $b \neq 0$.

Finding Positive and Negative Square Roots

The tables list the squares for the whole numbers 1 through 15 and their opposites. You can use the tables to find the positive and negative square roots of any number n^2 by looking at the values in the corresponding n column.

n	n^2
±1	1
±2	4
±3	9
±4	16
±5	25

n	n^2
±6	36
±7	49
±8	64
±9	81
±10	100

n	n^2
±11	121
±12	144
±13	169
±14	196
±15	225

Think About It

NOTATION The plus-minus sign ($\pm$) is convenient shorthand for a quantity with two possible values. For example, ± 7 means $+7$ or -7.

The square roots of 25 are 5 and -5 because $5 \cdot 5 = 5^2 = 25$ and $(-5) \cdot (-5) = (-5)^2 = 25$.

EXAMPLE 1

Find the square roots of the number.

A 81

SOLUTION

Because $9 \cdot 9 = 81$, the positive square root of 81 is 9.

Because $(-9) \cdot (-9) = 81$, the negative square root of 81 is -9.

B $\frac{16}{9}$

SOLUTION

Because $\frac{4}{3} \cdot \frac{4}{3} = \frac{16}{9}$, the positive square root of $\frac{16}{9}$ is $\frac{4}{3}$.

Because $\left(-\frac{4}{3}\right) \cdot \left(-\frac{4}{3}\right) = \frac{16}{9}$, the negative square root of $\frac{16}{9}$ is $-\frac{4}{3}$.

C -4

SOLUTION

Whenever you multiply a real number by itself, the product is positive. So -4 has no real square roots. ■

Solving Equations with Square Roots

When solving equations with square roots, you must note both the positive and the negative square roots of a number.

Square Root Property

For nonnegative values of a,	**Example**
if $x^2 = a$, then $x = \pm\sqrt{a}$.	If $x^2 = 49$, then $x = \pm 7$.
	If $x^2 = 100$, then $x = \pm 10$.

EXAMPLE 2

Solve.

A $x^2 = 121$

SOLUTION

$x^2 = 121$	Write the equation.
$x = \pm\sqrt{121}$	Square Root Property
$x = \pm 11$	Simplify.

▸ **Think About It** Check the answer by substituting it into the original equation.

CHECK

$$11^2 = 121 \text{ and } (-11)^2 = 121 \checkmark$$

Since $x^2 = 121$, $x = \pm 11$.

B $m^2 = \frac{4}{9}$

SOLUTION

$m^2 = \frac{4}{9}$	Write the equation.
$m = \pm\sqrt{\frac{4}{9}}$	Square Root Property
$m = \pm\frac{2}{3}$	Simplify.

C Solve $t^2 + 1 = 50$

SOLUTION

$t^2 + 1 = 50$	Write the equation.
$t^2 = 49$	Subtract 1 from both sides.
$t = \pm\sqrt{49}$	Square Root Property
$t = \pm 7$	Simplify.

Application: Interior Design

EXAMPLE 3

The area of a square rug is 36 ft^2. Write an equation to represent the area of the rug. What is the length of one side of the rug?

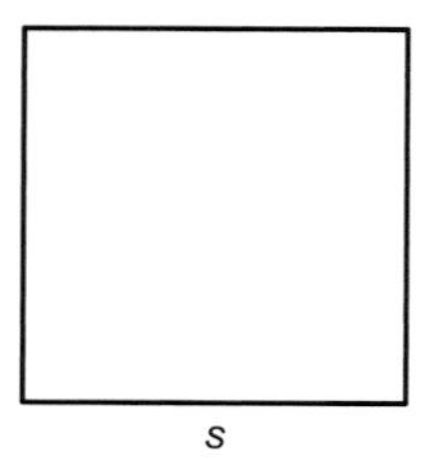

SOLUTION

Because the rug is a square, you know that all four sides have the same measure. The area of a square with side length s is $A = s^2$.

$A = s^2$	Write the formula for the area of a square.
$36 = s^2$	Substitute 36 for A.
$\pm\sqrt{36} = s$	Square Root Property
$\pm 6 = s$	Simplify.

▶ **Think About It** When solving a real-life problem, be sure to check that the solution makes sense.

The solutions are $s = +6$ and $s = -6$. Because a measurement cannot be negative, choose the principal square root. The length of one side of the rug is 6 ft. ■

Cube Roots

The opposite of squaring is taking a square root. Similarly, the opposite of raising to any power n is taking the nth root.

Definition

For all numbers a and b, if $a^n = b$, and n is an integer greater than 1, then a is the ***n*th root** of b.

Think About It

NOTATION The expression $\sqrt[n]{b}$ indicates the principal nth root of b when n is an even number.

Properties of Even and Odd Roots

An even root has two real answers. If n is even and b is nonnegative, then $\sqrt[n]{b}$ indicates the principal, or positive, root and $-\sqrt[n]{b}$ indicates the negative root.

An odd root has one real answer. If n is odd and b is positive or negative, then $\sqrt[n]{b}$ indicates the only root, which may be positive or negative.

For instance, 3 is the third root, or cube root, of 27 because $3 \bullet 3 \bullet 3 = 3^3 = 27$. Just as 9 is a perfect square, 27 is a **perfect cube**.

Although you cannot take the square root (or any other even root) of a negative number, you can take an odd root of a negative number. The cube root of -27 is -3 because $(-3)^3 = -27$, which can be written as $\sqrt[3]{-27} = -3$.

Evaluating Cube Roots

EXAMPLE 1

Evaluate the radical expression.

A $\sqrt[3]{8}$

SOLUTION

Because $2^3 = 8$, you know that $\sqrt[3]{8} = 2$.

B $\sqrt[3]{-125}$

SOLUTION

So $\sqrt[3]{-125} = -5$ because $(-5)^3 = -125$. ■

Simplifying Cube Roots

Variable expressions can also be perfect *n*th powers. Assume that all variables are nonnegative.

Multiplication Property of Radicals

For all a and b when n is odd, and for all nonnegative a and b when n is even, $\sqrt[n]{a} \bullet \sqrt[n]{b} = \sqrt[n]{ab}$ when n is an integer greater than 1.

EXAMPLE 2

Simplify the expression.

$\sqrt[3]{54}$

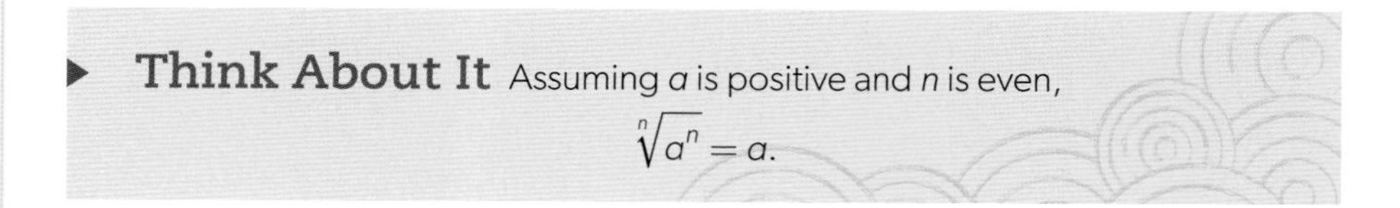

SOLUTION

$$\begin{aligned}\sqrt[3]{54} &= \sqrt[3]{27 \bullet 2} \\ &= \sqrt[3]{27} \bullet \sqrt[3]{2} \\ &= \sqrt[3]{3^3} \bullet \sqrt[3]{2} \\ &= 3\sqrt[3]{2} \quad \blacksquare\end{aligned}$$

Using Square Roots to Solve Equations

An equation can have zero, one, two, or even an infinite number of solutions. When a solution to an equation is substituted for the variable, the statement is a true statement.

Solving Equations with the Form $x^2 = a$

Consider the equation $x^2 = 9$. This equation has two solutions because both 3 and -3, which are the square roots of 9, make the equation true. To solve an equation in which the variable is squared, take the square root of each side of the equation. Because $\sqrt{x^2} = |x|$, and both the positive and the negative square roots are solutions, write $x = \pm\sqrt{9}$.

EXAMPLE 1

Solve the equation. Round your answer to the nearest tenth, if necessary.

A $n^2 = 25$

SOLUTION

$n^2 = 25$

$n = \pm\sqrt{25}$ Take the square root of each side.

$n = \pm 5$ Simplify $\sqrt{25}$.

The solutions are 5 and -5.

Remember For nonnegative values of a, if $x^2 = a$, then $x = \pm\sqrt{a}$.

B $5t^2 = 35$

SOLUTION

Isolate the variable and take the square root of each side.

$5t^2 = 35$

$t^2 = \frac{35}{5}$ Divide both sides by 5.

$t = \pm\sqrt{\frac{35}{5}}$ Take the square root of both sides.

$t = \pm\sqrt{7}$ Simplify the radicand.

The solutions are exactly $\sqrt{7}$ and $-\sqrt{7}$, or about 2.6 and -2.6.

C $9x^2 - 64 = 0$

SOLUTION

Use inverse operations to isolate the variable.

$9x^2 - 64 = 0$

$9x^2 = 64$ Add 64 to both sides.

$x^2 = \frac{64}{9}$ Divide both sides by 9.

$x = \pm\sqrt{\frac{64}{9}}$ Take the square root of both sides.

$x = \pm\frac{\sqrt{64}}{\sqrt{9}}$ Write the square root as a quotient.

$x = \pm\frac{8}{3}$ Simplify $\sqrt{64}$ and $\sqrt{9}$.

The solutions are $\frac{8}{3}$ and $-\frac{8}{3}$. ■

Applications: Geometry and Physics

EXAMPLE 2

The area of a circle is 40 cm^2. Estimate the radius to the nearest tenth of a centimeter.

SOLUTION

Solve the area formula $A = \pi r^2$ for r.

$40 = \pi r^2$	Substitute 40 for A.
$\frac{40}{\pi} = r^2$	Divide both sides by π.
$\pm\sqrt{\frac{40}{\pi}} = r$	Take the square root of both sides.
$\pm 3.6 \approx r$	Use a calculator to estimate.

Because length cannot be negative, disregard the negative answer. The radius is about 3.6 cm. ■

EXAMPLE 3

Solve $-16t^2 + 80 = 0$ to estimate the number of seconds, t, it takes for an object dropped from 80 ft above the ground to hit the ground.

SOLUTION

$-16t^2 + 80 = 0$

$-16t^2 = -80$	Subtract 80 from both sides.
$t^2 = 5$	Divide both sides by -16.
$t = \pm\sqrt{5} \approx \pm 2.236$	Take the square root of both sides.

Since time cannot be negative, disregard the negative answer. The time is about 2.24 s. ■

Using Cube Roots to Solve Equations

You can use cube roots to solve equations of the form $x^3 = a$, where a is any real number.

Solving Equations with the Form $x^3 = a$

Consider the equation $x^3 = 8$. The solution is 2 because 2^3 equals 8. To solve an equation in which the variable is cubed, take the cube root of each side of the equation.

▶ **Q&A**

Q The equation $x^2 = 4$ has two solutions: $x = 2$ or $x = -2$. Does the equation $x^3 = 8$ also have two solutions?

A No, $2^3 = 8$, but $(-2)^3 = -8$. Therefore, the eqution has exactly one solution, $x = 2$.

EXAMPLE 1

Solve the equation. Round your answer to the nearest tenth, if necessary.

A $n^3 = 64$

SOLUTION

$n^3 = 64$

$n = \sqrt[3]{64}$ Take the cube root of both sides.

$n = 4$ Simplify.

The solution is 4.

B $8d^3 = 1$

SOLUTION

$8d^3 = 1$	
$\frac{8d^3}{8} = \frac{1}{8}$	Divide both sides by 8.
$d^3 = \frac{1}{8}$	Simplify.
$d = \sqrt[3]{\frac{1}{8}}$	Take the cube root of both sides.
$d = \frac{\sqrt[3]{1}}{\sqrt[3]{8}}$	$\sqrt[3]{\frac{1}{8}} = \frac{\sqrt[3]{1}}{\sqrt[3]{8}}$
$d = \frac{1}{2}$	Simplify.

The solution is $\frac{1}{2}$.

C $4c^3 - 5 = 891$

SOLUTION

$4c^3 - 5 = 891$	
$4c^3 - 5 + 5 = 891 + 5$	Add 5 to both sides.
$4c^3 = 896$	Simplify.
$\frac{4c^3}{4} = \frac{896}{4}$	Divide both sides by 4.
$c^3 = 224$	Simplify.
$c = \sqrt[3]{224}$	Take the cube root of both sides.
$c \approx 6.1$	Use a calculator to estimate $\sqrt[3]{224}$.

The solution is about 6.1. ■

Application: Geometry

You can use cube roots to solve problems related to volume.

EXAMPLE 2

Alexander has a cube-shaped box.

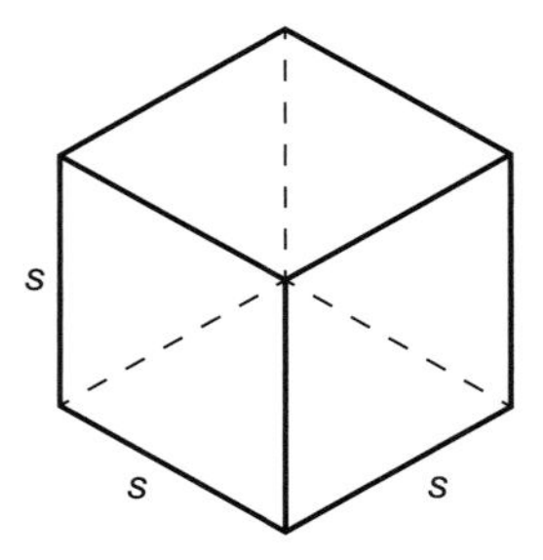

A Let s be the side length of the box. Write an equation that relates the volume of the box to its side length.

SOLUTION

A cube is a rectangular prism with equal side lengths s.

$V = lwh$

$V = s \bullet s \bullet s$ Replace l, w, and h with s.

$V = s^3$ $s \bullet s \bullet s = s^3$

The equation that relates the volume V to the side length s is $V = s^3$.

B The volume of Alexander's box is 512 in^3. What is the side length of the box?

SOLUTION

Let $V = 512$, and solve for s.

$512 = s^3$ Let $V = 512$.

$\sqrt[3]{512} = s$ Take the cube root of each side.

$8 = s$ Simplify.

The side length of the box is 8 in. ■

The Pythagorean Theorem

Topic List

- Using the Pythagorean Theorem
- Proofs of the Pythagorean Theorem
- Distances with the Pythagorean Theorem
- Applications of the Pythagorean Theorem
- Pythagorean Theorem in 3-D
- More Pythagorean Applications

After basic computation, discovering and using some version of the Pythagorean theorem was the next step in many civilizations' mathematical development. The relationship described by the theorem has applications in a long list of areas, including building and surveying.

Using the Pythagorean Theorem

Squaring and taking square roots of numbers can help you solve many geometric problems, such as those involving triangles.

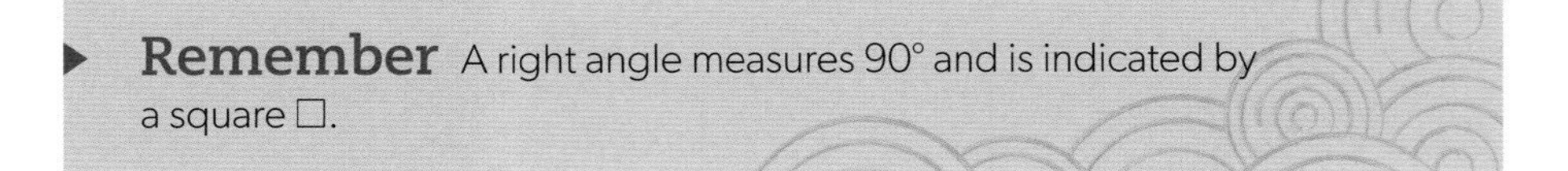

Remember A right angle measures 90° and is indicated by a square □.

Definitions

A triangle with a right angle is a **right triangle**.

The two sides of the triangle that form the right angle are the **legs**.

The side opposite the right angle is the **hypotenuse**.

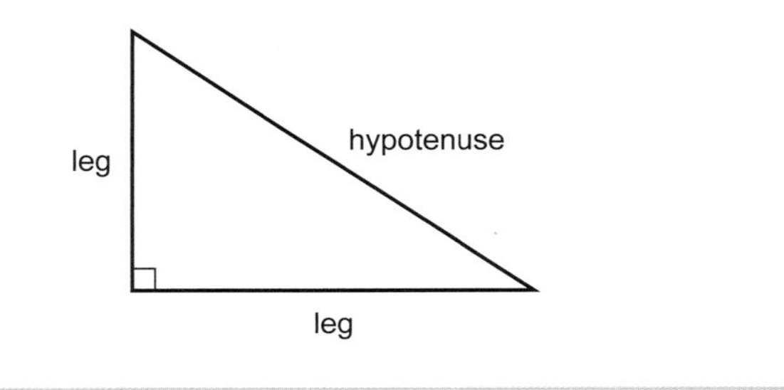

Understanding the Pythagorean Theorem

The Pythagorean theorem states the relationship between the lengths of the sides of a right triangle.

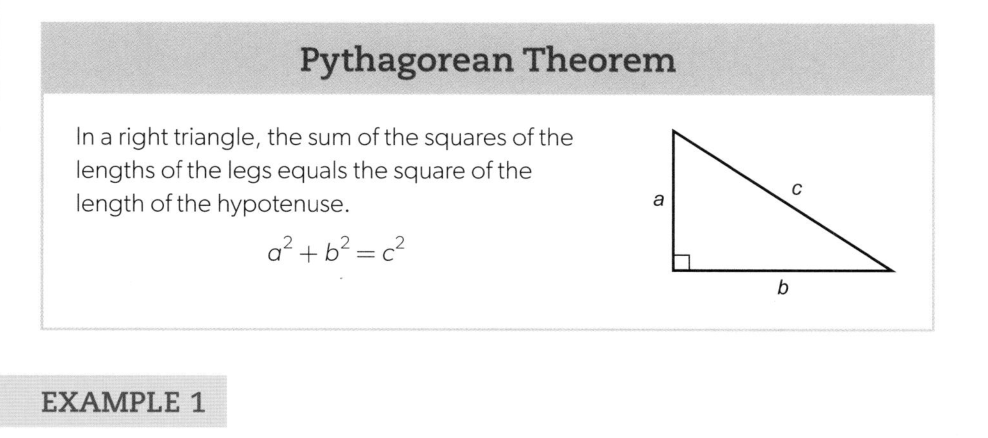

EXAMPLE 1

Find the value of x.

A

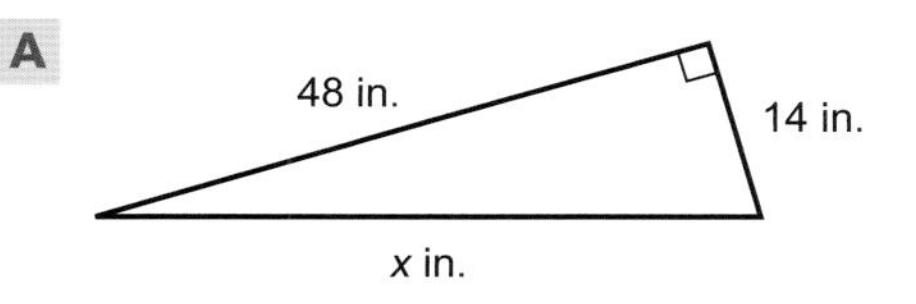

SOLUTION

The unknown side is the hypotenuse c.

$$a^2 + b^2 = c^2$$

$$\mathbf{14}^2 + \mathbf{48}^2 = \boldsymbol{x}^2 \qquad \text{Substitute 14 for } a\text{, 48 for } b\text{, and } x \text{ for } c.$$

$$196 + 2304 = x^2 \qquad \text{Simplify the left side.}$$

$$2500 = x^2$$

$$\pm\sqrt{2500} = x \qquad \text{Take the square root of each side.}$$

$$\pm 50 = x$$

Disregard the negative answer because lengths must be nonnegative. The length is 50 in.

▶ **Think About It** You would get the same answer by substituting 48 for a and 14 for b.

B

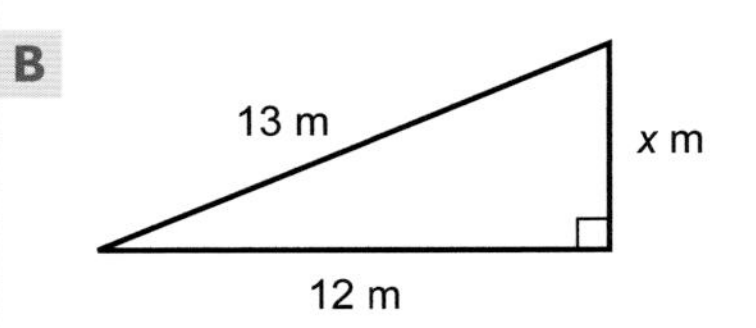

SOLUTION

The unknown side is a leg.

$a^2 + b^2 = c^2$	
$x^2 + 12^2 = 13^2$	Substitute x for a, 12 for b, and 13 for c.
$x^2 + 144 = 169$	Evaluate the powers.
$x^2 = 25$	Subtract 144 from each side.
$x = \pm\sqrt{25}$	Take the square root of each side.
$x = \pm 5$	

Disregard the negative answer. The length is 5m.

▶ **Think About It** The hypotenuse is always the longest side of a right triangle. You know you have made an error if the length of a leg is greater than the length of the hypotenuse.

Using the Converse of the Pythagorean Theorem

The Pythagorean theorem tells you how to find the length of a side of a triangle given that the triangle is a right triangle. The converse of the Pythagorean theorem tells you how to determine whether a triangle is a right triangle given the lengths of all three sides.

Converse of the Pythagorean Theorem

If the sum of the squares of the lengths of the shorter sides of a triangle equals the square of the length of the longest side, then the triangle is a right triangle.

EXAMPLE 2

Determine whether a triangle with the given side lengths is a right triangle.

A 15 ft, 32 ft, and 36 ft

SOLUTION

Substitute 15 for a, 32 for b, and 36 for c, and then simplify.

$$\begin{aligned} a^2 + b^2 &= c^2 \\ \mathbf{15}^2 + \mathbf{32}^2 &\stackrel{?}{=} \mathbf{36}^2 \\ 225 + 1024 &\stackrel{?}{=} 1296 \\ 1249 &\neq 1296 \end{aligned}$$

The two sides of the equation are not equal, so the side lengths do not form a right triangle.

B 20 ft, 16 ft, and 12 ft

SOLUTION

Substitute 20 for c, 16 for a, and 12 for b, and then simplify.

$$\begin{aligned} a^2 + b^2 &= c^2 \\ \mathbf{16}^2 + \mathbf{12}^2 &\stackrel{?}{=} \mathbf{20}^2 \\ 256 + 144 &\stackrel{?}{=} 400 \\ 400 &= 400 \end{aligned}$$

The two sides of the equation are equal. The side lengths form a right triangle. ■

Determining the Relative Measure of the Greatest Angle

The greatest angle in a triangle is opposite the longest side c.

Pythagorean Inequalities

For a triangle with side lengths of a, b, and c, where $c > a$ and $c > b$,

- If $c^2 > a^2 + b^2$, then the angle opposite side c has a measure greater than 90°.
- If $c^2 < a^2 + b^2$, then the angle opposite side c has a measure less than 90°.

▶ **Think About It** The inequalities $c > a$ and $c > b$ mean that c is the longest side in the triangle.

EXAMPLE 3

The side lengths of a triangle are 9 m, 12 m, and 14 m. Does the greatest angle in the triangle measure 90°, more than 90°, or less than 90°?

SOLUTION

Determine whether c^2 is less than, greater than, or equal to $a^2 + b^2$.

$$c^2 \;\blacksquare\; a^2 + b^2$$
$$14^2 \;\blacksquare\; 9^2 + 12^2$$
$$196 \;\blacksquare\; 81 + 144$$
$$196 < 225$$

Because $c^2 < a^2 + b^2$, the angle opposite side c, which is the greatest angle, has a measure that is less than 90°. ■

Proofs of the Pythagorean Theorem

You can prove the Pythagorean theorem and its converse using models, equations, and geometry.

Visualizing the Pythagorean Theorem

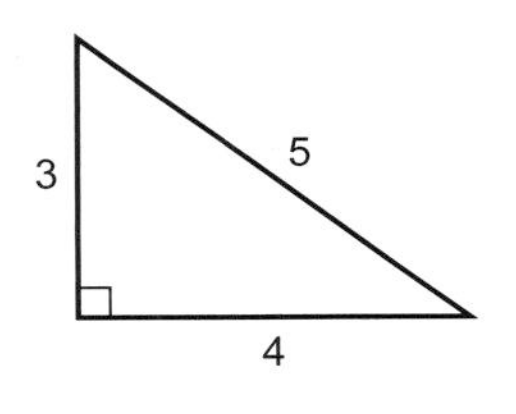

There are a number of ways to visualize the Pythagorean theorem. One way is to use a model. Consider a right triangle whose side lengths are 3 units, 4 units, and 5 units.

Imagine that each side of the triangle is also a side of a square. One square has a side length of 3 units, another has a side length of 4 units, and the third has a side length of 5 units. Then divide each square into unit squares.

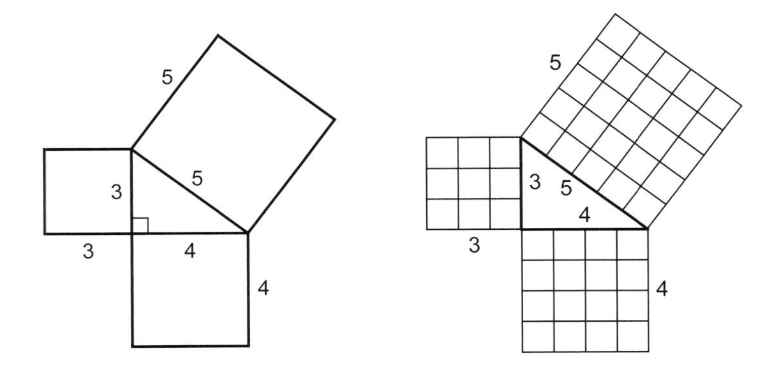

In the 3×3 square, there are 9 unit squares. In the 4×4 square, there are 16 unit squares. In the 5×5 square, there are 25 unit squares. The sum of the areas of the two smaller squares equals the area of the larger square.

$$9 + 16 = 25$$

Since $9 = 3^2$, $16 = 4^2$, and $25 = 5^2$, you can write this equation as

$$3^2 + 4^2 = 5^2.$$

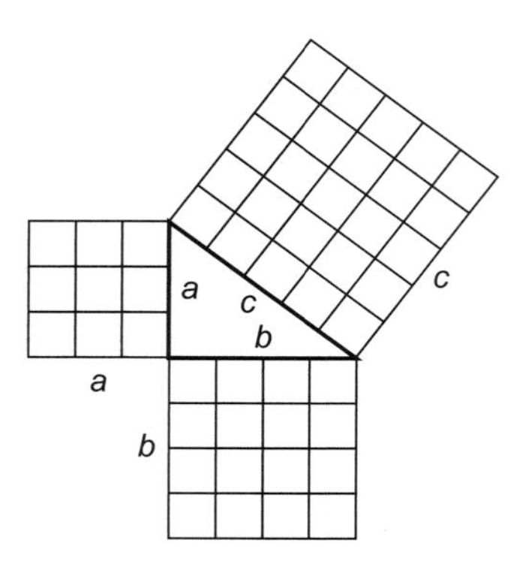

The legs of the right triangle are 3 units and 4 units, and the hypotenuse is 5 units. Therefore, this equation tells you that the sum of the squares of the legs of the right triangle equals the square of the hypotenuse.

Replacing 3 with a, 4 with b, and 5 with c, you can infer the Pythagorean theorem: $a^2 + b^2 = c^2$.

Using Models and the Converse of the Pythagorean Theorem

The converse of the Pythagorean theorem states that if the sum of the squares of two sides of a triangle equals the square of the third side, the triangle is a right triangle. You can use models to determine whether a triangle is a right triangle.

EXAMPLE 1

Determine whether the triangle is a right triangle.

A

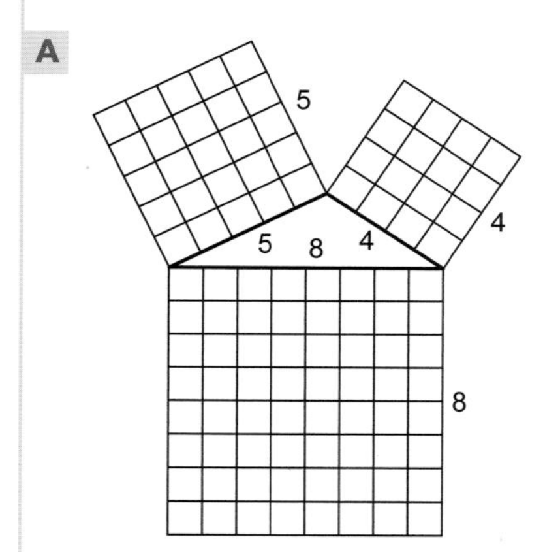

SOLUTION

The side length of each square is equal to the length of one side of the triangle. Squaring a side of the triangle is equal to the area of that side's corresponding square. Therefore, the triangle is a right triangle if the sum of the areas of the two smaller squares equals the area of the largest square.

The 4×4 square has 16 unit squares, the 5×5 square has 25 unit squares, and the 8×8 square has 64 unit squares. Since $16 + 25 \neq 64$, the triangle is not a right triangle.

B

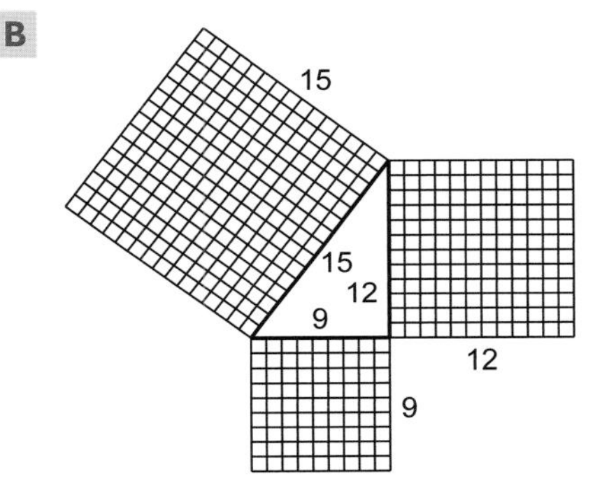

SOLUTION

The 9×9 square has 81 unit squares, the 12×12 square has 144 unit squares, and the 15×15 square has 225 unit squares. Since $81 + 144 = 225$, the triangle is a right triangle.

Proving the Converse of the Pythagorean Theorem

You can use what you know about congruent triangles to prove the converse of the Pythagorean theorem.

EXAMPLE 2

Prove that $\triangle ABC$ is a right triangle.

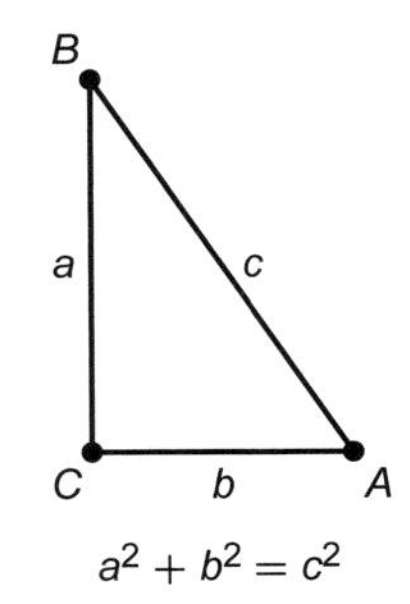

SOLUTION

Consider $\triangle ABC$. It's given that the length of leg $\overline{BC}$ is a, the length of leg $\overline{AC}$ is b, and the length of hypotenuse $\overline{AB}$ is c. It is also given that $a^2 + b^2 = c^2$. The measures of the angles of the triangle are unknown.

Consider $\triangle XYZ$. It's given that $\angle Z$ is a right angle. It's also given that the length of leg $\overline{ZY}$ is a, the length of leg $\overline{ZX}$ is b, and the length of hypotenuse $\overline{YX}$ is r.

$\triangle XYZ$ is a right triangle. Therefore, by the Pythagorean theorem, $a^2 + b^2 = r^2$.

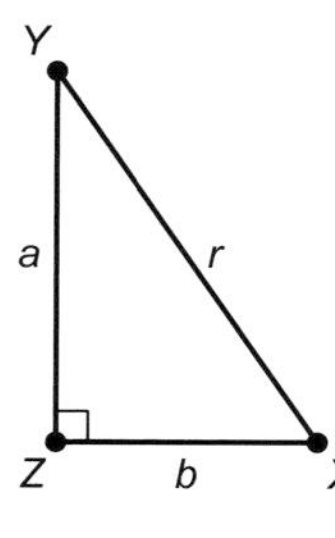

Since $c^2 = a^2 + b^2$ and $r^2 = a^2 + b^2$, $c^2 = r^2$. Therefore, $c = r$.

When all of the corresponding sides of two triangles are congruent, the triangles are congruent by the side-side-side (SSS) congruence postulate. $\overline{ZY} \cong \overline{CB}$, $\overline{ZX} \cong \overline{CA}$, and $\overline{YX} \cong \overline{BA}$. Therefore, $\triangle ABC \cong \triangle XYZ$.

When two triangles are congruent, all of their corresponding parts are congruent. Since $\triangle ABC \cong \triangle XYZ$, $\angle A \cong \angle Z$. Since $\angle Z$ is a right angle, $\angle A$ is also a right angle. Therefore, $\triangle ABC$ is a right triangle. ■

Distances with the Pythagorean Theorem

You can use the Pythagorean theorem to find the distance between points in the coordinate plane.

Finding the Length of a Nonvertical, Nonhorizontal Line Segment

In the coordinate plane, a right triangle can be drawn so that a given line segment is the hypotenuse of that triangle. You can then use the Pythagorean theorem to find the length of the given segment.

EXAMPLE 1

Find the length of $\overline{AB}$.

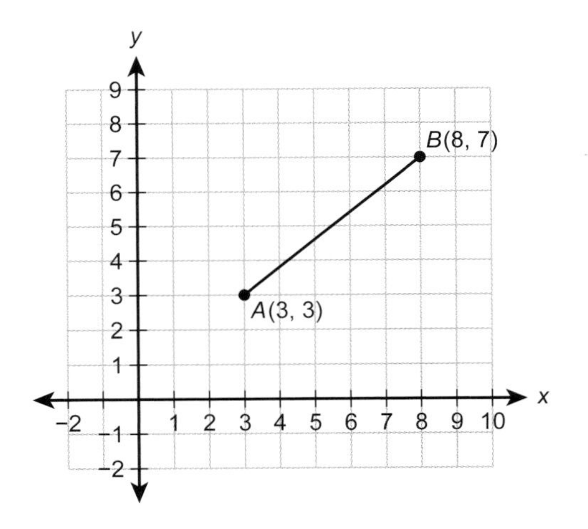

SOLUTION

Think of $\overline{AB}$ as the hypotenuse of right triangle $\triangle ABC$. Plot point C at (8, 3) to form right angle ACB.

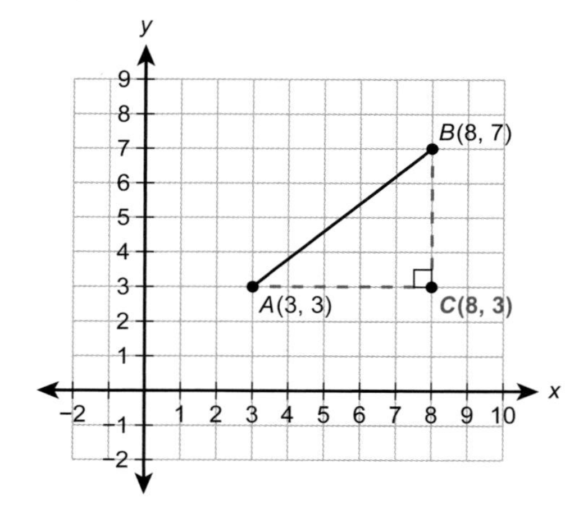

Find the lengths of the legs $\overline{AC}$ and $\overline{BC}$.

▶ **Remember** $\overline{AC}$ and $\overline{BC}$ are horizontal and vertical line segments. Therefore, to find the lengths of these segments, you take the absolute value of the difference of their *x*- or *y*-coordinates.

$$AC = |8 - 3| = |5| = 5$$

$$BC = |7 - 3| = |4| = 4$$

The length of $\overline{AC}$ is 5 units, and the length of $\overline{BC}$ is 4 units.

Use the Pythagorean theorem to find the length of the hypotenuse $\overline{AB}$.

$$\begin{aligned} AC^2 + BC^2 &= AB^2 \\ 5^2 + 4^2 &= AB^2 \\ 25 + 16 &= AB^2 \\ 41 &= AB^2 \\ \sqrt{41} &= AB \\ 6.4 &\approx AB \end{aligned}$$

The length of $\overline{AB}$ is about 6.4 units. ■

Finding the Distance Between Two Points

You can use the Pythagorean theorem to find the distance between two points.

EXAMPLE 2

Find the distance between the points with coordinates $(-2, 5)$ and $(4, -1)$.

SOLUTION

Draw a segment between the points. Let this segment be the hypotenuse of a right triangle.

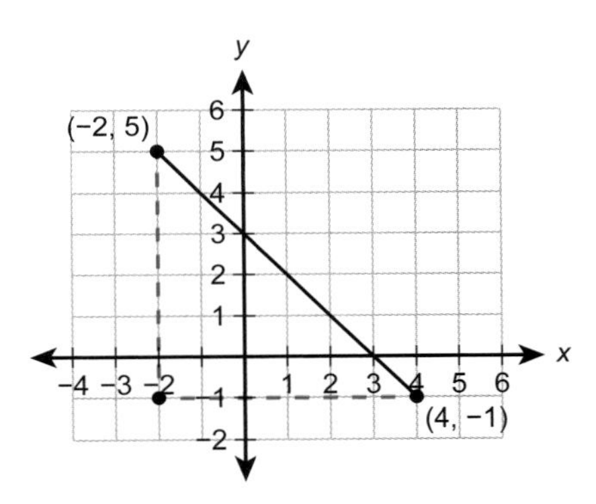

To find the length of the horizontal leg, subtract the x-coordinates of the endpoints and take the absolute value of the difference.

$$\text{length of the horizontal leg} = |4 - (-2)| = |6| = 6$$

The horizontal leg is 6 units long.

To find the length of the vertical leg, subtract the y-coordinates of the endpoints and take the absolute value of the difference.

$$\text{length of the vertical leg} = |-1 - 5| = |-6| = 6$$

The vertical leg is 6 units long.

Use the Pythagorean theorem to find the length of the hypotenuse. Let $a = 6$ and $b = 6$, and then solve for c.

$a^2 + b^2 = c^2$	
$6^2 + 6^2 = c^2$	Substitution
$36 + 36 = c^2$	Simplify.
$72 = c^2$	Add.
$\sqrt{72} = c$	Take the square root of both sides.
$8.5 \approx c$	Simplify.

The length of the hypotenuse is about 8.5 units, so the distance between points $(-2, 5)$ and $(4, -1)$ is about 8.5 units.

Finding Perimeter in the Coordinate Plane

To find the perimeter of a polygon, you must know the lengths of the polygon's sides. Use the Pythagorean theorem to find the lengths of any nonhorizontal, nonvertical sides.

EXAMPLE 3

Find the perimeter of trapezoid $ABCD$.

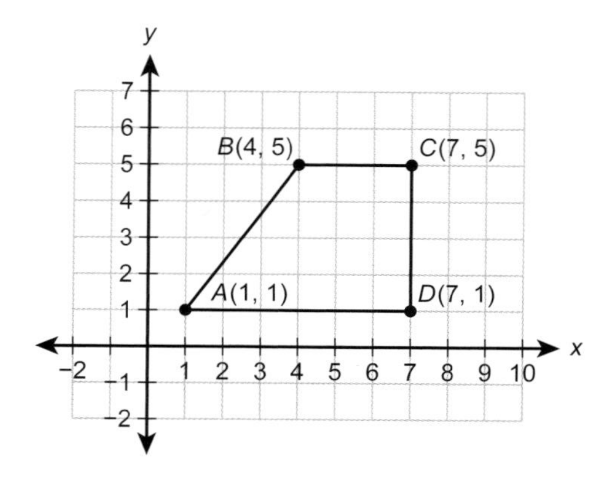

SOLUTION

Step 1 Begin by finding the lengths of horizontal sides $\overline{AD}$ and $\overline{BC}$. Subtract the x-coordinates of their endpoints and take the absolute value of the differences.

$$AD = |7 - 1| = |6| = 6$$

$$BC = |7 - 4| = |3| = 3$$

The length of AD is 6 units, and the length of BC is 3 units.

Step 2 Find the length of vertical side $\overline{CD}$. Subtract the y-coordinates of its endpoints and take the absolute value.

$$CD = |5 - 1| = |4| = 4$$

Step 3 Use the Pythagorean theorem to find the length of side AB. Place point E at $(4, 1)$ to create a right triangle ABE so that side AB is the hypotenuse.

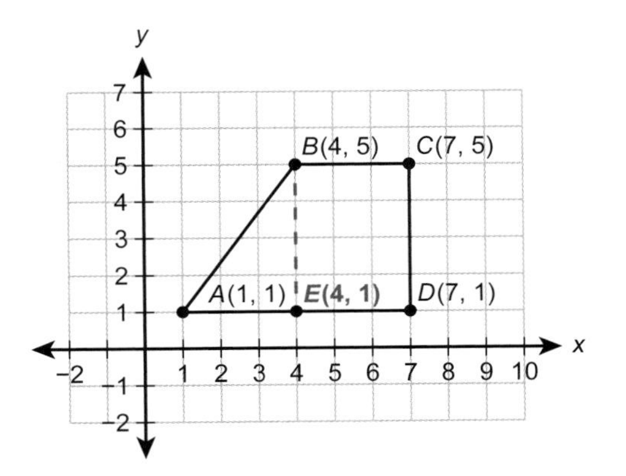

Find the lengths of the horizontal and vertical sides of the triangle, $\overline{AE}$ and $\overline{BE}$.

$$AE = |4 - 1| = |3| = 3$$

$$BE = |5 - 1| = |4| = 4$$

Use the Pythagorean theorem to find the length of the hypotenuse, side AB.

$$\begin{aligned} AE^2 + BE^2 &= AB^2 \\ 3^2 + 4^2 &= AB^2 \\ 9 + 16 &= AB^2 \\ 25 &= AB^2 \\ \sqrt{25} &= AB \\ 5 &= AB \end{aligned}$$

Side AB is 5 units long.

Step 4 Find the perimeter. Add the lengths of sides AB, BC, CD, and AD.

$$\begin{aligned} \text{perimeter} &= AB + BC + CD + AD \\ &= 5 + 3 + 4 + 6 \\ &= 18 \end{aligned}$$

The perimeter of the trapezoid is 18 units. ■

Applications of the Pythagorean Theorem

You can use the Pythagorean theorem to solve many real-world problems.

Many real-world problems involving right triangles can be solved using the Pythagorean theorem. To solve these types of problems, it's helpful to draw a diagram if one is not provided for you.

Applications: Boating and Kites

EXAMPLE 1

A boat leaves a dock and travels 3.5 mi due north and 6 mi due west. How far is the boat from the dock? Round your answer to the nearest tenth of a mile.

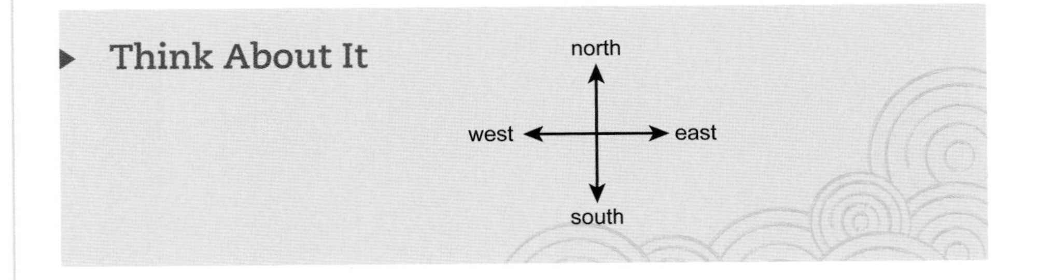

SOLUTION

Draw a diagram.

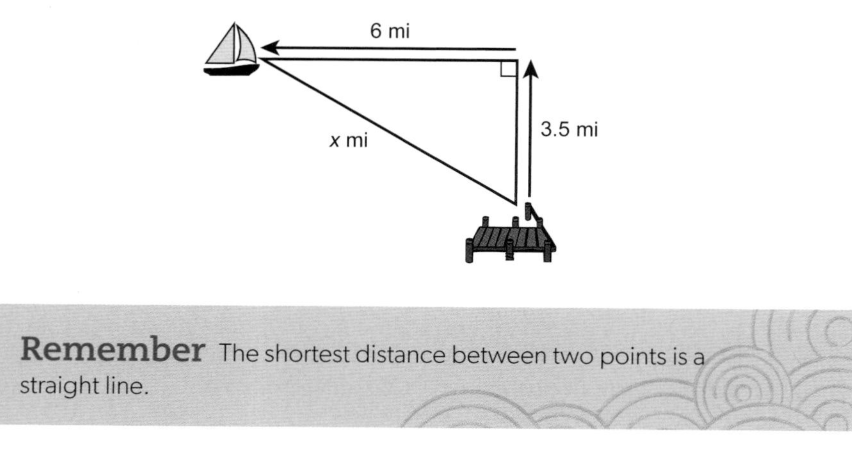

> ▶ **Remember** The shortest distance between two points is a straight line.

The unknown distance x is the length of the hypotenuse of a right triangle. Use the Pythagorean theorem.

$$\begin{aligned} a^2 + b^2 &= c^2 \\ \mathbf{3.5}^2 + \mathbf{6}^2 &= \boldsymbol{x}^2 \\ 12.25 + 36 &= x^2 \\ 48.25 &= x^2 \\ \pm\sqrt{48.25} &= x \\ \pm 6.946 &\approx x \end{aligned}$$

Disregard the negative answer. The boat is about 6.9 mi from the dock. ■

EXAMPLE 2

Eduardo is flying a kite on a string that is 75 m long. The kite is 62 m above the ground. Estimate the distance between Eduardo and the spot on the ground directly beneath the kite.

SOLUTION

Draw a diagram.

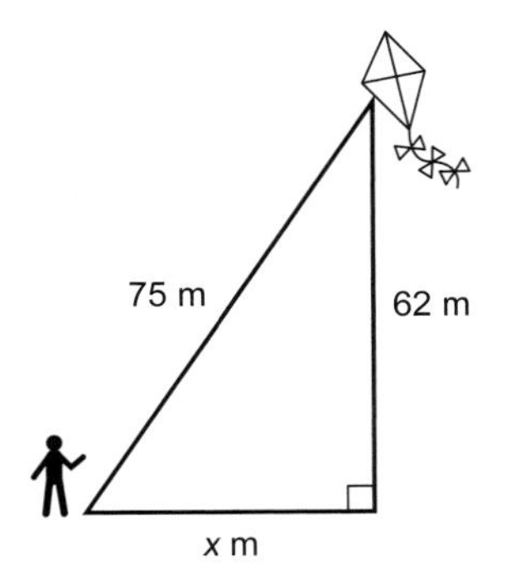

The unknown distance x is the length of a leg of a right triangle. Use the Pythagorean theorem.

$$
\begin{aligned}
a^2 + b^2 &= c^2 \\
x^2 + \mathbf{62}^2 &= \mathbf{75}^2 \\
x^2 + 3844 &= 5625 \\
x^2 &= 1781 \\
x &= \pm\sqrt{1781} \\
x &\approx \pm 42.2
\end{aligned}
$$

Disregard the negative answer. Eduardo is about 42.2 m from the spot on the ground directly beneath the kite. ■

Pythagorean Theorem in 3-D

You can use the Pythagorean theorem to find missing measures in three-dimensional figures.

Using the Pythagorean Theorem to Solve Problems Involving 3-D Figures

To use the Pythagorean theorem to find missing measurements in 3-D figures, you must be able to identify right triangles in the figure.

EXAMPLE 1

Consider the prism.

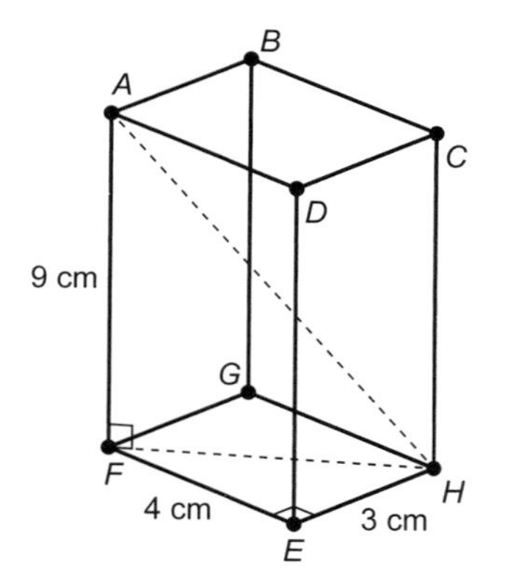

A Find FH.

SOLUTION

Consider $\triangle FEH$. $\overline{FH}$ is the hypotenuse, and $\overline{EF}$ and $\overline{EH}$ are the legs of the triangle. Use the Pythagorean theorem to find FH.

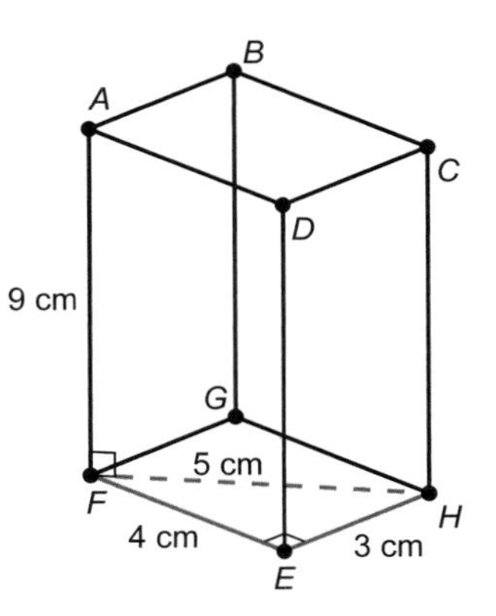

$$
\begin{aligned}
EF^2 + EH^2 &= FH^2 \\
4^2 + 3^2 &= FH^2 \\
16 + 9 &= FH^2 \\
25 &= FH^2 \\
\sqrt{25} &= FH \\
5 &= FH
\end{aligned}
$$

FH is 5 cm.

B Find AH.

SOLUTION

Consider $\triangle AFH$. $\overline{AH}$ is the hypotenuse, of the triangle and a diagonal of the prism. $\overline{FA}$ and $\overline{FH}$ are the legs of the triangle. Use the Pythagorean theorem to find AH.

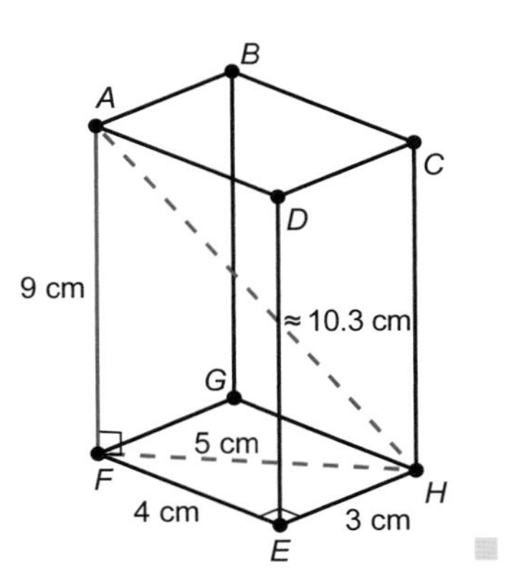

$$
\begin{aligned}
FA^2 + FH^2 &= AH^2 \\
9^2 + 5^2 &= AH^2 \\
81 + 25 &= AH^2 \\
106 &= AH^2 \\
\sqrt{106} &= AH \\
10.3 &\approx AH
\end{aligned}
$$

AH is about 10.3 cm.

Solving Real-World Problems

You can use the Pythagorean theorem to find measurements in 3-D figures in real-world contexts.

EXAMPLE 2

The top of a steeple has the shape of a square pyramid. The side length of the steeple's base is 8 ft long, and the steeple's slant height is 20.4 ft. How high is the top of the steeple?

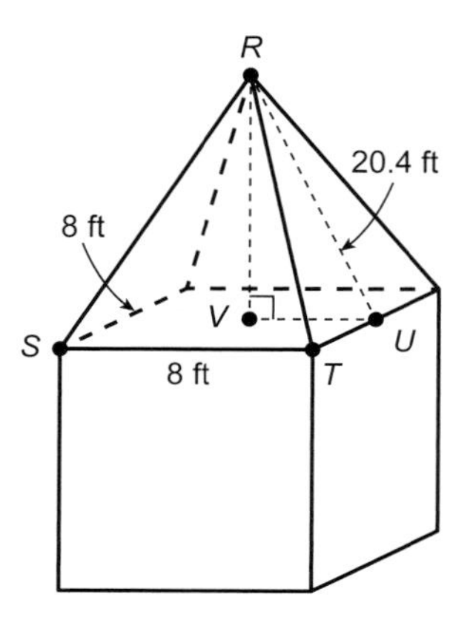

SOLUTION

$\overline{VR}$ represents the pyramid's height, $\overline{RU}$ is the pyramid's slant height, and $\overline{VU}$ is one-half the length of the pyramid's base. $\overline{VR}$, $\overline{RU}$, and $\overline{VU}$ form right triangle RVU, where $\overline{VR}$ and $\overline{VU}$ are the legs and $\overline{RU}$ is the hypotenuse.

It's given that RU is 20.4 ft. Since $\overline{VU}$ is one-half the length of the pyramid's base, VU is 4 ft. Use the Pythagorean theorem to solve for VR.

$$
\begin{aligned}
VR^2 + VU^2 &= RU^2 \\
VR^2 + 4^2 &= 20.4^2 \\
VR^2 + 16 &= 416.16 \\
VR^2 + 16 - 16 &= 416.16 - 16 \\
VR^2 &= 400.16 \\
VR &= \sqrt{400.16} \\
VR &\approx 20
\end{aligned}
$$

The top of the steeple is about 20 ft high. ■

More Pythagorean Applications

You can use the Pythagorean theorem to solve many geometry problems, including ones involving area.

Using the Pythagorean Theorem in Area Problems

The Pythagorean theorem can be a useful tool for finding the area of polygons. To use the Pythagorean theorem, you must be able to identify right triangles in the given figure.

EXAMPLE

Find the area of the equilateral triangle.

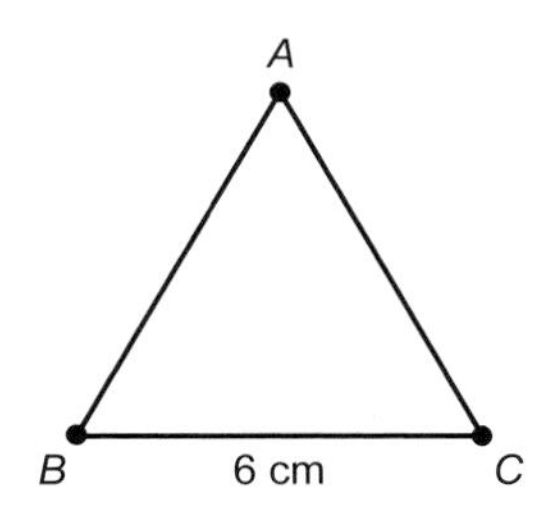

SOLUTION

The formula for finding the area of a triangle is $A = \frac{1}{2}bh$. The base b of this triangle is 6 cm, but the height h is unknown. You can use the Pythagorean theorem to find the height of the triangle.

Draw $\overline{AD}$ perpendicular to $\overline{BC}$.

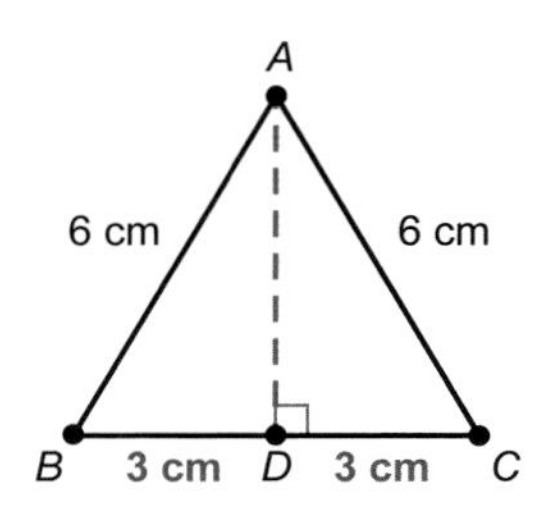

Point D is the midpoint of $\overline{BC}$. Therefore, BD and CD are each 3 cm.

$\overline{AD}$ is an altitude of $\triangle ABC$, and it forms two right triangles: $\triangle ABD$ and $\triangle ACD$.

▶ **Think About It** A line segment that represents the height of a triangle is called an altitude. An altitude always extends from a vertex and intersects the opposite side at a right angle. When the triangle is equilateral, the altitude bisects the side it intersects.

Consider $\triangle ACD$. $\overline{AD}$ and $\overline{CD}$ are the triangle's legs, and $\overline{AC}$ is the hypotenuse. Use the Pythagorean theorem to solve for AD.

$$AD^2 + CD^2 = AC^2$$
$$AD^2 + 3^2 = 6^2$$
$$AD^2 + 9 = 36$$
$$AD^2 + 9 - 9 = 36 - 9$$
$$AD^2 = 27$$
$$AD = \sqrt{27}$$
$$AD \approx 5.2$$

AD is about 5.2 cm. Therefore, the height of $\triangle ABC$ is about 5.2 cm.

Find the area of $\triangle ABC$.

$A = \frac{1}{2}bh$

$A \approx \frac{1}{2} \bullet 6 \bullet 5.2$ Let $b = 6$ and $h = 5.2$.

≈ 15.6

The area of $\triangle ABC$ is about 15.6 cm^2. ■

Pronunciation Guide

Pronunciation Guide

The tables provide sample words to explain the sounds associated with specific letters and letter combinations used in the respellings in this book. For example, *a* represents the short "a" sound in *cat*, while *ay* represents the long "a" sound in *day*.

Letter combinations are used to approximate certain more complex sounds. For example, in the respelling of *trapezoid*—TRA-puh-zoyd—the letters *uh* represent the vowel sound you hear in *shut* and *other*.

VOWELS

a	short a: **a**pple, c**a**t
ay	long a: c**a**ne, d**ay**
e, eh	short e: h**e**n, b**e**d
ee	long e: f**ee**d, t**ea**m
i, ih	short i: l**i**p, act**i**ve
iy	long i: tr**y**, m**igh**t
ah	short o: h**o**t, f**a**ther
oh	long o: h**o**me, thr**ow**
uh	short u: sh**u**t, **o**ther
yoo	long u: **u**nion, c**u**te

LETTER COMBINATIONS

ch	**ch**in, an**ci**ent
sh	**sh**ow, mi**ss**ion
zh	vi**s**ion, a**z**ure
th	**th**in, heal**th**
th	**th**en, hea**th**er
ur	b**ir**d, f**ur**ther, w**or**d
us	b**us**, cr**us**t
or	c**our**t, f**or**mal
ehr	**er**ror, c**are**
oo	c**oo**l, tr**ue**, r**u**le
ow	n**ow**, **ou**t
ou	l**oo**k, p**u**ll, w**ou**ld
oy	c**oi**n, t**oy**
aw	s**aw**, m**au**l, f**a**ll
ng	so**ng**, fi**ng**er
air	**Ar**istotle, b**ar**rister
ahr	c**ar**t, m**ar**tyr

CONSONANTS

b	**b**utter, **b**a**b**y
d	**d**og, cra**d**le
f	**f**un, **ph**one
g	**g**rade, an**g**le
h	**h**at, a**h**ead
j	**j**u**dg**e, gor**g**e
k	**k**ite, **c**ar, bla**ck**
l	**l**i**l**y, mi**l**e
m	**m**o**m**, ca**m**el
n	**n**ext, ca**n**di**d**
p	**p**rice, co**pp**er
r	**r**ubber, f**r**ee
s	**s**mall, **c**ircle, ha**ss**le
t	**t**on, po**tt**ery
v	**v**ase, **v**i**v**id
w	**w**all, a**w**ay
y	**y**ellow, ka**y**ak
z	**z**ebra, ha**z**e

Glossary

abscissa the first number in an ordered pair of numbers; also called the x-coordinate

absolute deviation the absolute value of the difference between a data value and the mean

absolute value the distance from zero to the graph of a number on a number line; The absolute value of a number a is denoted by $|a|$.

acute angle an angle that measures greater than 0° and less than 90°

acute triangle a triangle with three acute angles

addends numbers that are added

addition pattern a pattern formed by adding the same addend to each term to get the next term

additive identity a number whose sum with any given number is the given number; The additive identity for the real numbers is zero.

additive inverses two numbers whose sum, when added together, is zero; A number's additive inverse is its opposite.

adjacent angles angles in the same plane that share a vertex and a side but do not share any interior points

algebraic expression an expression containing variables as well as constant values

algorithm a step-by-step way to solve a problem

alternate exterior angles the outside angles that do not share the same vertex and are on opposite sides of a transversal crossing two lines

alternate interior angles the inside angles that do not share the same vertex and are on opposite sides of a transversal crossing two lines

altitude a line segment that extends from a figure's vertex and intersects the opposite side at a right angle

angle a figure formed by two rays, called sides, that share the same endpoint

angle of rotation the number of degrees a figure is rotated

apothem a line segment that joins the center of a polygon to the midpoint of one of its sides

approximate solution an estimate for the answer to a problem

area the number of square units contained in the interior of a figure

arrangement the order or placement of numbers or objects

average the sum of the data divided by the number of data values; the mean of the data

axis a number line that appears in a graph, such as the x-axis or y-axis in a coordinate plane; The plural of *axis* is *axes*.

bar graph a graph that uses bars to display and compare data

base a number or variable that is raised to a given power; For example, in 5^2, 5 is the base.

base of a cylinder one of the parallel, congruent faces of the cylinder; A base of a cylinder is a circle.

base of a figure the bottom side or face of a geometric figure

base of a parallelogram the side of a parallelogram that is chosen as the bottom side; Any side of a parallelogram can be its base.

base of a prism one of two parallel congruent faces in a prism

bias the error that can arise when a sample is not representative of its population

biased sample a sample that is not representative of its population

bisector a line that divides a line segment, an angle, or another figure into two equal parts

boundary number the upper or lower limit used to round a number to a given place value

box-and-whisker plot a diagram that shows the distribution or spread of data with the minimum, the maximum, and the three quartiles of the data

capacity a measure indicating an amount a container can hold

Cartesian coordinate system method of locating points in a plane in which the coordinates of the points are their distances from two intersecting perpendicular lines called axes

categorical variable a variable that has two or more categories

center of rotation the point about which a figure is rotated

chord a segment with endpoints that are points on a circle

circle the set of all points in a plane that are equidistant from a given point called the center

circle graph a circular chart that shows divisions according to how data results are distributed

circumference distance around a circle

clockwise in the same direction that the hands on a clock rotate

closed a set is closed under an operation if the operation performed on any two numbers in the set produces another number in the set

cluster a group of points that are close together in comparison to other points

coefficient the numerical factor in a term in a variable term

coincident system of linear equations consistent system of linear equations with infinitely many solutions; also called a consistent dependent system

collinear points points that lie on the same line

combination a collection of items in which the order of the items is not important

common factor a factor that two or more given numbers have in common; For example, 9 and 12 have a common factor of 3.

compass a tool used to draw circles and to measure in constructions

complementary angles a pair of angles for which the sum of their measures is 90°

complementary events two events such that one must occur, but both cannot occur at the same time

complex fraction a fraction that has a fraction in the numerator or the denominator (or both)

composite number a whole number greater than 1 that is not prime

compound interest interest paid on both the principal (the original amount of money) and the interest an account has already earned

cone a three-dimensional figure with one base that is a circle, a curved lateral surface, and a point called a vertex

congruent having exactly the same size and shape, even though orientation may vary

congruent angles angles that have the same measure

congruent figures figures that have the same size and shape

congruent polygons polygons that have the same size and shape

congruent triangles triangles that are identical to each other

conjecture an idea that might be true on the basis of observations but is not yet proven to be true

consecutive whole numbers whole numbers that increase by 1, such as the numbers 3, 4, and 5

consistent dependent system of linear equations a system of linear equations with infinitely many solutions; also called a coincident system

consistent independent system of linear equations a system of linear equations with exactly one solution

consistent system of linear equations a system having exactly one solution or infinitely many solutions

constant a numerical term that has no variables

constant function a function that neither rises nor falls as the input variable increases

constant of variation the ratio of two directly proportional quantities; also the nonzero constant k defined by $y = kx$ in a direct variation; also called the constant of proportionality

constant rate a rate that does not change over time

construction a method showing how a figure can be drawn accurately with a specified set of tools

continuous data values that all make sense within a range of data

contradiction an equation that is true for no values of the variable

convenience sampling sampling in which members of the population who are close at hand are selected

coordinate a number that indicates the location of a point on a number line

coordinate plane a plane that has an x-axis and a y-axis perpendicular to each other on which points can be located

corresponding angles angles that lie in the same position or match up with respect to the transversal when the transversal crosses two lines

counterclockwise in the opposite direction than the hands on a clock rotate

cross products the product of the numerator of one fraction and the denominator of a second fraction and the product of the denominator of the first fraction and the numerator of the second fraction

cross section a plane figure that results from the intersection of a plane and a solid

cube a solid figure made up of six square faces that meet at right angles

cubed the result of the operation where a number has been multiplied by itself two times, such as 5 cubed $= 5^3 = 5 \bullet 5 \bullet 5 = 125$; When the volume of a cube is found, the dimensions are cubed, and the volume is expressed in units cubed.

cube root a number that when multiplied by itself 3 times equals a given number

cubic unit a cube that is 1 unit on each side; a measure of volume

cylinder a three-dimensional figure with two congruent, parallel bases that are circles and a curved lateral surface that joins them

data numerical information that has been gathered; The term *data* is plural.

data skewed left the graph of the distribution of data with a longer tail to the left side

data skewed right the graph of the distribution of data with a longer tail to the right side

decimal a number written with a decimal point

decreasing function a function whose output values decrease as the input values increase

degree a unit used to measure angles

degree of accuracy the place value that is to be used to report an answer, such as in tens or hundredths

denominator the bottom number of a fraction

dependent events two events that are related in such a way that knowing about one event's occurrence has an effect on the probability of the other event

dependent variable the output variable

diameter a chord that passes through the center of a circle

diameter of a sphere a line segment passing through the center of a sphere that joins two points on the sphere

difference the solution to a subtraction problem

dilation the change in size of a figure without a change in shape

direct linear variation a function where y varies directly with x following the equation $y = kx$ where k is a nonzero constant

directly proportional a relationship in which two quantities vary directly with each other

direct variation a relationship between two quantities in which one quantity increases in proportion to the other; The relationship can be shown as a line on a graph.

discount a decrease in the price of an item

discrete data values that are distinct or have distinct intervals; values between the intervals that do not make sense as part of the data set

distribution of a data set the shape of the plotted data over the range of the data set's values

distributive property a rule that says that multiplying a number by a sum gives the same answer as multiplying the number by each addend of the sum and then adding the products

dividend the number to be divided; The dividend divided by the divisor equals the quotient.

divide out a common factor to simplify an expression by dividing a numerator and denominator by a common factor

divisor the number that divides the dividend; The dividend divided by the divisor equals the quotient.

domain the set of allowable inputs of a relation

equally likely having the same chance of happening

equation a number sentence that indicates that two expressions are equal

equiangular polygon a polygon with all angles congruent

equiangular triangle a triangle with three 60° angles

equilateral polygon a polygon with all sides congruent

equilateral triangle a triangle in which all three sides have equal length

equivalent having the same value, such as $\frac{1}{2}$, 0.5, and 50%

equivalent equations equations with the same solution or solutions

equivalent fractions fractions with the same value

equivalent inequalities inequalities that have the same solution set

equivalent ratios ratios that describe the same numerical relationship

estimate (n.) a very good guess or rough calculation of an answer, when the exact answer is not necessary

estimate (v.) to make a very good guess or rough calculation of an answer when the exact answer is not necessary

evaluate to find the value of an expression

evaluate a variable expression to replace all the variables in the expression with numbers and simplify

event a set of one or more outcomes; a subset of the sample space; also called actions

exact solution a solution that is not an estimate or an approximation

experiment any process or action that has a result

experimental probability probability based on actual observations or results of an experiment

exponent a number or variable attached to the base to show how many times the base will be a factor; For example, in 5^2, the exponent is 2.

expression a group of mathematical symbols that represents a numerical value; Most expressions contain numerals as well as operation signs or grouping symbols or a combination of these elements. An expression containing one or more variables is a variable expression or an algebraic expression.

exterior angle of a triangle an angle formed by two sides of a triangle, one of which extends outside the triangle; Each interior angle of a triangle forms a linear pair with an exterior angle.

extrapolation the process of inferring, estimating, or predicting an unknown value that is outside of known values

extremes in a proportion, the first and last numbers or variables; In $a : b = c : d$ or $\frac{a}{b} = \frac{c}{d}$, a and d are the extremes.

factor any of two or more numbers multiplied to form a product

favorable outcome the outcome you are investigating

flip the movement of a figure that shows the figure and its mirror image, sometimes called a reflection

formula an equation that is used to compute values, such as area, perimeter, or volume

fraction a number that shows part of a set, a point on a number line, a part of a whole, a quotient, or a ratio

frequency the number of times one item appears in a data set

frequency table a table that shows how often each item appears in a set of data

friendly numbers numbers such as 5 and 10, or multiples of 5 and 10, that are easier to add, subtract, multiply, and divide

function a relation in which every element of the domain is assigned to exactly one element of the range

geometric probability the probability of an event equal to the ratio of the area of success to the area of the entire region

graph (n.) a diagram that shows the relationship between quantities

graph (v.) to draw a visual representation of data

graph of a one-variable inequality the set of points on a number line that represents all the solutions of the inequality

greatest common factor (GCF) the greatest number that divides evenly into two or more numbers

grouping symbols symbols such as parentheses, brackets, and fraction bars used to set apart an expression that should be simplified before other operations are performed

height in a geometric figure, the length of an altitude that is perpendicular to a base

height of a triangle the length of the perpendicular segment that joins a base to the opposite vertex

histogram a graph with adjoining bars; used to show the frequency of data or data groups

horizontal intercept the value of the variable on the horizontal axis at the point where a graph crosses the horizontal axis

hypotenuse the side opposite the right angle in a right triangle

identity an equation that is true for every value of the variable

image the new figure that results from a transformation

improper fraction a fraction in which the numerator is greater than or equal to the denominator

inconsistent system of linear equations a system with no solution

increasing function a function whose output values increase as input values increase

independent events two events that are related in such a way that one event's occurrence has no effect on the probability of the other event

independent variable the input variable

inequality a mathematical sentence that compares numbers or expressions using one of the symbols $<, >, \leq,$ or $\geq$

inference a conclusion reached from facts, evidence, and reasoning

input a number that will be used in a rule to determine the value of the output

integers the set of whole numbers and their opposites $\{\ldots -2, -1, 0, 1, 2, \ldots\}$

intercept the value at which a graph crosses one of the coordinate axes

interest the cost to borrow money or the amount earned by lending money

interest rate the percentage of the original amount of money on which the interest will be calculated

interior angle any angle inside a polygon

interpolation the process of inferring, or estimating, an unknown value that is between known values

interquartile range (IQR) a measure of variation found by subtracting the first quartile Q_1 from the third quartile Q_3: $IQR = Q_3 - Q_1$; represents the range of the middle half of the data

intersecting lines lines that cross at one point

interval the distance between two points, as between two numbers on a number line

inverse operations opposite operations that undo each other; Subtraction and addition are inverse operations. Division and multiplication are inverse operations.

irrational number a real number that cannot be written in the form $\frac{a}{b}$ for integers a and b, with $b \neq 0$

irregular polygon a polygon that does not have all sides and angles equal in measure

isosceles triangle a triangle that has at least two sides equal in length; An equilateral triangle is a special type of isosceles triangle.

label one of the informative indicators at various places on data displays such as tables and graphs

lateral area the sum of the areas of a figure's lateral faces only

lateral face one of the parallelograms that form a prism and is not a base

lateral surface the curved surface of a cylinder or cone; in a prism, any surface that connects the two bases; in a pyramid, any surface that rises from the base to the vertex

lateral surface area the sum of the areas of all surfaces of a three-dimensional figure except the base(s)

law of large numbers a law that states that the relative frequency of an event becomes closer to the theoretical probability of the event as the number of trials increases

least common denominator (LCD) in a set of fractions, the least common multiple of the denominators

least common multiple (LCM) the least number that is a multiple of all numbers in a set

leg of a right triangle one of the two sides of a right triangle that form the right angle

like denominators denominators that are exactly the same in two or more fractions

like fractions fractions with the same denominator

like terms terms that have the same variable part(s) raised to the same powers; Constants (numbers without variables) are also like terms.

line a straight path of points that extends without end in both directions

linear association in a scatter plot, points following a pattern that resembles a line

linear equation an equation whose graph is a line

linear function a function whose graph is a straight line

linear pair two angles that have a common side and whose other sides point in opposite directions

line graph a display in which a set of information is shown as a series of points connected by straight line segments; A line graph is used to reveal trends.

line of reflection the line across which a figure is reflected

line plot a number line that shows all the data values with a mark or marks above each data value to show how many times that data value occurred

line segment part of a line including two points on the line and all the points between those points

literal equation an equation with two or more variables; Formulas are common examples of literal equations.

lower bound estimate an estimate for a problem that is less than the actual solution could be

lowest terms when the numerator and the denominator of a fraction have no common factors other than 1

magic square a square made up of an equal number of rows and columns of numbers such that the sum of any column, row, or diagonal is the same

maximum the greatest value for a data set

mean absolute deviation (MAD) the mean of all the absolute deviations of a data set

means in a proportion, the second and third numbers or variables; In $a : b = c : d$ or $\frac{a}{b} = \frac{c}{d}$, b and c are the means.

mean the sum of the values in a data set divided by the number of values

measure of center a measure that represents the center of the distribution of values for a data set, such as mean, median, and mode

measure of spread a measure that represents the extent to which the values of a data set are spread out, such as the range

measure of variation a measure, such as the interquartile range, that compares the range or spread of data to a measure of center

median the middle value when the data are ordered; If there is an even number of data values, the median is the average of the two middle values.

minimum the least value for a data set

minuend a number from which another number is subtracted

mixed number a number consisting of both a whole number and a fraction, or the opposite of such a number

mode the most common value; A data set can have no mode, one mode, or more than one mode.

multiple of a number the product of the given number and a counting number

multiplication pattern a pattern formed by multiplying each term by the same factor to get the next term

multiplicative identity the number 1

multiplicative inverse the reciprocal of a number

mutually exclusive events events that cannot happen at the same time

negative association in a scatter plot, a relationship between two variables for which an increase in one variable corresponds to a decrease in the other variable

negative correlation a trend that develops with two variables when the value of one variable increases while the other value decreases; In a scatter plot, the data points form a pattern that slants down.

negative sign the sign $(-)$ indicating that a number's value is less than zero, such as -6

net a two-dimensional pattern that can be folded into a three-dimensional figure

net gain or net loss the sum of the individual values when a situation includes several gains and losses

no association in a scatter plot, a relationship between two variables for which an increase in one variable doesn't correspond to any particular pattern for the other variable

nonlinear association in a scatter plot, points following a pattern that does not resemble a line

nonlinear function a function whose graph is not a straight line

nonrepeating decimal a nonterminating decimal that has no repeating pattern of digits

nonterminating decimal a decimal that does not terminate or end

nonzero opposites two numbers that are the same distance from zero on a number line

nth root any number x such that x raised to the n power equals some given number a for a whole number $n > 1$

number line a line that has equally spaced intervals labeled with coordinates

numerator the top number of a fraction

numerical expression an expression consisting of numbers and one or more operations

obtuse angle an angle that measures greater than 90° and less than 180°

obtuse triangle a triangle with an obtuse angle

open sentence an equation or inequality that contains one or more variables

opposites a pair of numbers whose distance on both sides of zero is the same, such as -5 and $+5$

ordered pair a pair of numbers in which the first number is the x-coordinate, or abscissa, and the second number is the y-coordinate, or ordinate, of a point's location in the coordinate plane

order-of-magnitude estimate an estimate expressed as a power of 10

order of operations mathematical order that should be followed to simplify an expression when there is more than one operation

ordinate the second number in an ordered pair of numbers; the y-coordinate

origin on a number line, the point with coordinate zero; on a coordinate plane, the point where the x-axis and the y-axis intersect; The ordered pair at the origin is $(0, 0)$.

outcome a result of an experiment

outlier a point that is far from other points in a data set

output the result of applying a function rule to the value of an input

parallel lines lines on the same plane that never intersect

parallelogram a quadrilateral with two pairs of parallel sides

percent a ratio that compares a number to 100

percent error the ratio of the absolute error of a measurement to the actual value, written as a percent

percent of change the ratio of the amount of change to the original amount, expressed in percent form

perfect square a rational number with a rational square root

perimeter distance around a figure; The perimeter of a polygon is the sum of the lengths of all the sides.

perpendicular lines lines that intersect and form angles that measure 90°

place value the value of a digit depending on its position, or place, in a number

plane a flat surface with infinite length and width but no thickness

point a location in space with no length, width, or depth

point on a coordinate plane a dot that marks a coordinate; a location on a coordinate plane, designated by an x-value and a y-value

point-slope form of a linear equation $y - y_1 = m(x - x_1)$ where m is the slope of the line and x_1 and y_1 are the coordinates of a point through which the line passes

polygon a closed figure formed by three or more line segments in a plane, such that each line segment intersects two other line segments at their endpoints only

population a group of individuals or objects about which information is wanted

positive association in a scatter plot, a relationship between two variables for which an increase in one variable corresponds to an increase in the other variable

positive correlation a trend that describes when two variables increase or decrease together; In a scatter plot, the data points form a pattern that slants up.

positive sign the sign $(+)$ indicating that a number's value is greater than zero, such as $+6$; The positive sign is not always shown.

power the product that results when a number, called the base, is multiplied by itself the number of times indicated by its exponent

power of ten any number that can be written in the form $10n$, where n is an integer

precision an indication of how exact a calculation or measurement is

predict to state how future events will happen

pre-image the original figure in a transformation

prime factorization an expression showing a positive integer as a product of its prime factors

prime number a whole number greater than 1 that has only two whole-number factors, 1 and itself

principal money that earns interest at a given rate over time; The principal is the original amount of money on which the interest is based.

principal square root the nonnegative square root, indicated by the square root sign

prism a three-dimensional figure whose surfaces, called faces, are polygons; At least two faces are parallel and congruent and are called bases, and all other faces are parallelograms. (In a right prism, all other faces are rectangles.)

probability a number from 0 to 1 that describes how likely an event is to occur

product the result of multiplying two or more factors together

proper fraction a fraction in which the numerator is less than the denominator

proportion an equation stating that two ratios are equal

proportional relationship a relationship that can be described by an equation of the form $y = kx$ where k is the constant of proportionality

protractor a tool to measure the degrees in an angle

pyramid a three-dimensional figure with one base that is a polygon and all other faces (called lateral faces) are triangles that meet at a single vertex

quadrant one of the four regions into which the coordinate axes separate the coordinate plane

quadratic variation a relationship between x and y in which you can write the function describing the relationship in a form of the general equation, $f(x) = kx^2$ where k is a nonzero constant

quadrilateral a polygon with four sides

quartile one of the three values that separate an ordered data set into four equal parts; The second quartile Q_2 is the median of the data set. The first quartile Q_1 is the median of the lower half of the data set. The third quartile Q_3 is the median of the upper half of the data set. Note: A quartile also refers to the entire set of data in any quarter of the data.

quotient the result of division

radius (of a circle) a segment whose endpoints are the center of the circle and a point on the circle. The plural of *radius* is *radii.*

radius (of a sphere) a line segment joining the center of the sphere and a point on the surface of the sphere. The plural of *radius* is *radii.*

range the set of allowable outputs of a relation

range of a data set the difference of the maximum and minimum values in the data set

rate a ratio of two quantities measured in different units

rate of change the ratio of a change in one quantity to a change in a second quantity

ratio a comparison of two quantities by division

rational expression a fraction that includes expressions for the numerator or the denominator

rational number a number that can be expressed as a ratio $\frac{a}{b}$ where a and b are integers and $b \neq 0$; A rational number can be written as a fraction, a decimal, or a percent.

rational square root a square root that is a rational number

ray part of a line that begins from an endpoint and extends infinitely in one direction

reasonableness the sense that an answer is correct, given the facts

reasoning the series of thoughts and steps used to understand a problem, to create a plan to solve the problem, to reach a solution, and to accurately explain results

reciprocal a number by which a given number must be multiplied to get a result of 1; also called the multiplicative inverse

rectangle a parallelogram with four right angles; A square is a special type of rectangle.

reflection a transformation of a figure by flipping it across a line or line segment, creating a mirror image of the figure

regular polygon a polygon with all its sides congruent and all it angles congruent

relation a mapping from a set of inputs to a set of outputs

relatively prime numbers two or more numbers that have no common factors other than 1

remainder the amount left over after dividing

repeating decimal a decimal in which a digit, or a group of digits, other than zero repeats forever after the decimal point

replacement set the given set of numbers that a variable may represent

representation a way of displaying information, such as a model, a number, a graph, or an equation

rhombus a parallelogram with four congruent sides; A square is a special type of rhombus.

right angle an angle that measures 90°

right triangle a triangle with a right angle

rigid transformations transformations that do not change the size or shape of a figure

rise the vertical change between two selected points on a line

rotation the turning of a figure around a given point

round (v.) to change a number to the nearest place value asked in a problem; For example, the result of rounding 532 to the nearest ten would be 530.

ruler a tool to measure length, typically marked in centimeters or inches

run the horizontal change between two selected points on a line

sale price the price of an item after a discount

sales tax a percent of the price of an item paid to a government when the item is sold

sample part of a population

sample space the set of all possible outcomes of an experiment

scale factor the ratio of two corresponding sides in two similar figures

scalene triangle a triangle that has no sides equal in length

scatter plot a graph that displays data as points

scientific notation a system of writing numbers as the product of a number that is greater than or equal to 1 but less than 10 and an integer power of 10

semicircle half of a circle

sides of a polygon the segments forming a polygon

similar figures two figures in which each pair of corresponding angles is congruent and the ratio of the lengths of corresponding sides is constant

simple interest interest earned at a fixed percent of the initial deposit, or principal amount

simple random sampling sampling in which all members of the population have an equal probability of selection

simplest form of a fraction a fraction in which the numerator and the denominator have no common factor other than 1 or -1

simplify a numerical expression to find the value of a numerical expression

slide the movement of a figure along a line without turns or flips, also known as translation

slope-intercept form of a linear equation $y = mx + b$ where m is the slope of the line and b is the y-intercept

slope of a line the ratio of the vertical change, or rise, between any two points on the line to the horizontal change, or run, between the same two points

solution the answer to a problem or the process used to find the answer

solution of an open sentence a number that makes the open sentence true

solution set the set of all solutions to a given open sentence

solve to find the value(s) of the variable(s) that make an equation true

speed the ratio of distance traveled to time

sphere the set of all points in space that are a given distance from a point called the center

square a parallelogram with four congruent sides and four right angles

squared the result of the operation where a number has been multiplied by itself, such $5^2 = 5 \bullet 5 = 25$; When the area of a square is found, the dimensions are squared, and the area is expressed in units squared.

square of a number the product of a number and itself

square root a factor of a number that when multiplied by itself results in the number; The nonnegative square root is called the principal square root and is indicated by the square root sign.

square unit a square with sides of a particular side length, such as a square meter, used to measure area

standard form of a linear equation $Ax + By = C$ where A, B, and C are integers, and A and B are both nonzero

standard form of a number a number expressed using digits and place values

stem-and-leaf plot data display that lists the last digits (leaves) of the data values to the right of the earlier digits (stems)

straight angle an angle that measures 180°

strategy a technique used to solve a problem, such as working backward or drawing a diagram

stratified random sampling sampling in which the population is first organized into separate categories, and then each is sampled as an independent subpopulation

substitution the replacement of an equivalent value for another

subtrahend a number that is subtracted from another number

sum the result of an addition; The numbers added are addends.

supplement one of two supplementary angles

supplementary angles a pair of angles for which the sum of their measures is 180°

surface area the sum of the areas of all surfaces of a three-dimensional figure

surface area of a rectangular prism the sum of the areas of a prism's lateral faces and two bases

surface of a solid figure all of the polygons that are faces of the solid figure

survey a strategy for collecting data by asking questions of a group of people

systematic sampling sampling in which the population is ordered, and then members are selected at regular intervals through that ordered list

system of linear equations two or more linear equations using the same variables

tax a sum of money collected by a government

term a part of an expression that can be a number, a variable, or a product of numbers and variables

term in a pattern each number or object in a pattern

terminating decimal a decimal that has a finite number of nonzero digits to the right of the decimal point

term number the position of a term in a pattern

tessellation a pattern of shapes that fit together with no overlaps or gaps and can extend to fill a figure

theoretical probability the ratio of the number of favorable outcomes to the total number of possible outcomes

three-dimensional object a figure with length, width, and height; often called 3-D

tip an amount of money given to someone who provides a service

transformation (geometric) a movement or change of a figure, such as a translation, reflection, rotation, or dilation

transformation (of an equation) any change to an equation that results in an equivalent equation

translation a sliding of a figure in a straight path without rotation or reflection

transversal a line that intersects two or more lines in a plane

trapezoid a quadrilateral with exactly one pair of parallel sides

tree diagram a branching diagram used in probability to show outcomes of several events that occur one after the other

trend a consistent pattern in data

triangle a figure made up of three segments joined at their endpoints; Each endpoint is a vertex.

turn the movement of a figure a certain number of degrees around a given point, sometimes called a rotation

two-dimensional shape a figure with length and width, but no height; often called 2-D

two-way relative frequency table a table that shows the relative frequencies of each data value in a two-way table

two-way table a frequency table for two categorical variables

unbiased sample a sample that is representative of the population

unit an object or an amount used to measure, such as kilograms as a standard unit for mass

unit rate a rate in which the second quantity in the ratio is 1

unlike denominators denominators that are different in two or more fractions

upper bound estimate an estimate for a problem that is greater than the actual solution could be

variable a symbol that represents a value

variable expression an expression consisting of one or more variables, one or more operations, and possibly one or more numbers; also called an algebraic expression

vector a line segment with a direction indicated with an arrow

Venn diagram a drawing that shows relationships among sets of numbers or objects

vertex a point where two sides of a polygon meet. The plural of *vertex* is *vertices*.

vertical angles two nonadjacent angles that share a vertex and are formed by two intersecting lines

vertical intercept the value of the variable on the vertical axis at the point where a graph crosses the vertical axis

volume a measure of space inside a figure

whole number any member of the set $\{0, 1, 2, 3, 4, \ldots\}$

***x*-axis** in a coordinate plane, the horizontal line, or axis

***x*-coordinate** the first number in an ordered pair of numbers; also called the abscissa

***x*-intercept** the x-coordinate of a point where a graph intersects the x-axis

***y*-axis** in a coordinate plane, the vertical line, or axis

***y*-coordinate** the second number in an ordered pair of numbers; also called the ordinate

***y*-intercept of a graph** the y-coordinate of the point where the graph intersects the y-axis; also called the vertical intercept

Symbols

Symbol	Meaning
$\mid$	such that
$\in$	is an element of
$\varnothing$ or $\{\}$	null or empty set
$\sqrt{a}$	principal square root of *a*
$\sqrt[3]{a}$	cube root of *a*
A'	*A* prime; the result of transforming point *A*
$\ldots$	continuation of a pattern
Q_1	first quartile
x_1	first value of *x*
π	pi
$(\ )$	parentheses
$[\ ]$	brackets
$\approx$	is approximately equal to
$=$	is equal to
$\neq$	is not equal to
$\cong$	is congruent to
$\sim$	is similar to
$<$	is less than
$>$	is greater than
$\leq$	is less than or equal to
$\geq$	is greater than or equal to
$\lvert x \rvert$	absolute value of *x*
$-a$	the opposite of *a*
a^n	*a* to the *n*th power
$\{\ldots\}$	description or list of all elements in a set; roster notation
$\%$	percent
$\overline{}$	placed over a digit or a block of digits in a decimal to show that the digit or block of digits repeats
$\pm$	plus or minus
$a : b$	ratio of *a* to *b*
$^\circ$	degree
$\overline{AB}$	line segment *AB*
AB	length of line segment *AB*
$\overrightarrow{AB}$	ray *AB*
$\overleftrightarrow{AB}$	line *AB*
$\triangle ABC$	triangle *ABC*
$\angle ABC$	angle *ABC*
$m\angle ABC$	the measure of angle *ABC*
⦜	right angle
$\parallel$	is parallel to
$\perp$	is perpendicular to

Properties

Real Number Properties

Let a, b, and c be any real numbers.

Addition Property of Equality	If $a = b$, then $a + c = b + c$ and $c + a = c + b$.	
Addition Property: Addends with Like Signs	For all $a > 0$ and $b > 0$, $a + b = \|a\| + \|b\|$. For all $a < 0$ and $b < 0$, $a + b = -\|a\| + \|b\|$.	
Addition Property: Addends with Unlike Signs	For all $a > 0$ and $b < 0$, If $\|a\| > \|b\|$, then $a + b = \|a\| - \|b\|$. If $\|a\| < \|b\|$, then $a + b = -\|b\| - \|a\|$.	
Subtraction Property of Equality	If $a = b$, then $a - c = b - c$.	
Substitution Property of Equality	If $a = b$, then a may be replaced with b in any expression or equation.	
Multiplication Property of Equality	If $a = b$, then $c \bullet a = c \bullet b$ and $a \bullet c = b \bullet c$.	
Division Property of Equality	If $a = b$ and $c \neq 0$, then $\frac{a}{c} = \frac{b}{c}$.	
Distributive Property	$a(b + c) = ab + ac$	
	Addition	Multiplication
Commutative Properties	$a + b = b + a$	$a \bullet b = b \bullet a$
Associative Properties	$(a + b) + c = a + (b + c)$	$(a \bullet b) \bullet c = a \bullet (b \bullet c)$
Inverse Properties	$a + (-a) = 0$ and $(-a) + a = 0$	$a \bullet \frac{1}{a} = 1$ and $\frac{1}{a} \bullet a = 1, a \neq 0$
Identity Properties	$a + 0 = a$ and $0 + a = a$	$a \bullet 1 = a$ and $1 \bullet a = a$

Absolute Value Equations

If $|x| = a$ for some positive number a, then $x = a$ or $x = -a$.

Properties of Exponents

Let a and b be nonzero real numbers. Let m and n be integers.

If n is a positive integer, then $a^n = a \bullet a \bullet a \bullet \ldots \bullet a$ (n factors).

Zero Exponent Property	$a^0 = 1, a \neq 0$
Negative Exponent Property	$a^{-m} = \frac{1}{a^m}, a \neq 0$
Product of Powers Property	$a^m \bullet a^n = a^{m+n}$

Square Root Properties

For nonnegative values of m, n, and p, if $m < n < p$, then $\sqrt{m} < \sqrt{n} < \sqrt{p}$.

Product Property	For real numbers a and b, $\sqrt{ab} = \sqrt{a} \bullet \sqrt{b}$ and $\sqrt{a} \bullet \sqrt{b} = \sqrt{ab}$.
Quotient Property	For real numbers a and b with $b \neq 0$, $\sqrt{\frac{a}{b}} = \frac{\sqrt{a}}{\sqrt{b}}$.

Reciprocal Properties

Reciprocal Property of Multiplication	For any nonzero real number a, $a \bullet \frac{1}{a} = 1$.

For all nonzero real numbers a and b, the reciprocal of $\frac{a}{b}$ is $\frac{b}{a}$.

For any nonzero real number a, $\frac{1}{-a} = \frac{-1}{a} = -\frac{1}{a}$.

For all nonzero real numbers a and b, $\frac{1}{ab} = \frac{1}{a} \bullet \frac{1}{b}$.

Division Properties

For any real number a and nonzero real number b, $a \div b = a \bullet \frac{1}{b}$.

For all real numbers a and b and nonzero real number c, $a + \frac{b}{c} = \frac{a}{c} + \frac{b}{c}$.

For all $a > 0$ and $b > 0$, $a \div b > 0$.

For all $a < 0$ and $b < 0$, $a \div b > 0$.

For all $a < 0$ and $b > 0$, $a \div b < 0$.

Properties of Order

Comparison Property of Order	If $a > b$, then $b < a$. If $a < b$, then $b > a$.
Transitive Property of Order	If $a > b$ and $b > c$, then $a > c$. If $a < b$ and $b < c$, then $a < c$.
Addition Property of Order	If $a > b$, then $a + c > b + c$. If $a < b$, then $a + c < b + c$.
Subtraction Property of Order	If $a > b$, then $a - c > b - c$. If $a < b$, then $a - c < b - c$.
Multiplication Property of Order, Positive Multiplier	If $a > b$ and $c > 0$, then $ca > cb$ and $ac > bc$. If $a < b$ and $c > 0$, then $ca < cb$ and $ac < bc$.
Multiplication Property of Order, Negative Multiplier	If $a > b$ and $c < 0$, then $ca < cb$ and $ac < bc$. If $a < b$ and $c < 0$, then $ca > cb$ and $ac > bc$.
Division Property of Order, Positive Multiplier	If $a > b$ and $c > 0$, then $\frac{a}{c} > \frac{b}{c}$. If $a < b$ and $c > 0$, then $\frac{a}{c} < \frac{b}{c}$.
Division Property of Order, Negative Multiplier	If $a > b$ and $c < 0$, then $\frac{a}{c} < \frac{b}{c}$. If $a < b$ and $c < 0$, then $\frac{a}{c} > \frac{b}{c}$.

Comparison Property of Rational Numbers

For nonzero integers a and c and positive integers b and d,

$\frac{a}{b} > \frac{c}{d}$ if, and only if, $ad > bc$.

$\frac{a}{b} < \frac{c}{d}$ if, and only if, $ad < bc$.

Properties of Proportions

Let a, b, c, and d be real numbers.

Means-Extremes Product Property	$\frac{a}{b} = \frac{c}{d}$ if, and only if, $ad = bc$, given that b and d are not 0.
Reciprocal Property	If $\frac{a}{b} = \frac{c}{d}$, then $\frac{b}{a} = \frac{d}{c}$, given that a, b, c, and d are all nonzero.

Formulary

Geometry

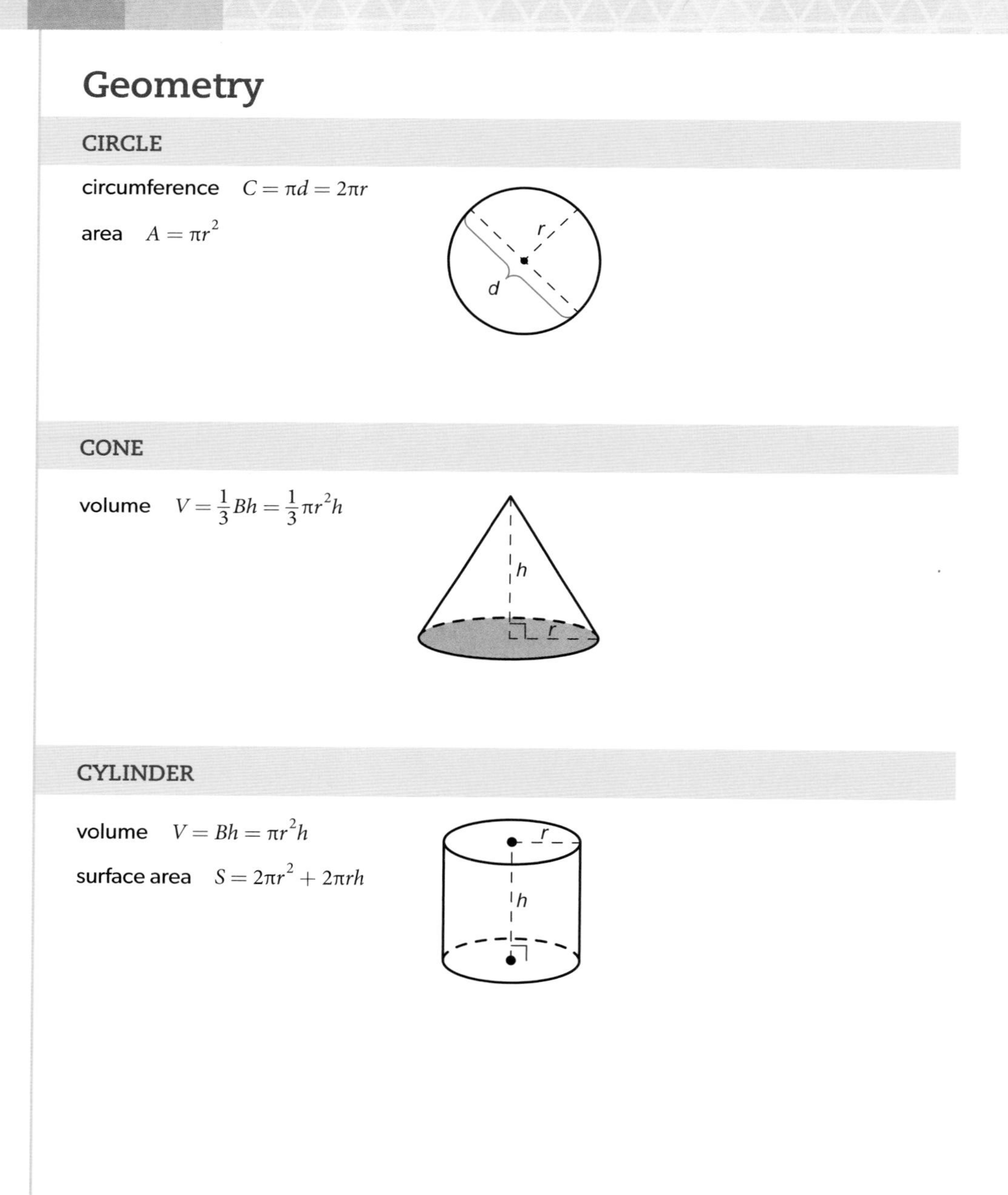

CIRCLE

circumference $C = \pi d = 2\pi r$

area $A = \pi r^2$

CONE

volume $V = \frac{1}{3}Bh = \frac{1}{3}\pi r^2 h$

CYLINDER

volume $V = Bh = \pi r^2 h$

surface area $S = 2\pi r^2 + 2\pi rh$

PARALLELOGRAM

area $A = bh$

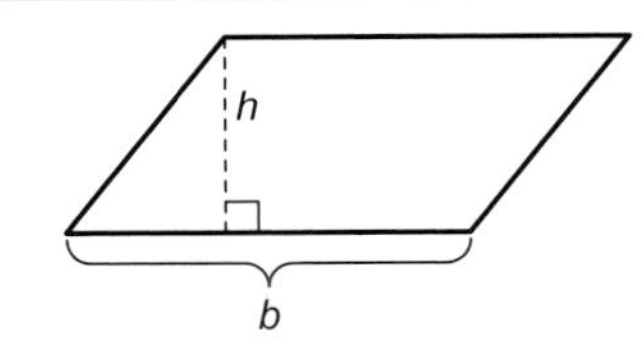

PRISM: CUBE

volume $V = s^3$

surface area $S = 6s^2$

lateral area of a prism $L = Ph$

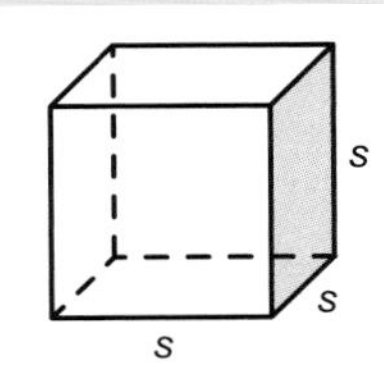

PRISM: RIGHT RECTANGULAR

volume $V = lwh$

surface area $S = 2lw + 2lh + 2wh$

length of diagonal $d = \sqrt{l^2 + w^2 + h^2}$

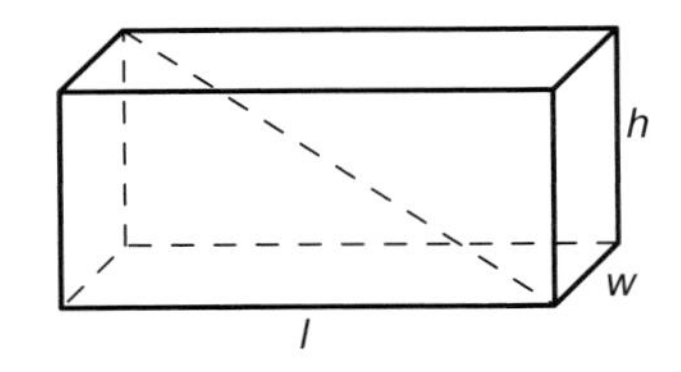

PYRAMID

volume $V = \frac{1}{3}Bh$

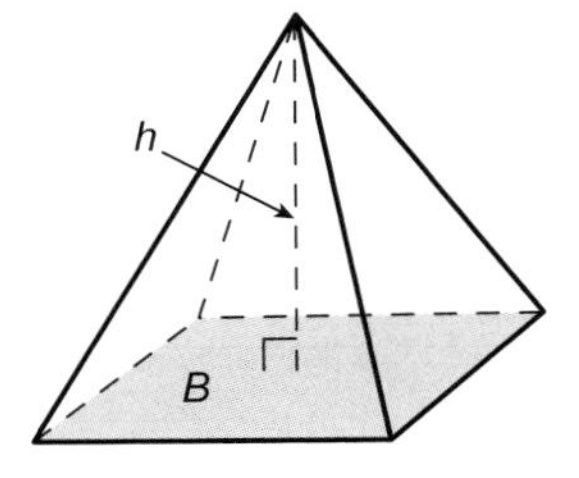

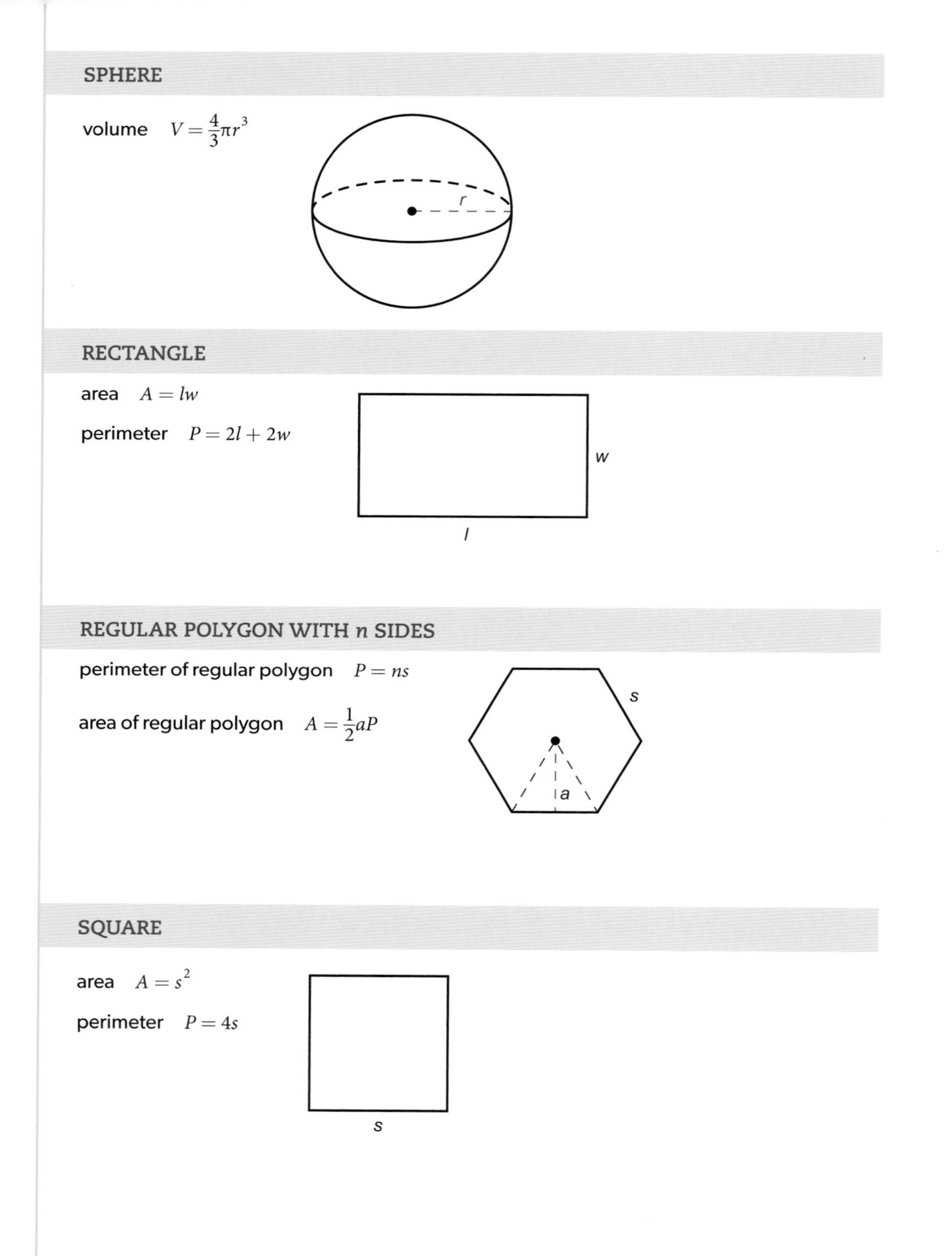

SPHERE

volume $V = \frac{4}{3}\pi r^3$

RECTANGLE

area $A = lw$

perimeter $P = 2l + 2w$

REGULAR POLYGON WITH n SIDES

perimeter of regular polygon $P = ns$

area of regular polygon $A = \frac{1}{2}aP$

SQUARE

area $A = s^2$

perimeter $P = 4s$

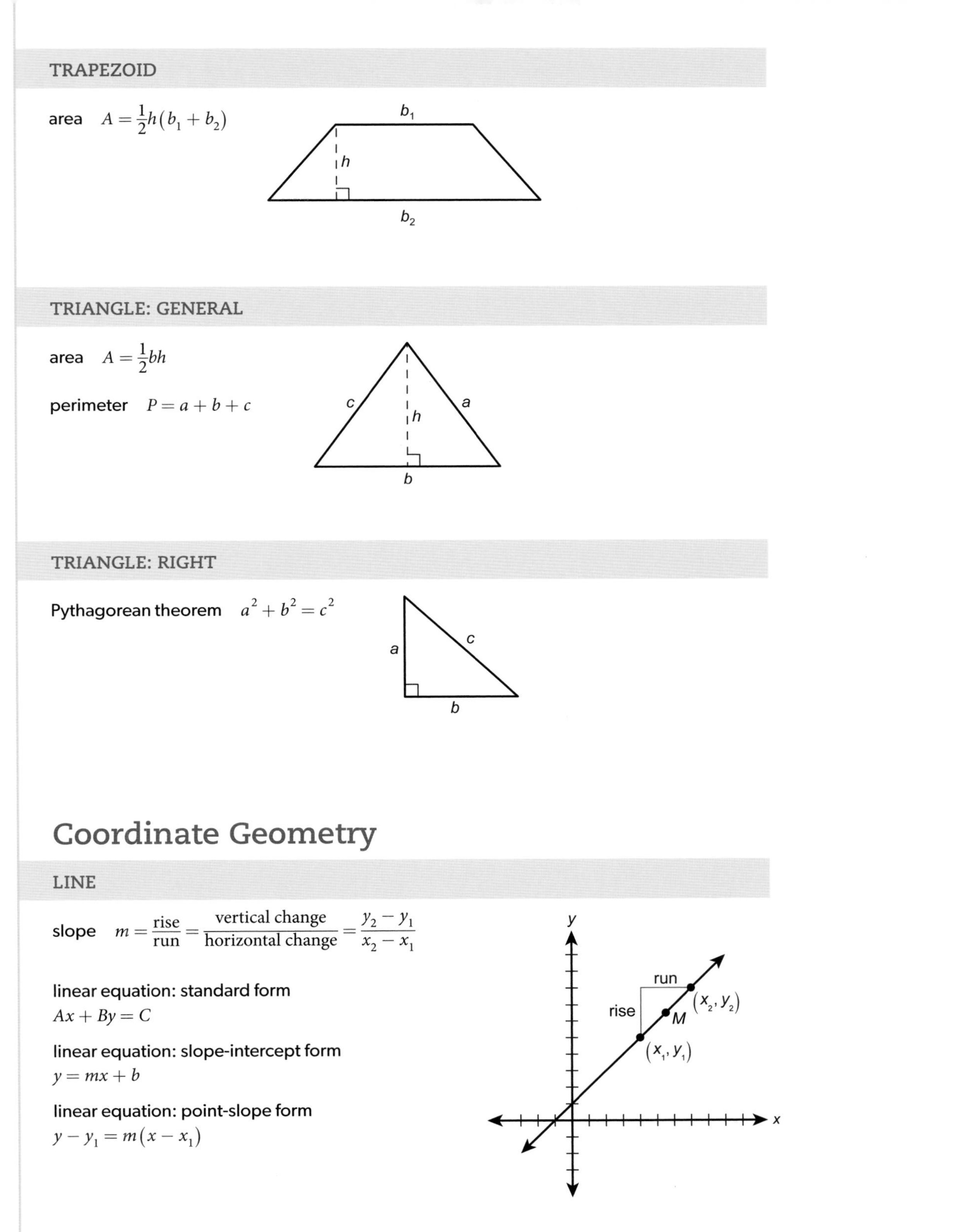

TRAPEZOID

area $A = \frac{1}{2}h(b_1 + b_2)$

TRIANGLE: GENERAL

area $A = \frac{1}{2}bh$

perimeter $P = a + b + c$

TRIANGLE: RIGHT

Pythagorean theorem $a^2 + b^2 = c^2$

Coordinate Geometry

LINE

slope $m = \frac{\text{rise}}{\text{run}} = \frac{\text{vertical change}}{\text{horizontal change}} = \frac{y_2 - y_1}{x_2 - x_1}$

linear equation: standard form
$Ax + By = C$

linear equation: slope-intercept form
$y = mx + b$

linear equation: point-slope form
$y - y_1 = m(x - x_1)$

VERTICAL DISTANCE

same x-value $d = y_2 - y_1$

HORIZONTAL DISTANCE

same y-value $d = x_2 - x_1$

DIRECT LINEAR VARIATION

general formula $y = kx \quad k \neq 0$

QUADRATIC VARIATION

general formula $y = kx^2 \quad k \neq 0$

Probability

SIMPLE THEORETICAL PROBABILITY

$$P(E) = \frac{\text{number of outcomes in event } E}{\text{total number of outcomes in sample space } S} = \frac{n(E)}{n(S)}$$

PROBABILITY OF MUTUALLY EXCLUSIVE EVENTS

$$P(A \text{ or } B) = P(A) + P(B)$$

RELATIVE FREQUENCY OF AN EVENT (EXPERIMENTAL PROBABILITY)

If n is the number of trials of an experiment or number of observations in a study, then the relative frequency of an event E is

$$P(E) = \frac{\text{number of times event } E \text{ has occurred}}{n}.$$

PROBABILITY OF INDEPENDENT EVENTS

For independent events A and B,

$$P(A \text{ and } B) = P(A) \bullet P(B).$$

PROBABILITY OF DEPENDENT EVENTS

For dependent events A and B,

$$P(A \text{ and } B) = P(A) \bullet P(B \text{ after } A)$$

where $P(B \text{ after } A)$ is the probability of B knowing that event A has already occurred.

GEOMETRIC PROBABILITY

$$P(E) = \frac{\text{area of region of success}}{\text{area of entire region}}$$

Statistics

MEAN

$$\overline{x} = \frac{x_1 + x_1 + \ldots + x_n}{n}$$

ABSOLUTE DEVIATION

The absolute deviation is the absolute value of the difference between a data value and the mean.

MEAN ABSOLUTE DEVIATION (MAD)

The MAD is the mean of all the absolute deviations. Calculate the absolute deviation for each data value and add. Then divide the sum by the number of data value.

MEANS-TO-MAD RATIO

$$\frac{|\overline{x}_1 + \overline{x}_2|}{\text{MAD}_{\text{larger}}}$$

MEDIAN

Arrange the values in order from least to greatest. For an

Odd number of values, use the middle value.

Even number of values, use the average of the middle two values.

MODE

The mode is the value that occurs most often in a set of data. If no one value occurs most often, then there is no mode for the set.

RANGE

$$\text{range} = \text{maximum} - \text{minimum}$$

Conversions

CONVERSION FOR LENGTH

English Units	Metric Units
1 ft = 12 in.	1 cm = 10 mm
1 yd = 36 in.	1 m = 100 cm
1 yd = 3 ft	1 km = 1000 m
1 mi = 5280 ft	

CONVERSION OF CUBIC UNITS

English Units	Metric Units
1 ft^3 = 1728 in^3	1 cm^3 = 1000 mm^3
1 yd^3 = 27 ft^3	1 m^3 = 1,000,000 cm^3

SCALE FACTOR FORMULAS

If SA_F is the surface area of a figure that is enlarged or reduced with a scale factor, then the surface area of the scaled image, SA_I, is $SA_I = (\text{scale factor})^2 \bullet SA_F$.

General Applications

PERCENT OF CHANGE

$$\text{percent of change} = \frac{\text{amount of change}}{\text{original amount}} \bullet 100\%$$

SIMPLE INTEREST

$$I = Prt$$

where I is the amount of interest, P is the principal (the money you start with or your first deposit), r is the annual interest rate, and t is the time in years.

COMPOUND INTEREST

$$A = P(1 + r)^t$$

where P is the principal (the money you start with or your first deposit), r is the interest rate, and t is the number of years.

PERCENT ERROR

$$\text{percent error} = \frac{|\text{measured value} - \text{actual value}|}{\text{actual value}} \bullet 100\%$$

PERCENT OF TOTAL COST

$$\text{percent of total cost} = \frac{\text{individual cost}}{\text{total cost}} \bullet 100\%$$

FINAL PRICE FORMULA

$$\text{final price} = \text{pre-tax price} + \text{tax paid}$$

Illustrations Credits

All illustrations © K12 Inc. unless otherwise noted

Front cover Cheetah. © Dobrynina Elena/Shutterstock.com

Back cover Pink-blue watercolor. © Gloria Elpis/Shutterstock; Cheetah pattern. © Dobrynina Elena/Shutterstock.com

K[12] Summit Curriculum Computer monitor. © antpkr/Shutterstock; Tablet and phone. © Radu Bercan/Shutterstock

Number Properties Preamplifiers. © Damien Jemison/LLNL

Linear Equations Woman carrying bananas. © Martin Puddy/Corbis

Linear Relationships and Slope Backcountry skiing. © Jeff Diener/Aurora Photos

Lines Central Park tunnel. © Sozdate/Dreamstime.com

Systems of Equations Tulip fields. © Image Source/Alamy Stock Photo

Function Basics Kerr Dam. © Aurora Photos/Alamy Stock Photo

Linear Data Models Red jets. © wildpixel/Thinkstock

Basic Geometric Shapes Bank of China. © Thierry Dosogne/Getty Images

Volume Ice cream. © margouillat photo/Shutterstock

Transformation, Congruence, and Similarity Woven baskets. © Mike Copeland/Getty Images

Real Numbers Rhind Papyrus. © The Trustees of the British Museum/Art Resource, NY

The Pythagorean Theorem Louvre at night. © Padsaworn Wannakarn/Getty Images

Data Sources

FUNCTIONS

U.S. Census Bureau. 2015. “Resident Population and Apportionment of the U.S. House of Representatives.” Accessed January 16, 2015. http://www.census.gov/dmd/www/resapport/states/northcarolina.pdf.

LINEAR DATA MODELS

Coates, Jennifer. 2014. “How Long Do Dogs Live?” PetMD. Accessed June 16, 2014. http://www.petmd.com/dog/wellness/evr_dg_how_long_do_dogs_live.

Modern Puppies. 2014. “Breed Weight Chart.” Accessed June 16, 2014. http://modernpuppies.com/breedweightchart.aspx.

Statista. 2014. “Average selling price of desktop PCs worldwide from 2005 to 2014 (in U.S. dollars).” Accessed June 24, 2014. http://www.statista.com/statistics/203759/average-selling-price-of-desktop-pcs-worldwide/.

Tax Foundation. 2015a. “State Individual Income Tax Rates, 2000–2014.” Accessed March 3, 2015. http://taxfoundation.org/article/state-individual-income-tax-rates.

———. 2015b. “State Sales, Gasoline, Cigarette, and Alcohol Tax Rates by State, 2000–2014.” Accessed March 3, 2015. http://taxfoundation.org/article/state-sales-gasolinecigarette-and-alcohol-tax-rates.

The President’s Challenge. 2014. “Physical Fitness Test.” Accessed June 19, 2014. https://www.presidentschallenge.org/challenge/physical/benchmarks.shtml.

Watkins, Thayer. 2014. “Animal Longevity and Scale,” San Jose State University. Accessed June 11, 2014. http://www.sjsu.edu/faculty/watkins/longevity.htm.

Wu, Sen-Yuan. 2010. “New Jersey Population: 1790 to 2010,” Division of Labor Market & Demographic Research. State of New Jersey Department of Labor and Workforce Development. Accessed March 5, 2015. http://lwd.dol.state.nj.us/labor/lpa/dmograph/est/nj1790_2010.pdf.